£10

GREAT FARMERS

GREAT FARMERS

by
JAMES A. SCOTT WATSON
and
MAY ELLIOT HOBBS

FABER AND FABER LIMITED
24 Russell Square
London

First published in this edition mcmli
by Faber and Faber Limited
24 Russell Square London W.C.1
Printed in Great Britain
at the Bowering Press Plymouth
All rights reserved

FOREWORD

Great Farmers was first published in 1937. It was written at a time when, as events were to prove, British agriculture was nearing the end of a long period of tribulation and neglect.

The purpose of the book was to give some account, mainly in terms of personalities, of the British contribution, during a hundred years, to the advancement of the ancient craft.

Much has now been added and much changed. It is no longer necessary, as it was in the 'thirties, to urge the importance of producing food in greater abundance, or to plead for a reasonable measure of encouragement to the improver; and it is no longer true that our country is lagging behind others in agricultural education or research. Naturally, some of the earlier judgments have had to be modified in the light of all that has happened during the years between.

One of the new chapters—that on 'Poultry Farmers'—has been contributed by Dr. R. Coles.

But the story, as we now retell it, is still one of which our farmers can be very proud.

J. A. S. W.
M. E. H.

April 1951

CONTENTS

9

ILLUSTRATIONS

MARSH, MOOR AND FEN

FIELD DRAINAGE

'Whereof in these our times a wonder happened; for whereas antiently time out of mind, they were neither accessible for man or beast, affording only deep mud with sedge and reeds, and possessed by birds (yea much more by devils, as appeareth in the life of St. Guthlas who, finding it a place of horror and great solitude, began to inhabit there) is now changed into delightful meadows and arable ground.'

Quoted by Dugdale from a thirteenth-century writer on the Fens

Arthur Young's *Tours* leave us with the impression of a waterlogged England; of clay lands still sodden until late in the spring, and strangers to the new turnip husbandry which was in process of vastly increasing the productivity of the poor dry sands and chalks. The only artificial drainage, on much of the heavy arable land in the Vales, was afforded by laying up the soil into ridges or 'stetches' from ten to thirty feet wide, with deep furrows between—all, indeed, carefully planned in relation to the natural contours, so as to form a complete system for carrying off surface water. On the heaviest land the ridges were sometimes so high that men sitting in adjacent furrows were hidden from each other. Even Mr. Pusey, as late as 1841, was surprised to learn of the ancient practice of brush-draining in Essex and Suffolk, which was almost unknown elsewhere. In this, the earliest system of covered drainage, faggots of brushwood or hedge clippings performed the function of the modern tile.

After heavy rains the anxious clayland farmer was to be seen, 'spud in hand, wading through his open furrows trying to lead stagnant little pools into the adjoining ditches.' It is little wonder that the records of the old Spitals, such as Kelso, show that ague was very prevalent. Over most of Scotland, with gradually increasing cultivation and better drainage, ague had almost disappeared when the New Statistical Accounts were written about 1840. But it persisted longer in the Fens and the Essex Marshes. Scottish labourers who went harvesting in Lincolnshire often returned with the infection, and 'uplanders' who settled in the Essex flats had a short expectation of life.

In the latter half of the eighteenth century, Joseph Elkington, a Warwickshire farmer, devised a useful system of dealing with spring waters which oozed to the surface of sloping ground, producing boggy patches where rushes grew instead of corn, and in which the unwatchful carter might bog his team. Elkington's 'system' was to intercept each spring at its source by means of a short length of deep stone-filled drain (running almost on the contour) and to lead the waters from several adjacent springs into a common 'main'. But Elkington's crowbar—sometimes likened to the rod of Moses—dealt only with a minor problem. The major ones, of near-level fields of impervious clay, and of areas where the winter water-table approached or reached the surface, were still unsolved; the wheat 'drowned out' in winter and the land lay too wet for tillage until far on in the spring. A new era opened in 1831 when John Smith published his *Remarks on Thorough Draining and Deep Ploughing*.

James Smith was born at Glasgow in 1789. His father was a Glasgow merchant, and his mother the daughter of James Buchanan a landed proprietor in the western part of Stirlingshire. The elder Smith died whilst his children were still very young, and the Smith family, mother and three children, made their home with their mother's brother, Archibald Buchanan, then the working manager of the Deanston Cotton Works, between Callandar and Dunblane in Perthshire.

Archibald Buchanan seems to have been a gentleman of exceptional attainments. He had been a pupil of Thomas Arkwright, and himself had invented self-acting mules and carding and other machines. James Smith described him as 'a man of singular genius, sound judgment and great application and perseverance.' It was fortunate that Smith came under such an influence, for the qualities of the uncle were possessed to an equal degree by the nephew.

Whilst Smith was at Glasgow University his uncle moved to the Catrine Works in Ayrshire where, in his vacations, James studied mechanics and engineering under him. His holidays were not confined to the works. Archibald Buchanan, like many other manufacturers of his time, had, for his pleasure and recreation, a small farm; and there the nephew learned also the principles and practice of farming.

When he was eighteen Smith was appointed manager of the Deanston Cotton Works and found plenty to keep him busy. He first threw his vast energy into the reorganization of the works. This done to his satisfaction, he turned his attention to more philanthropic works. With an understanding unusual in mill owners of his time he concerned himself seriously with the well-being of his workpeople. He installed a teacher, paid by the works, to educate the children. He encouraged athletic games—in short he imposed his superabundant energy upon the whole of his neighbourhood. The model village of Deanston was built under his direction, and he knew every inhabitant of the two villages which housed his workpeople. He had an extraordinary aptitude for selecting his workers and for getting the utmost out of them, and withal was a popular and well-beloved employer.

He had not lost his liking for farming and soon became a member of the Gargunnock Farmers Club. In 1812 he invented a reaping machine which he entered for the £500 prize offered by the Dalkeith Farmers' Club. He was unsuccessful, but tried the following year with an improved machine. Here he came up against the nature of the ground, which later he was to do so much to improve. His machine 'fell into a sudden hollow, the cutter stuck fast, and part of the mechanism was broken.' He was however awared a fifty-guinea piece of plate for his 'meritorious endeavours' and, later, received another piece of plate from the Highland Society. A model of his machine got as far as St. Petersburg, and the Emperor of Russia sent him a Gold Medal. Smith was now well aware of the difficulties of devising a machine to work successfully on the uneven ridges, and the lesson went home

His inventions and improvements for the Deanston Works still kept him busy. There was the Deanston Weir and its salmon ladder, his improved self-acting mules, and his assistance to the Gargunnock Road Trustees in carrying a bridge over a tributary of the River Forth.

In 1823, when he was thirty-three, he took over a farm at Deanston and started, of course, to improve it. His uncle had preceded him in the use of 'thorough' draining, and both he and James Smith had lamented the waste of money and land through lack of real knowledge of its principles.

It was not a promising farm. 'The land was bad, consisting chiefly of the drifted debris of the Old Red Sandstone—some parts of the subsoil being of hard compact soil with stones, and some in the hollows of sandy clay, composed of the soil which had been washed from the higher parts of the ground. The whole was thickly interspersed with large boulder stones, some of them very near the surface. The active soil was in general very thin, in most places not exceeding 4 inches. Much of the surface was studded with rushes and other water plants, while the dry knolls were covered with heath, fern, and broom.'

Smith first attempted draining. In the old days at the Catrine Works farm his uncle had drained his fields at a depth of 18 inches, but James Smith saw that this had been a mistake. He laid his main drains along the hollower parts of the field at a depth of 4 feet, the receiving drains at 3 feet, and the network of parallel drains covering the whole farm he put at 2 feet 6 inches and at 16 to 20 feet apart. These parallel drains were filled with stones—the broken boulder stones of the district—to within about 18 inches of the surface. After this Smith departed from the general practice and laid all his fields flat.

That done, he was disappointed. To a certain extent the drains were efficient, but he had not satisfied himself that he had achieved the utmost that was possible. So he applied himself to a second operation. It occurred to him that if he could stir up and break the subsoil without bringing it to the surface, the water could the more easily escape through the soil to the drains, air would be admitted with the passage of the water and the whole soil made friable. He invented for this purpose his subsoil plough. Here is his own description of its purpose:

'I saw it was of the greatest importance to break up the subsoil, especially where it was tenacious. I saw that the common trench plough, when used to break up the subsoil, at the same time turned over the recently moved subsoil, to mix with the surface soil, which induced a partial sterility for a time. I then bethought me of having a plough that would move the subsoil, still retaining the active soil above the surface.'

The subsoil plough was a heavy implement, weighing 400 lb. At least four, and sometimes as many as eight, horses were required to draw it, and it penetrated to a depth of 16 inches. When his ploughman was first given the job of using it he complained of fatigue. It was too heavy, he said, too hard on the horses and on the man. However, when he was given a lighter implement he found it less satisfactory, for it was more often jerked out of the ground. He consented to go back to the heavier plough, and soon grew so adept at managing it that he could cover three-quarters of an acre per day.

The results of this combined underdraining and subsoiling were surprising. Deanston became famous. Farmers and land-owners came crowding to visit it. They received a kindly and hospitable welcome from James Smith and his sister, who had succeeded her mother as mistress of the house. The orderliness and benevolent organization of the cotton works and the village were admired, and the farm was viewed with scientific interest. Those who had seen it spread its fame all over Scotland and England. Two hundred acres of waterlogged, sour, cold land had been turned into what was described as a garden, 'as pleasing to the eye as it was interesting to the intellect and heart. The fields were conveniently laid off, kept very clean, and fenced generally with pretty whitethorn hedges; or where the situation required it, with ornamental belts of thriving plantations, which afforded protection to the crops and shelter to the flocks. Water for the supply of the fields was obtained from tanks fed by the drains, and pumped into water-troughs by an ingenious but simple arrangement; and there was not an open ditch on the whole farm. The crops in their season were usually luxuriant, a thorough and uniform dryness having been acquired over the whole surface by the new system of working.' All this had been accomplished by draining and subsoil ploughing.

Smith's neighbours and friends of the Gargunnock Farmers' Club imitated his method, with the same good results. Smith became famous. He was required to write and speak of his improvement. He was called upon to give evidence in 1836 before the Committee on Agricultural Distress, where he was firm in maintaining that, provided his 'frequent' drain system had preceded it, one operation of subsoil ploughing was a permanent improvement to the land—that the character of the subsoil was thus entirely changed by the action of air and water, becoming mellow, warm, and friable. Not only that, but where turnips could not before have been grown it was now possible to obtain good crops; where sheep could not have been run it was now possible to fold them over the turnips without their suffering from rot.

Those who heard the evidence went away to try the new improvement on their own lands. Gentlemen riding together spoke of his improvements, and passed on the good news. The agricultural papers of the day were full of his praises. Smith was followed by many who sought to improve their land in the same way. Sir James Graham of Netherby in Cumberland, for instance, experimented with a field of 8 acres of the poorest and wettest of land. A surface soil of 5 inches deep, consisting of black peaty earth, overlay a subsoil of 'weeping retentive clays and sand and rusty gravel mixed.' The pasture was coarse and overrun with rushes. He drained at 30 inches deep in every furrow, placing the drains 10 yards apart, and laying tiles instead of stones. After the first crop of potatoes (which yielded 12 tons to the acre) the land remained flat, but there was no recurrence of waterlogging nor sourness. Before draining the field was valued at 4s. 6d. an acre, but the incoming tenant was willing to rent it, on a 14 years' lease, at 20s.

Similar results were being obtained in widely different parts of the country. The subsoil plough was imitated by other makers, and in some cases improved upon. Tile-making works grew up, as well as a new profession of agricultural engineers, who devoted themselves to the study and undertaking of farm drainage.

It appeared that Smith's claims were substantiated. Here and there, however, were farmers and landowners who had been disappointed. The subsoil plough was being too indiscriminately used, and the 'frequent' drainage too slavishly imitated, without regard to the nature of the particular soil. What was required was the elucidation of the principles of drainage and this was begun by a notable member of the new profession—Josiah Parkes, the Consulting Engineer to the Royal Agricultural Society.

Parkes, third son of a manufacturer, born at Warwick in 1793, had, like Smith, worked from the age of seventeen in his father's mill, where he devoted himself to mechanics. In 1820 he moved to Manchester, experimenting with a process for the prevention of smoke; later he went to Woolwich, concerning himself with a salt-refining process. He had lived in France between the years 1825 and 1830, but, having fought in the revolution and having lost his business, he returned to England as an engineer, concerned with the draining of agricultural land and particularly with the reclamation of bogs.

Such reclamation had been attempted before. The famous Drummond Moss near Stirling had been turned into valuable land by the cutting away of the peat and floating it down the River Forth; but that had proved a costly venture.

In 1833 Parkes was engaged in draining part of Chat Moss, in the county of Lancashire. Chat Moss was an immense peat bog, some dozen square miles in extent. In most places it was incapable of supporting a man or a horse, a mass of spongy vegetable pulp extending to a depth of 20 or 30 feet. Although semi-fluid in consistency its surface was higher than the surrounding country. The railway, by a considerable feat of engineering, had been laid across the moss and, when it was opened in 1830, the passengers on the first journey were lost in amazement. They 'perceived they were on a floating road', and they saw, as the train progressed, the bog undulating on either side.

It was on this seemingly impossible land that Josiah Parkes was experimenting, and it was while he was so occupied that the principles of deep drainage occurred to him. He had noticed that shallow draining did not lay strong and wet land sufficiently dry,

B

and was fearful that, throughout the whole country, labour and expense had been incurred without achieving the sufficient drying of the land. He saw that it was from the deeper drains which he had laid on Chat Moss that the water began to flow first, and he deduced that the pressure of water from below was at least partly responsible for the surface wetness. He concluded that Smith had been wrong, and that field drains should be sunk at least as deep as 4 feet, if not 5. An experiment in deep drainage on a field at Bolton was successful. In 1843 he gave evidence before the Committee of the House of Lords, and the long and often bitter controversy of shallow *versus* deep drainage began.

In 1842 James Smith had left Deanston, to which he was so attached. His reasons are not clear, but probably a philanthropic mill manager was something of a handicap in those times, and Smith's ideas must have been at times costly to the Deanston works. However he had a connection in Ireland and in England, and was henceforth to concern himself with giving advice to intending improvers in both countries. He established himself in London as an agricultural engineer, giving advice on drainage and irrigation as well as on systems of cultivating and the arrangement of farm buildings, tanks and compost heaps. Thus were both the protagonist and the antagonist of 'shallow frequent drainage' established in the same capacities in London.

James Smith has been described as a man who had a charm of person and the ability to profit from the experience of others. On the other hand, Josiah Parkes was jealous and obstinate, intolerant of advice, and, what was more, had no capacity to manage men. Much of his work was badly executed, and so brought disrepute on his system. The controversy resolved the great underlying principles of draining. Until that time every farmer with a spirit-level considered himself qualified to drain his land, and often the consulting engineer had to be called in to find the cause of failure of the undertaking. But gradually a body of scientific knowledge was built up, and in the end it was discovered that no uniform system of drainage could be applicable to all soils and climates.

Apart from his work in drainage Josiah Parkes did other valuable service to agriculture, especially in his capacity of consulting engineer to the Royal Agricultural Society. It was through him that the first set of special tools for draining was made and adopted.

The actual conduit to carry away the water was still a difficulty in field drainage. Stones were expensive in a stoneless district and tiles (which had been made since 1810) were expensive too. It was in 1843 that John Reade, a gardener (and incidentally the inventor of the stomach pump) made clay cylindrical pipes with which to heat his master's hotbeds, and Parkes immediately saw their possibilities for the cheapening of land drainage. These 1-inch-bore clay pipes were exhibited at a Royal Show, and Parkes, talking to the Earl Spencer and holding one in his hand, said: 'My Lord, with this pipe I will drain all England.' Smith contemptuously called them 'Pencil cases'. Reade had made the pipes by wrapping a lump of clay round a mandrill and rubbing it smooth with flannel. Parkes investigated the use and merits of pipes in Kent.

The pipe-making machine of those days was a rude and unsatisfactory affair, but again through Parkes' encouragement, a satisfactory machine was at last invented by Thomas Scragg, and the heavy cost of pipes was a thing of the past. From a model making 1,000 pipes a day, at an average cost of 21s. per 1,000, they advanced to a machine making as many as 20,000 pipes a day at a cost of 6s. per 1,000.

In 1840 an Act was passed which enabled landowners to meet the cost of draining by loans to be repaid by way of mortgage, the approval of the loans to be made by the Court of Chancery. In 1843 a company was formed to advance money—the Yorkshire Land Drainage Company—of which James Smith was a Director. This company did not function for long, but through its agency a bill was brought forward which resulted, in 1846, in Peel's Public Money Drainage Act, administered by the Inclosure Commissioners. Under this Act the Government offered a loan of two million pounds, to be repaid by rent-charge over twenty-two years. But the 'canny' farmers of Scotland availed themselves of the greater part of this loan almost before the English landowners had had time to make up their minds!

Another two millions were offered, and the Private Money Drainage Act, in 1849, was passed to enable private companies to be formed to lend further monies for land improvement. Great companies, such as the General Land Drainage and Improvement Company, the Lands Improvement Company, the Scottish Drainage and Improvement Company, and the Land Loan and Enfranchisement Company, were formed in the 'fifties and 'sixties, and some of these are still in existence.

The impetus towards improvement was enormous. In the ten years before 1856 it was estimated that sixteen million pounds had been spent on land drainage.

It was John Bailey Denton and his colleagues on the Lands Improvement Company who eventually settled the controversy between the two schools of drainers. The varying nature of soils was by this time better understood, and it was found that depth and distance apart had to be adjusted to this. Land drainage had become a science, and the demands of individual localities and soils were studied and met individually. The long period of trial and error is recorded in many of our fields, where are to be found drains of various kinds at varying depths, some still functioning, others long since choked and dried, and others still well preserved because they have never functioned at all. Again, the conduit pipes of 1-inch bore which Parkes had approved, and which in theory were big enough, proved unsatisfactory in practice and pipes of greater bore now found favour.

Lord Stanley, in 1841, summed up the attitude of agriculturists to this great movement towards land improvement when he said: 'There is no bank in the whole country—no commercial speculation—no investment, so sure and profitable as that in which even borrowed capital may be engaged by investing it underground.'

The work on drainage and subsoiling which took place from the year 1835 onwards made possible the full realization of all the discoveries and inventions which followed. New manures like guano, nitrate of soda and superphosphate, could be used, and were used extensively, without fear that much of their potency would be lost in the mire. The greater stock-carrying capacity of the drained lands led to a general improvement of breeds. Drills, hoes and other cultivating machinery could be used in every district, thus stimulating their invention and improvement. Horse labour was considerably reduced, one man and two horses being able to plough an acre of land more quickly than the old cavalcade of four or five with a man and a ploughboy. Instead of the old bare fallows, with their long-continued summer tillage, green crops were widely introduced.

James Smith, while on a visit to his cousin Archibald Buchanan, at Kingencleugh, in Ayrshire, in 1850, died in his sleep, after a day of great exertion. He was then sixty-one years of age. Like so many others who contributed to the advancement of his fellow men, he died a poor man.

Parkes lived to carry out work for the War Department in the Isle of Wight, and two years after his retirement he died there in 1871.

Smith and Parkes left behind them a body of men well qualified to carry on their work, and a generation of farmers and landowners who made English farming famous all over the world.

THE RECLAMATION OF MOORLAND

The conversion of a stretch of barren moorland into fertile fields has been the ambition of vast numbers of improvers. The task is inevitably a heavy one, involving often the removal of boulders and the making of complete and costly drainage systems as well as deep ploughing, liming, manuring, and fencing. Sometimes the history of a scheme has been one of physical failure; the obstacles have been greater than expected, or the improver's purse has not been as deep as the height of his ambition. Sometimes complete success has been achieved, farms have been made and the work has returned some margin of profit. But probably the commonest story is one of schemes begun in periods of prosperity and of calculations based upon a continuance of existing price levels; of work accomplished and farms made, and of a subsequent fall in prices that left the owner with a poor investment. The country has gained but the improver has lost—unless indeed he happens to have had enough philosophy to think more of his acres and of his workers than of his guineas.

23

If this be broadly true, the story of the reclamation of Exmoor is typical. On the Moor the story of the Knight family is still well remembered, and the history of the reclamation of their great estate has been told by Dr. C. S. Orwin; but the names of the early farmers who colonized Exmoor are mostly forgotten. Some survived and prospered; others, like Hannam, whose diaries provide a vivid picture of vicissitudes and hardships, were worsted in their fight with the soil and the climate. But in the end, through their trials and errors, a system of farming suitable to the moor was evolved.

The reclamation started with the enclosure of the whole district and the sale, in 1818, of the Crown Allotment of over 10,000 acres to John Knight, a Worcestershire squire of a family whose fortunes, as ironmasters in Shropshire, dated back to the Commonwealth.

Three distinct periods may be recognized in the process of reclamation, beginning with the first-hand exploitation by Knight of his property; the second was the colonization of the estate; and the final one the conversion of the land into the present day sheep grazings.

Knight, having added to his original purchase the Bamfylde and Acland allotments, amounting to another 5,000 acres, started the scheme. Even to-day parts of Exmoor are remote and wild, but a century and a half ago it was a desolate waste, unenclosed, uncultivated, without roads except packhorse tracks, and tenanted only by the few shepherds who saw to the summer-feeding of the stock. Such cultivation as existed was on the primitive system of cropping the soil to exhaustion and moving on. Smuggling, sheep-stealing, venison poaching and pony-rounding were the part-time or whole-time occupations of the permanent inhabitants.

Steal the sheep and sell the wool
Say the Bells of Withypool.

The same processes which, during long ages, have produced highland moors elsewhere had been going on in Exmoor. Accumulations of peat on the thin clay pan, impervious to water, had swallowed up the remains of the trees which once had clothed the hills. The land lay continually wet like a sponge. Fortunately these processes had not been operating so very long, and, where the clay pan had been worn away and the yellow subsoil exposed, forest grass grew in profusion, and on this large flocks of sheep fed in summer. Apart from some small sums from the sale of native ponies, these sheep provided John Knight's only return from his new estate. He made his home at the old house at Simonsbath. Enclosing his property by a forty-mile dry-stone wall, he established home farms at Honeymead and Cornham, and these he started to farm, rather unsuccessfully, on the Norfolk four-course system. He put in hand the making of roads on the routes of the old pack-horse tracks, thus opening up the moor for the first time to market towns and ports. Paring, burning, and liming of the land were done according to the usual practice of the time. 'Bullock teams in yokes of six supplied the power for the cultivation of land which had never before been moved by man.' Instead of using the dry improved land as pasture, admirably suited as it was for this purpose, he persisted in his arable farming and bought his experience dearly. Wheat does not ripen fully or often at altitudes like a thousand or fifteen hundred feet.

At this time he travelled far to buy the best Highland and Hereford cattle, and set up a pony stud of Dongola Arabs and mares of the Cleveland type with the idea of improving the native Exmoor pony.

When Frederick Knight succeeded his father, the colonizing period began in earnest. He employed an agent from Devon and started to build numbers of farmhouses and homesteads for tenants. Farms were to let at low rents and on liberal leases, but the burden of improvement was to be on the tenant. Although the farmers in the immediate neighbourhood knew too much about the moor to be tempted by low rents, 'foreigners' from Dorset, Somerset, and Wiltshire, some of them dairy farmers, entered into competition for the new farms. Amongst the buyers who went up to the sales of Knight's stock was a certain Hannam from the neighbourhood of Wincanton in Somerset. His son William, fascinated by his father's glowing accounts of the farming on the moor, decided to have a try, and took Cornham farm, of about

1,000 acres, on a twelve years' lease at a rental of £240 a year. The sitting tenant, discouraged after two years of farming, which had included one very severe winter, was selling off. The building and the alterations were hardly begun.

In March the little family, with their furniture and farming stock, courageously set out on their great adventure, leaving the kindly lanes of Somerset for the inclement loneliness of the high moorland.

'The 25th March being a Sunday,' he wrote, 'we got loaded on a Sadderday and started Monday. We had three wagons with three horses each and two carts with one horse each. I had a covered cart with my wife, servants and child, but got no further than Exford as the roads were bad after frost so that the horses could scarcely stand.' Leaving his family at Simonsbath farmhouse he returned to meet the heavy wagons, which had intended to travel steadily all through the night. Conditions, however, had been so bad that they got no farther than Rawley Cross. Fifteen horses had to be housed, and the stables held no more than four or five. 'It was then five o'clock and a tremendous mist or thick fog. I said to the men it is no use staying here. Night is coming on. We shall not see our way over the hills. No one knew the road, darkness set in, and the wheels of the wagons sank in the wet ground. At length the White Horse Inn at Exford was reached, where the horses and men laid down for a few hours.'

The third day saw them at Cornham.

The costs of liming, breaking, and draining proved to call for unexpectedly heavy drafts on Hannam's capital. Then, too, prices of farm produce had been high when he first went on to Exmoor, and now they began to fall. His estimates of his probable returns were proved to have been far too optimistic, and he laboured under the disadvantage of having to pay as much as £50 a year interest on borrowed money. His costs of cultivating the land he gives as follows:

Paid for lime bills (over 8 years) ..	..	£400
Broke 100 acres which had never been broken before, £5 an acre ..	.. ..	£500

| Manure on grass, 100 acres per year for 10 years, at £1 an acre .. | .. | .. | £1,000 |
| Rent during term .. | .. | .. | £3,600 |

It was only a matter of two years until he began 'to have great anxiety of mind'. Already he found that rent days came round before he was ready with the cash.

Other tenants were coming and going, some only staying a year or two before selling up their stock and leaving for America.

About 1848, however, a new agent, Robert Smith from Lincolnshire, was appointed. A better mode of leasing farms was initiated, based on the Lincolnshire custom, under which tenancies ran for twenty-one years, and embodied compensation for any durable improvements, undertaken by the tenant with the owner's sanction. Men of different calibre and capital, and from further afield, were attracted. Even so the first years of his agency saw a succession of changes and bankruptcies—tenants 'came in their po'chaises and went in their dung carts'.

Broadly speaking, the farming policy of the Moor was now changing. Sheep were gaining favour, and the dairy farmers almost disappeared. Hannam, seeing the changes around him, but not in the least understanding them, writes bitterly that the 'gentlemen farmers' would not improve the Moor, but rather 'they are more likely to bring some of the old men's words true, that they should "see it Exmoor again and as before a sheep walk" with the farmhouses occupied by shepherds and herdsmen.'

Hannam was passing through a bad time. 'For a year or two we could not get more than 5d. or 6d. retail for our cheese, there was such a quantity of American cheese brought over.' In 1850, he 'had over one Hundred Cheese in number that averaged over 56 lb. each', which he tried to sell by auction at Barnstaple Market, but for which he could get no more than the above sum. His butter was selling at 7d. or 7½d. a pound, and he 'could get no more than 7s. a score for good fatt pigs.' He killed a lot of pigs rather than sell for this price, and 'salted and dried Baken and Hams, but could get no more than 6d. a lb. for Baken, Hams and Lard.'

Hannam had been persuaded by Smith to buy some South Downs which some preferred to the wandering native breed, but severe winters with insufficient food wrought havoc with Down flocks on the high Moor. In one such, Hannam was obliged to winter his flock in yards, but even so lost nearly forty ewes and a hundred and fifty lambs.

In 1852 the arrival of a new tenant, the fifth on Wintershead farm since 1844, proved to be an important step in the evolution of Exmoor farming. Gerald Spooner, a Scot, brought with him his native sheep, Cheviots and Blackfaces, which, he maintained, would do best on the native grass as 'nought but powder and shot would kill them.' He introduced the Scottish sheep-farming system, whose object was the breeding and fattening of lambs for the butcher. His ewes lambed down later than either Exmoors or South Downs, and by November the lambs were off to the market.

Although Spooner stayed on the Moor only for six years, and, so far as his own farming was concerned, cannot be said to have had much success, his system had been adopted by the landowner, with whom the Scottish shepherds remained. Ponies and store stock gradually gave place to ewes got by the Scottish rams. Cultivations and rotations were adapted to changing practice. Turnips and three-years' ley were followed by oats and well-manured roots. The growing demand for meat, along with the opening up of railway traffic to the markets of Bristol, Birmingham, and London, favoured the new methods.

By 1857 the population on Exmoor had so increased that it was created a Civil and Ecclesiastical Parish.

Meanwhile the Hannams fared from bad to worse. Men were attracted away from the farms to work in the supposed iron-ore deposits. Many a time Hannam had neither man nor maid, and the milking had to be done by himself and his two little girls, not then eleven years old. He was pressed on all sides for repayment of borrowed money, and was forced to sell his stock to meet demands. Like some of his neighbours he took to summering of stock for lowland farmers, but this was a retrograde step in the eyes of the owner, who wished the land to be steadily improved.

Just as he thought better times were ahead, and that, left alone with his pony and his sheep-dog, he could make a living, Hannam was overtaken by his debts and a threatened increase of rent in a new lease. His business was put in the hands of the sheriff and the sale of the remainder of his stock arranged. Pathetic entries in his diary show his troubled mind. 'I rode round the farm after they (the executors) were gone. I satt on my pony on Little Cornham where I had a sight of the farm and a feeling came over mee. I must confess I shedd maney tears.' Had he been of a less tenacious character, like many others, he might have fled the Moor or been found on the roadside 'with his brains blown out by a pistol', but he had conceived a deep love for the Moor and for his gaunt farmhouse. Fighting to the end he finally left, beaten and penniless, not only by adverse circumstances or, as he bitterly felt, by the unfriendliness of neighbours, but rather by lack of knowledge and by an obstinate inadaptability of mind. He wandered about without work and without money, unable to stray far from Exmoor, always brooding over the beautiful cattle he had had to sell. From some wistful words written in retrospect one feels that he realized at last the causes of his failure. 'I wished myself away when I suffered such severe losses with my stock in severe winters and could not tell how to prevent it. Still, I made up my mind it was no use to frown, we were not by ourselves and no doubt it was ordained to teach us a lesson to adopt a different system and not to depend on wintering such a lot of cattle.'

Things on Exmoor were now moving rapidly. A new agent, accustomed to moorland farming, solved the problem of winter crops by substituting rape for turnips, which change also lowered the cost of improvement. Nothing fed sheep so well on the hills. Hay-making machinery was introduced and the steam plough arrived for subsoiling. The gap between November and Midsummer, when no rape was available, was filled up by kale.

By 1885 West Country farmers were thriving on the Moor, and when farms fell vacant competition was keen. On the higher parts, still in the hands of the owners, ranged flocks of ewes, the produce of pure-bred Cheviot rams. Scottish shepherds—Davidsons, Johnsons, Grahams, McDougals and Murrays—from the

Highlands and the Borders, lived on their herdings with their wives and families, a cow and grazing ground. Accustomed to the loneliness of their native hills, they tended the sheep with the traditional skill of their forebears.

And so 'the third and last experiment, the conversion of forest grass into permanent pasture for ranch farming with hill breeds of sheep began.' The new system enabled the Exmoor farmers to weather the depression of the late 'eighties and the early 'nineties. Even in the disastrous season of 1879-80 sheep rot was unknown on the heathy moorland.

In 1880 Mr. Little, one of the Assistant Commissioners on the Richmond Commission, reported signs of continued progress. There were some forty farms, ranging in size from 20 to 1,000 acres, with rents from 5s. to 25s. an acre. New pastures were being made. Steam ploughs were at work on the Moor 1,300 feet above sea-level. Mr. Knight's own flock of 4,000 Cheviot ewes lay out on the moors all winter and lambed there, and his Cross Shropshire lambs, fattened off and consigned to London as dead meat, yielded him in wool and mutton 20s. per head. When he died in 1879 Knight was farming 9,000 acres, with a stock of some 9,000 ewes and lambs and 14 farm horses, with Devon cattle and down-calving Shorthorn heifers for summer grazing. To quote Dr. Orwin's closing words, 'From an uninclosed waste of some 20,000 acres; untraversed save by packhorse tracks; uninhabitated save by one family; untilled save for a few acres; unstocked save for summer grazing [Exmoor became] accessible from all sides by good roads; giving shelter and support to a population of 300 people, working for the most part on some 15 adequately equipped farms comprising in all about 5,000 acres of improved and enclosed lands, permanently stocked with some 200 horses, 1,000 cattle and 10,000 sheep exclusive of lambs. . . . Here and for all time there has been created a thriving community contributing in men and material to the welfare of the State.'

The wild intractable moorland, which, almost as if resentful of man's interference, had beaten so many, was in the end moulded to man's will, conquered by the indomitable spirit of the pioneer.

THE FENS

The history of the Fenlands of England, going back to Roman times or earlier, is one of a long succession of attempts at drainage and reclamation, alternating with periods of neglect and the occasional reconquest of land by river and sea. No other district has experienced such vast improvements and changes; no other has repaid so fully the skill and perseverance spent upon it.

The soil of the area is partly silt, partly the black vegetable mould to which the name fen is properly applied, and partly 'skirt' which is a mixture of the two. How long the process of overflow and deposit had been going on none can say. In 1635 boats were found buried 8 feet deep below the bed of the river at Wisbech, and a smith's forge and tools were dug up near Boston some 16 feet below the surface. In the early days the Church, wishing to extend its fat pastures from the little islands round Ely and Crowland, made great cuts to carry off the waters to the rivers and to the sea. But these were only tiny patches in the Great Level, which comprised over 700,000 acres in six counties. In past ages this country was 'the haunt of the crane, the heron, wild duck and teal, the savoury snipe, the swallow kite, the swarth raven, the vulture, the eagle and the gay goose hawk.' Wild buck, and the grey wolf and wild boar roamed at will. Young novices on their way to Ely or Peterborough or Crowland carried poles in their hands to leap the ditches; the same were still used by the inhabitants of the Fens eight hundred years later.

Even in Elizabeth's reign, when the first law of drainage was passed, the district was described as having been 'for the space of many ages a vast and deep fen affording little benefit to the realms other than fish or fowl, with over much harbour to a rude and almost barbarous sort of lazy and beggarly people.' In the seventeenth century Francis, Earl of Bedford, with thirteen other gentlemen adventurers, undertook, not without the prospect of reward in the shape of 95,000 acres of new land, to drain the whole level. Cornelius Vermuyden, a Zeelander who had come over to drain Hatfield Chase, was made director of works. The great stretch was divided into the North, the Middle and the South Levels. The banks of the Welland, Nene and Ouse were built up, sluices were erected and cuts made, and 'the face of the country began to assume an appearance of fertility and agricultural prosperity.' By 1652 Vermuyden could say of the North and Middle Levels that they were 'so far improved that there were about 40,000 acres then sown with coleseed, wheat, and other winter grain, besides innumerable quantities of sheep and cattle and other stock, where never any had been before.'

Vermuyden's work has long been the subject of controversy and even now there is no agreement. The one view is that, with the knowledge and resources then available he did as well as could have been expected. The other is that he botched the job, and left little but trouble to his successors.

The work of the seventeenth-century 'undertakers' was successful only so far as the works were carefully maintained. On the least relaxation of effort the outfalls were once more choked up, water from the tidal rivers swept once more over the land and the natives, who had bitterly resented the disturbance of their ancient habits, returned to their cutting of rushes and turf and pasturing of geese. Their attitude is well described in the old ballad:

> *Come trekmen of the water, and let us all assemble*
> *To treat upon this matter, which makes us quake and tremble.*
> *For we shall rue it, if it be true the fens be undertaken*
> *And where we feed on fen and reed, they'll feed both beef and*
> *bacon.*
> *They'll sow both beans and oats, where never man yet thought*
> *it,*
> *Where men did row in boats ere undertakers bought it;*
> *But Ceres, thou behold us now, let wild oats be their venture,*
> *And let the frogs and miry bogs destroy where they do enter.*

During the Civil Wars, when Cromwell was otherwise engaged, the fenmen had their opportunity and renewed the age-long battle with the enclosers, destroying embankments and sluices. Although Cromwell took measures to protect the adventurers, much of the reclaimed land went back to swamp, and the amphibian inhabitants triumphed for a time. But neither rhymes nor indignation deterred the improvers.

The Restoration saw the foundation of the Bedford Level Corporation. Wind engines began to discharge the waters, and
throughout the eighteenth century many acts of Parliament, both
public and private, were passed to effect the proper drainage of
the Fens. Even so, after the disastrous floods of 1790, Marshall
wrote of the disgraceful state of the Huntingdonshire Fens and
the reporter to the Board of Agriculture added that 'they were
generally unproductive, constantly either covered with water or
in too wet a state for cultivation.' Young speaks of Wildmore Fen
as covered with thistles and nettles four feet high or more, where
in winter horses were driven to such distress for food that they
ate every remaining dead thistle and were said to devour the hair
off the manes and tails of each other. In one year over 40,000 sheep
rotted, and even the young geese died of the cramp on the waterlogged commons. The *Reporter* of 1811 describes the 'awful
reservoir of stagnant water which poisons the air for miles round
about, and sickens and frequently destroys many of the inhabitants, especially such as are not natives.' These 'ague-stricken,
opium-eating fenmen' still opposed attempts at reclamation, but
nothing could arrest the progress of enclosure. More and more
acres were added to the great area where, in the later years of last
century, the 'perfection of farming' was reached. The aspect of
hundreds of square miles of country was completely changed.
The rich marsh life so dear to the naturalist vanished. The bittern
and the crane disappeared before the advance of the reclaimer.

One of the last great incidents of the history of fenland improvement took place in the middle of the nineteenth century,
when the waters of the largest inland lake in the country were
drained away, and its site converted into thriving farms. Whittlesea Mere lay in the Middle Level, right in the centre of the tract
of black fen to the south-east of Peterborough. Camden, in the
sixteenth century, describes it as 'a clear lake, well stocked with
fish. Six miles in length, three in breadth, in a very fenny part of
the country.' He also records the first attempt to control its waters.
Whilst the sons and servants of King Canute were 'sailing along
cheerfully amusing themselves with singing', they suddenly found
themselves in great danger from a violent storm. The King there-

fore caused a dyke to be marked with swords in the marches between Ramsey and Whittlesea.

Throughout the early and middle eighteenth century the network of cuts and sluices extended in the Mere district. The Nene, a main artery of the Middle Level, was scoured and deepened: the Eau Brink Cut, first made by Telford in 1821, was widened. By 1851 the new cuts and their principal drains were ready to receive the waters of the Mere. Holm Fen, once a great reed-shoal, and the adjacent Middlemore Fen, formerly a watery desert, were drained and enclosed. Mr. George Thornhill, M.P., could no longer get into a gunning boat from the windows of the dining-room on the ground floor of Conington Castle and paddle off to shoot coot or to set his dead-lines with eel hooks and trimmers. The days of Whittlesea were drawing to a close. Its waters had already decreased to 1,000 acres. Around its shores had formed great reed-shoals flanked by sedges. From its south and west margin there extended a peat-moss bog, dry for a time in summer, but submerged in winter. The lake side was inhabited only by fishermen, fowlers and reed cutters, who lived in the season in reed-thatched huts. Although the booming of the bittern was no longer heard round its banks, there was still wild fowl in plenty. But the waters had become so filled up with mud and grown with aquatic vegetation that they were of little value as fisheries, either to the owner or to the public. Still, it was not an entirely unproductive area and those who depended upon the Mere as their source of livelihood bewailed its passing. The 'great gulph' over which Canute's sons had sailed had dwindled to a depth of three or four feet. Indeed, in the drought of 1826 the Mere for a time quite dried up, the fish perished and 'lay like heaps of snow on the shore'. In hard winters, when the waters froze solid, there were great gatherings at Whittlesea. The whole countryside came to determine skating championships, to race for a cocked hat, a pig or a purse, and to regale themselves with hot chestnuts. But the last skating race had been run, the last regatta had been held. The point of outfall was chosen: the bank cut and the long-pent-up waters flowed through to the sea. Crowds of people from the neighbourhood and from distant parts of the Fens watched the

34

Mere's lowest ebb. Nine out of ten came with sacks and waded after eels and other fish. 'It was impossible to imagine a more singular scene, as the fading light of a blood-red sunset fell on the vast multitude of figures scattered in all directions over the dreary waste of slimy ooze.' Never again would Mr. Preston from Norwich sail his cutter, the *Bure*, up into the Mere. The landscape which 'teemed with the beauty embodied in the works of Cuyp, Hobbema and Ruysdael', would never again attract Mr. David Cox or Mr. Peter de Wint. Fortunately a pupil of the latter, Mr. J. M. Heathcote of Conington, has preserved for us in a series of sketches the various aspects of the Mere and the surrounding country.

The mud in the bed of the Mere revealed many strange curiosities, not least a fossil skeleton of a grampus. Lying in the bottom of a rudely made boat was found a silver-gilt censer and incense boat belonging to the Abbey of Ramsey, probably lost during the flight from Henry's commissioners.

William Wells of Holme, the owner of the Mere and the adjoining Holme Fen, in all 8,000 acres, was one of the many landowners in the Fens who had spent large sums on improvement.

After the drainage of the Mere it was his task to bring it into a state fit for cultivation. Such problems had been tackled with success by others all over the neighbourhood of the fens. The farming of the reclaimed marshes was by that time famous all over the world. Consequently he and his neighbours established no precedents in method. They followed the usual practices, surmounting in turn, by the light of others' experience, the particular difficulties that were met. The outline of the steps they followed serves as a picture of the perseverance commonly brought to bear on fenland improvement.

The promoters of the draining of Whittlesea Mere and district, of whom, of course, William Wells was one, had been attracted by a model of the Apfold pump which had been shown at the Great Exhibition of 1851. With their own difficulties in mind they installed such a pump, with a 25 h.p. engine, at the extreme eastern corner of what had been the Mere. This engine facilitated the work of shaping the land. Dykes were made, tapping the surrounding waters; roads and farm boundaries were mapped out; negotiations for letting the farms yet to come into being were set afoot. The following summer, 1852, was a time of great storms, rains and floods. It was disastrous to Whittlesea, for on the 12th November the rivers were so swollen that they broke back through the banks and in a few hours the whole was again a lake under 2½ feet of water. The installation of the Apfold pump proved to have been wise for, raising 20,000 gallons of water a minute and working incessantly for twenty-three days, it again accomplished the drainage. A luncheon was given in the engine-room, decorated with flowers, reeds and banners, in honour of the pump.

There were three distinct types of new land each requiring different treatment: the bed of the Mere, the skirting silt deposits on which the reeds had grown, and the low-lying peatlands abutting on these. The improvers had to meet in turn nearly all the ordinary difficulties to which fenland reclamation is subject and peculiar difficulties besides.

The Mere bed itself presented the least of the difficulties. The surface had to be levelled, but at first a horse and cart could not be trusted on the bed. It was difficult enough for the men engaged in cutting drains and levelling to move about. When the sticky mud hardened a further difficulty presented itself. The surface broke into deep cracks and fissures which persisted for three or four years. Even when the horses were shod with boards they could not safely work on the land. Consequently the whole of the preparation of the ground for the rape, which was to be the first crop, had to be done by hand.

Light harrows were drawn over the surface in some parts, and on others men dug and forked the land by hand. Then the seed was sown. Good crops were taken, and after this first harvest the land was ready for wheat and oats. 'The wind, which in the autumn of 1851 was curling the blue waters of the lake, in the autumn of 1853 was blowing in the same place over the fields of yellow corn.'

The ordinary practice in fenland reclamation had changed considerably through the discovery in the same century of 'frequent' drainage and subsoil ploughing, and by the greater knowledge of the necessary blend of clay subsoil with peat to make a good loam. The object of the fen farmer was to get rid of the turf, and then to get a sufficient quantity of earthy matter into the soil to give it solidity and consistency. Naturally, the first operation was the making of surface drains—either open or turf- or stone-filled, for pipe conduits were not yet manufactured at a cost which allowed them to be widely used. The peat thus treated became drier; in order still further to reduce its bulk, the land had used to be pared and burnt, that is, as soon as the east winds of spring arrived the surface was breast-ploughed, then pared and turned over. When it was dry the peat was piled into heaps and burned. The ashes were spread over the ground as manure and the first crop, usually rape seed, was sown. Sheep and cattle, feeding off the rape, helped still further to consolidate the peat. But by this time 'claying' was the universal practice. The benefits of claying, summed up by a farmer in 1842, were those of giving solidity to the soil, of stiffening the straw of corn, and, by preventing mildew, improving both the quantity and quality of corn; moreover, the clayed soil was healthy for turnips, and the clay added that which clover liked. In winter lines for trenching would be set out and the peat dug through to the clay stratum below. The clay was then thrown up on each side of the trench. After the winter frosts had played their part in breaking down the clay lumps and aerating the whole, the land was 'harrowed about' and the first crop sown with a dressing of the new artificial manures. When the clay lay too deep to allow trenching to be carried out economically a supply was carted on to the land from some nearby source and spread.

At first an attempt was made in the Whittlesea area to bring the bog into cultivation by the old system of paring and burning, which the East-fen farmer had observed to ruin those who followed it. Here, too, the succeeding crops were poor and the method failed to give an adequate return.

Ordinarily the lowland clay was found at a depth of from 2 to 5 feet. The bog round Whittlesea Mere was fast becoming dry, and its crust was consolidating. But when claying was contemplated it was found that the clay lay buried 15 feet below the peat.

At such a depth the cost of claying in the ordinary manner was prohibitive. However, there was clay in the bed of the Mere, besides fertile silt enough and to spare. Incidentally, the qualities of that silt deposit were well known—one old farmer used to say that he never fallowed his land but when providence did so, by a flood or the breach of a bank, the sediment left by the waters completely renovating the land. So, at the same time that the Mere bed was being cut through by deep channels for draining, the silt and clay thus excavated were applied as warp over the bog.

The assistance of one of the great land improvement companies—the West of England Drainage and Inclosure Company —was called in. This company directed most of the draining, warping and road-making on the estate. About 1,500 acres stood in need of warp, but, as a start, only a few hundred acres could be tackled. The stagnant water that remained was drawn off by means of turf-filled drains. Men could pick their way over the uneven surface with comparative ease. An iron railway, nearly two miles long, was laid down from the bed of the Mere to the site of the warping. Fifty trucks, drawn by teams of horses, carried the silt and gault clay along the track-way. It was at first decided that a warp of 6 inches for land which was to bear arable crops, and 4 inches for pasture, would be necessary. Later, at Dr. Voelcher's suggestion, the depth of the warp was lessened to 4 inches for arable and 3 for grass. So working at full speed, in fair weather, an acre and a half of land was covered by alluvial soil and gault in a day.

It was a scene of enormous activity. The bed of the Mere was under crops. Warping was in progress as fast as the land could be prepared to receive it. Roads, made from a ballast of burnt clay with peat, were being made. Farms were being laid out and houses and homesteads were being built. The cost of reclamation was high. The dry-warping alone, at this time, cost, for a 4-inch layer, between £15 and £16 an acre, and for a 6-inch layer as much as £18 to £19 an acre.

Farther afield still attempts were being made to bring the remoter parts of the bog into shape by deep ploughing, by which operation the 'moorband' of hard, impervious peat, which lay at a foot below the surface, was dragged up and burnt.

So much had been accomplished by 1860 that an estimate of the money-value of the produce of 3,000 acres reached a total of £12,350:

	£
600 acres of wheat at 4 qrs. per acre—2,400 qrs. at 40s.	4,800
500 acres of oats, at 6 qrs. per acre—3,000 qrs. at 20s.	3,000
150 acres seeds / 150 acres rape / 100 acres mangolds — carrying 150 beasts at £3 per head increase, and 400 sheep at £1 per head increase per year	850
200 acres wheat at 3½ qrs. per acre—700 qrs. at 40s.	1,400
200 acres oats at 5 qrs. per acre—1,000 qrs at 20s.	1,000
1,000 acres grass / 100 acres green crops — 100 beasts / 1,000 sheep	1,300
	£12,350

Although the tax on the land (under the Middle Level Act) amounted at that time to 12s. 3d. per acre, the difference between the lettable value of the land and the cost of reclamation was sufficient, it was said, 'to show results which may well encourage enterprise of a similar character'.

A visitor to the district, in the same period, noted that on the bed of the Mere two-thirds of each farm was under corn: that the size and numbers of the straw-stacks bore witness to the bulk of straw—more than enough to meet the requirements of the land for manure.

Six or seven years later another visitor described what he saw. Land that had been worth but a shilling an acre was then let at

20s. to 30s. He too found wonderful rickyards. Buildings and farmsteads were completed. There were some 'very neat labourers' cottages, constructed of wood, the walls being formed of feather-edged boards nailed to strong posts, and well plastered and finished inside, while the roofs are carefully and substantially tiled', which, the inmates told him, were most comfortable. The Great Cattle Plague happened at that time (1866) to have made it unsafe to buy in beasts, so that sheep, instead of cattle, were being wintered in the yards, and the straw trodden by the sheep was carted off to the fields. Mangolds, kohl rabi, and turnips were being grown and fed. Other crops, such as potatoes, were being tried on the land. Instead of manual labour or dangerous horse labour (often on the newly reclaimed bogs horses sank so low that they had to be pulled out with ropes) a steam engine was being used. A Fowler four-furrow plough and a Coleman culti-vator were dragged back and forth, uprooting the buried trees and breaking the peat.

Schemes of improvement were still proceeding. Instead of drawing the gault from the bed of the Mere it was now being carried from a much nearer point, near Mr. Wells' house at Holme, and the cost of claying was of the order of £9, against £18 to £19 previously.

But all these things had not been accomplished smoothly. Frost and drought and wind had brought their peculiar ills. Wherever in the fens the soil was neither pure peat nor pure silt, but peat with an admixture of silt, it was subject to the peculiar process of 'honey-combing'. The lowest and wettest lands at Whittlesea were of this alluvial deposit. When the young wheat was springing on the bed of the Mere, and on those silty deposits which had been the reed shoals, all might go well until frosts came. With the frosts the surface of the soil formed a hard crust, which pinched the young plants of wheat and drew their roots out of the earth. Also, the silt dried out and lost a great deal of its weight. After a spell of drought, followed by a high wind, the very soil itself was blown all about, to settle in the slight hollows and furrows. Sometimes it took the young plants with it, some-times it left them exposed to die. This 'honey-combing' and drifting had to be stopped, and large tracts of the alluvial soil had to receive clay dressings to improve its consistency.

Another great difficulty had been caused by the subsidence of the whole area, as the peat dried and shrank. When the homesteads were put up they had, owing to the nature of the land, to be built on piles. The sites chosen were always the highest ground, but even so the great subsidence of the land reduced the water level below the foundations, and the heads of the piles decayed. Buildings became unsafe, and the piles had to be renewed —all of which added to the cost of improving the estate.

But William Wells was satisfied with the results of the work. During its progress he wrote: 'The accomplishment of a success, on however small a scale, must be reckoned as a profit; and the satisfaction of contemplating the changed aspect of the district, as well as the improved condition of the neighbouring poor, both in respect of constant, well-paid employment and better health, is alone a never-failing and substantial interest for the capital expended.'

Wells died in 1889 after a long life, lived at a time when agricultural improvement made remarkable strides. His contribution to the improvement of the fens was not his only service to agriculture. He was interested in all the movements going on round him. Portable steam engines for farm use were brought out in the 'forties, and he encouraged their proper use by offering prizes to drivers at the Peterborough Agricultural Society's meetings. He was a member of the Council of the 'Royal', and later became its President. The records of the Canterbury 'Royal' disclose that he won many prizes and commendations for his stock; he was President of the Shire Horse Society in 1885, a Member of Parliament for many years, a Justice of the Peace and High Sheriff of Huntingdonshire. He fulfilled completely all those duties which fell to the lot of the landed gentlemen of his time.

The reclamation of his fenland estate was an undertaking which not only contributed to the general improvement which was 'silently changing the face of the countryside', but to an actual change on the map of England.

THE WORLD WAR ON THE LAND

By the time that the tall wheat was waving over the site of Wittlesea Mere, the time for ventures on the Wittlesea pattern was nearly gone. The 'Golden Age' was drawing to a close. Wheat, which had long been England's chief arable crop, had touched 75s. a quarter in 1855 and 64s. in 1868, fell to 45s. in 1870 and (after a short-lived rise during the Crimean affair) to 44s. in 1879, the year which yielded the poorest crop in a century. Worse was still to come. The flood of imports reached its height in the early 'nineties when good grain fetched no more than 23s. These were not the conditions to encourage the adventurer. Here and there, indeed, another bite was taken out of the foreshores of the Wash as the rich silt slowly built up to the level that would allow drainage at low tide. Here and there, in the uplands, a man of exceptional faith in the future, or with a lack of economic inhibitions, struggled to make another 'intake' from the moor. But these small gains were far more than offset by the fields and farms, but lately won from the waste, that went back to scrub or heath.

The next great effort was called for in the Second World War, in urgent haste and inevitably with but scant regard to profit or loss. Much of the land now to be made productive had borne useful crops in the good times, but had reverted to the condition in which Caird had seen it in 1850—'impenetrable thickets of gorse and thorn abandoned to rabbits; vast straggling hedgerows, waterlogged fields owing to choked-up drains; growth of bracken destroying pastures'. Even some fields that had been won back in the First World War were again wildernesses. For the rest, there were old and neglected common grazings and stretches of moor and marsh that were now to see the plough for the first time.

But new weapons of peace, as well as of war, were now at hand —bulldozers and gyrotillers, prairie-buster ploughs and monster disc harrows, giant excavators and flame-throwers. And the War Committees, under the inspiring and exacting generalship of a tireless Minister, set about the task of producing corn and potatoes from Cornish commons and Northumbrian moors, from

Midland thickets, Welsh hills and the reed-grown swamps of East Anglia. They took the trainer's gallops, the sportsman's duck-shoot, the townsman's park and golf-course and the nurseryman's rose garden. And, all things considered, the results were surprisingly good.

One of the most spectacular efforts was seen on the adjacent Feltwell and Methwold fens, running to some ten thousand acres and lying on the south-west corner of Norfolk between the sandy 'uplands' and the Little Ouse and Withy. Some considerable part of the land had once been farmed, but an inundation in 1913 had washed away the banks and roads, and had filled the ditches. The only cultivation was in small patches adjoining the upland. For the rest, the land was covered with tall coarse grass, sedges and rushes, interspersed with thorn and creeping willow. In 1942 there were some eight thousand acres of this desolate waste without shed or cottage, road or hedge. The soil was a black peat, fluffy when dry, overlying in some parts blue clay and in others running sand.

Before anything else could be done, means of access for tackle had to be provided, and some twenty miles of concrete roads were laid, mostly following the lines of the old 'droves'. The next operation was to instal a pumping plant, with sufficient power to lift water, at the rate of a hundred and twenty tons a minute, over the twenty-foot bank into the river. With the help of a dozen excavators and two bull-dozers a hundred miles of drains were dug—mains up to fifty feet wide drawing the water from six-foot field ditches. Rectangular fields of ten to twenty acres were laid out and, at four strategic points, groups of light farm buildings were set up on concrete rafts. Here, too, temporary housing was provided for the many workers.

The initial cultivations presented the expected difficulties. Crawler tractors and wide-wheeled implements were needed to traverse the soft wet land, and submerged tree trunks—'bog oaks'—some forty or fifty feet long, had to be dug, drawn or blasted out of the land. In one spring, too, came a spell of parching sun followed by a strong wind, bringing the calamity that the old fenland adventurers had feared. Clouds of sooty dust drifted off the fields and filled many of the ditches, so that the excavators had to go back over their newly accomplished work. But planned cropping, designed to avoid any wide expanses of bare soil in spring, prevented a recurrence. Again, there was the usual struggle with annual weeds—'fat hen', treacle mustard, willow-weed and more—that had to be controlled with chemical sprays. Moreover, a plentiful stock of wireworms, moving freely in the loose soil, caused a good deal of loss; and while potatoes, sugar beet and vegetable crops throve and yielded well, the corn crops, lush and often to all appearance healthy, gave but meagre yields of grain.

But by 1949, when the work was done, the fens could show fine crops of potatoes, vegetables, rye and others, and lush grass leys carrying big herds and flocks of thriving animals.

Such spectacular operations should not blind our eyes to the achievements of little men who, with but small financial resources, are continuously adding their mites to our treasury of farm land. They are to be found in the uplands of the Scottish Border Counties, in the Yorkshire Dales, along the flanks of Dartmoor and elsewhere. Starting with a patch of moorland hillside, they clear away boulders, drain, lime, reseed and enclose.

This 'pioneering at home' is nowhere so vigorously carried on as in the Isles of Orkney. It has been going on almost continuously during the present century, for to-day there is a goodly number of well established and sizable farms of which there is no sign on the map of 1902. If you ask the owner of one of these farms how it was created, he may relate how he bought, which his slender savings, perhaps ten or twenty acres of open heather hill; how he bought, too, a tiny flock of ewes and a cow, built a little stone house and a cowshed with his own hands, and marked out his land, piece by piece, to be ploughed with horses or oxen (or perhaps spade trenched), limed with locally abundant shell sand, dressed with basic slag and sown to oats and grass. Field after field was enclosed by stone wall, for stone, at least, is plentiful. Usually, the owner worked for wages during at least part of the year, while his wife built up a flock of poultry which made a useful contribution to the family fortune. Then another piece of land was bought, and dealt with in turn.

In recent years help has been provided. It has been possible to hire a crawler tractor with a strong single-furrow plough, which lays the heather in a deep grave, and heavy disc harrows to consolidate the furrows and produce a tilth. A sympathetic Government now provides half the cost of the transport and distribution of the lime. Half a century's work can be measured by a few figures: in 1900 Orkney had 28,000 cattle and 36,000 sheep, of rather poor quality. In 1948 the figures were 47,000 and 59,000, and the quality had vastly improved.

Our farmers are sometimes blamed for objecting, bitterly and unreasonably, to the taking of farmland for new towns or playing fields, opencast coal working, water reservoirs and other necessary uses or desirable purposes. But if we remember all the skill, sweat, and courage that has gone into our farms, we may perhaps understand their point of view.

What of the future? As these lines are being written, reclamation is still proceeding. Here and there along the shores of the Wash new sea walls are going up, which will hold back the tides and enable mud flats to be turned into fields of potatoes and wheat. In two dozen counties crawlers are at work, turning bracken- and heather-clad wastes into lush pastures. Up on the Sussex Downs are new fields waving with barley. But the possible addition to our farm area is limited. Some say a million acres, some three million, some ten. We get one figure—a large one—if we think only in terms of physical possibilities. We get another—and much smaller—if we think in the business man's terms of a reasonable return on our investment. The question that we must sometime decide is how far we are to be governed by economic considerations. Business is business, no doubt; but a starving man is in no good case to dicker about the price of bread.

2

MACHINES AND MEN

For man, who is so weak a thing
Assumes thereby
Mighty extension and titanic force.

J. REDWOOD ANDERSON

S ince the earliest beginnings of agriculture the farmer has
exercised his mind to discover less laborious methods of
tillage and harvesting. The first mechanized farmer was
he who invented the digging stick as a substitute for his finger-
nails. There were sickles, made of flint, before the discovery of
the way to make bronze; the plough goes back to remote antiquity;
prehistoric man threshed by means of the flail, or by the feet of
his oxen.

In the eighteenth century there were three important steps of
progress. The plough, as the arable farmer's most important
implement, had received a good deal of attention from men like
James Small; sufficient strength had been compressed into lesser
weight, and patient trials had resulted in a form of mould-board
that accomplished the inversion of the furrow with less friction
and reduced draft. Jethro Tull had invented his corn drill. In 1785
young Meikle had succeeded, where many others had failed, in
inventing a thresher that did the work of the flail; and by the end
of the century shakers and fans had been embodied in a machine
which was then able to separate the crop into grain, chaff and
straw. Watt's steam engine had been invented, but its use had
gone no further than that of substituting wind or water power as
a source of power for stationary machines.

Aberdeenshire Twelve-oxen Plough of the Eighteenth Century

THE REAPER

The first great achievement of the nineteenth century was the invention of the reaper. Majority opinion was at first all against the possibility. 'The construction of a reaping machine to cut down corn without loss or damage is hopeless and impracticable.' Reapers had in fact been built and subjected to trials. Four patents had been taken out before 1828, when the sentence above quoted was written; and one at least of the machines had been subjected to official trials and had won a favourable report. This was the invention of James Smith of 'Deanstonizing' fame and it was viewed at work by a Committee of the Highland and Agricultural Society in 1815. The Committee reported that it 'not only wrought expeditiously', but that in their 'humble opinion the machine was, next to the plough itself, the most valuable invention that has occurred in the annals of husbandry.' But the Committee was in error; the practical solution had not yet been found. For some time later the work of harvest was to depend on gangs of Irish or Highland labourers, or of weavers and other artisans who left their looms and workshops for a short season in the fields. Controversy was not on hand *versus* machine, but on sickle *versus* scythe.

The year 1828 saw the first notice of the first successful reaping machine, the invention of Patrick Bell. Bell was one of the large family of an Angus farmer who had worked his way as a student of Divinity at St. Andrews, eking out his resources by teaching and by farm work; he later became minister of the small parish of Carmyllie in his native county. As a lad he had a turn for mechanics. He had seen a plate of Smith's machine and had pondered over its principles. He foresaw the growing difficulty that the farmer must expect to face in the assembling of the necessary harvest gang, and having himself been often called from his books to the harvest field, his thought may probably have been stimulated by his own experience of long weary hours stooping over a sickle. It was in 1826, while walking in his father's garden, that a pair of garden shears, sticking in the hedge, gave him his idea— the idea that mechanical scissors rather than mechanical scythes might be made the basis of a reaper. He set to work making wooden patterns and had them copied in iron by the local blacksmith; he tried and rejected and tried again. His cutting-machine, when finally made, was tested in an old barn, with an artificial crop of oats planted stalk by stalk in soil brought in from the field. The next step was to add a travelling canvas to deliver the cut stalks in a swath alongside the machine, and a reel to hold the waving crop against the cutting mechanism. The next trial of 1828 may be described in Bell's own words:

'Before the corn was perfectly ripe (I had not the patience to wait for that), my brother . . . and I resolved to have a quiet and unobserved start by ourselves. That could not be got while the sun was in the heavens, nor for a considerable time after he was set; and accordingly, about eleven o'clock at night, in a darkish autumn evening, when every man, woman and child were in their beds, the machine was quietly taken from its quarters, the good horse Jock was yoked to it, and we trio wended our way across a field of lea to one of standing wheat beyond it—my brother and I speaking the meanwhile to one another in whispers. We reached our destination, and the machine was put into position right at the end of a ridge. My duty was to look ahead, and my brother's to guide the horse. I gave the word of command to go on, and on the implement went; but it had not proceeded above five or six yards when I called upon my brother to stop. Upon examining the work we found it far from satisfactory—the wheat was well enough cut, but it was lying in a bundle before the machine. For a moment we were both downcast. But, recollecting myself, I had yet great hope, and said so, the whole of the machine not being used, the reel or collector having been left behind. I ran across the field and brought the reel and everything connected with it, upon my shoulders, and adjusted it as well as the darkness of night would permit, and we were soon ready for a second start. Taking our positions respectively as before, the machine moved forward, and now all was right. The wheat was lying by the side of the machine as prettily as any that has been ever cut by it since. After this we merely took it back again to the end of the ridge, and made a cut with the open edge to ascertain how the swathes would lie upon the stubble, with which being well pleased we, after some pardonable congratulations, moved the machine back to its old quarters as quickly as possible.'

A contemporary writer, computing the financial benefits of a reaping machine to the agricultural industry, arrived at the conclusion that over the whole of Great Britain a saving of £1,000,000 per year was possible, and that a premium of £20,000 or even £30,000 would not be too high an encouragement for such an object. Patrick Bell, however, reaped no pecuniary reward. A sum of £50 awarded to him by the Highland Society in 1828 met, in part, the expenses he incurred in obtaining a copy of the original machine.

Thus in 1828 the doubts and fears expressed as to the practicability of a reaping machine were confuted. The new machine attained a quick notoriety. A description and a plate, by Bell, were published, and the machine itself was exhibited, in 1828 and 1829, at various farms. These exhibitions were attended by proprietors of land, farmers, and others. At the first public trial, a body of such men reported that two machines, one of them chiefly made by Mr. Patrick Bell himself and the other erected by a mechanic at Dundee, were seen cutting oats, barley, and wheat on land with uneven surface and a considerable declivity. A five-foot cut left a stubble 3 to 4 inches high, free from loose straw, and the cut corn deposited on the side of the machine in a regular manner. Without raking, the corn could be collected into compact and well-formed sheaves. Six to eight persons, gathering, binding, and setting, constituted the team of workers. One horse propelled the machine from behind. The estimated cost of the reaper was £30.

The inventor did not take out a patent, a deliberate abstention in order that the implement might go into the world free of any avoidable expense. A public-spirited nobleman, indeed, offered to bear the expense of a patent, but this offer Bell refused.

Bell took his M.A. degree, and became a Presbyterian Minister. He left for a stay in America in 1833, and his reaper, oddly enough, lapsed into comparative obscurity. As he himself later wrote, his invention was like a child born prematurely into a world which was not ready for it. It seems that the implement met with coolness from farmers (for there was still an adequate, if declining, supply of labour) and with opposition from the working classes. The replacement of men by machines was resented by the labourers, who looked upon it as taking the bread out of their mouths. Such an attitude was a painful surprise to the inventor, who was largely actuated by humanity towards those same workers. Actual failures of machines, too, were frequent, a trouble that was due, in part, to Bell's failure to take out a patent; had he done so, the implements would have been constructed more uniformly and of better-quality material, whereas, as it happened, individual smiths and wheelwrights experimented diversely with copies of the original. Lack of strength in the vital parts was the cause of many breakages in actual working. Drill husbandry was by no means universally practised: the drainage systems had not been re-volutionized by deep-draining and subsoil ploughing, and ridge-and-furrow land was an obstacle to the proper working of the early machines.

Not only were these difficulties to be reckoned with, but there was, then as now, a good deal of false sentiment about the amenities of the countryside. It was claimed that the 'gaiety and charm of rural life at the harvest season would be destroyed, and the beauties of autumn defaced'. But there were pertinacious farmers who stuck to the machine, and its continued existence, after the first years, we owe to such practical men. Patrick Bell's original machine was retained by his brother—that same brother who had joined in the congratulations over the secret trial on the unripe wheat. This brother, now farming on his own account at Inchmichael, in Perthshire, worked his machine year after year, replacing those parts which broke in action, strengthening those which proved to need strength, and keeping it alive. By the harvest of 1832 ten machines between them cut 400 acres of corn in Scotland. Ten more had been built, of which two had been sent to Australia and two to Poland.

During this time Patrick Bell did not hesitate, when called upon, to journey to the various farms and himself give instruction on the proper management of the machines. Even when he was in America we hear of his giving advice and explanation on the principles of reaping machines.

Farmers in the vicinity of Inchmichael grew accustomed to the drone of the reaper in the harvest fields, and many became acquainted with its mechanism. Some of these farmers left their homes in Scotland for the New World (emigration to America being at this time on the increase) and took with them this knowledge. Thus, although we have no record of an actual reaper being sent to America, it is possible that, through this agency, and by means of the journals in which detailed descriptions had been published, Bell's reaper influenced the inventors of the American machines that first obtained wide notice, and whose arrival in England in 1851 caused a considerable sensation.

Contemporary with Patrick Bell was another, whose name is more generally associated with reaping machines—Cyrus McCormick, who, in 1831, at the age of twenty-two, was said to have 'invented the first practical reaper that the world has ever seen.'

It is difficult to say which of these men should be given the first place as inventor of the reaper. Certainly the McCormick family, father and son, had been hard at work on the problem since the early years of the century, and had made several unsuccessful machines before 1831.

Robert McCormick, father of Cyrus, and a man of Scottish ancestry, was a farmer and inventor of Virginia, U.S.A. Cyrus was born in 1809. He grew up on the farm, watching his father

at work in his log workshop, interested in the repeated attempts
to build a reaper. When he was seven years old he saw a fantastic
machine, pushed from behind by two horses, utterly fail to
achieve his father's hopes. He saw it hauled from the field, the
jest of the countryside. But he himself set to work, when he grew
older, in the same log workshop on the same problem.

One day, late in the July of 1831, Cyrus put a horse between
the shafts of his reaper and drove it down the yellow cornfield.
His father and the rest of the family were the only witnesses of
the consummation of their common hopes.

But progress was not easy. Money was necessary and money
was scarce. Capital for the manufacture of reapers could not be
built up out of farming profits. An iron furnace which the family
had started failed, and the McCormicks were bankrupt. But news
of the wonderful machine had leaked out. In 1840 a rough-looking
farmer rode up to the McCormick homestead with fifty dollars
in his pocket, and bought the first reaper. By 1844 fifty had been
sold.

Away to the West there were the prairies—great stretches of
level land, millions of potential corn farms. When a friend suggested that it was on these prairies that the reaper would prove
itself, the McCormicks moved to an isolated little town called
Chicago. From that date, 1847, Chicago became the home of the
manufacture of harvesting machinery.

In 1851 England first saw two of the American reaping machines
—McCormick's and Hussey's. Their appearance at the Crystal
Palace Exhibition of that year created vast excitement. The reapers
had a brilliant press, and they came into general use almost at once.
It was then, or rather in the following harvest season, that Bell's
reaper, the same that had worked so long on his brother's farm at
Inchmichael, 'rose like a giant refreshed', and, with unimportant
modifications, challenged the American machines. Many people
learned for the first time that there had been a successful reaper in
their midst for over twenty years. At the Highland Society's Show
at Perth in 1852, Bell's machine—'Lass of Gowrie'—met and
completely defeated a Hussey champion: a challenge was issued
to McCormick, the contest to take place on Hugh Watson's farm

at Keillor, for a stake of £50; but the trial did not materialize. In 1853, however, the battle was staged between Bell's reaper, slightly improved by Crosskill, and a McCormick machine, and the first premium was awarded to Bell's.

Patrick Bell, then married and living quietly in his Manse at Carmyllie, was drawn into public notice once more, and achieved a fame overdue by some twenty-three years. Large fortunes were made by firms and individuals manufacturing reapers and patenting improvements, but this fact did not worry Patrick. The last we know of him, in connection with his reaper, was the acknowledgment of his genius in the form of the presentation, in 1868, of a piece of plate and £1,000 at the General Meeting of the Highland and Agricultural Society, 'by a large number of his countrymen in token of their appreciation of his pre-eminent services as the inventor of the first efficient reaping machine.' He died at Carmyllie in the following year, 1869. A window in the little church has since been dedicated to his memory.

As for the McCormicks—they were to develop into The International Harvester Company, of world-wide fame. By 1871 the factory at Chicago was turning out 10,000 harvesters a year. At the end of the century thousands of machines a week were being poured out and sent to all parts of the world. The subsequent history of the firm is one of phenomenal growth and success.

Cyrus H. McCormick, the original inventor, died a rich man in 1884. The French Academy had elected him a Member, he having 'done more for the cause of agriculture than any other living man.'

NOTABLE IMPLEMENT MAKERS

The next outstanding invention in the way of farm machinery was the steam plough. Before this, however, came an important development in the implement industry. Like most other manufactures in the eighteenth century, that of farm machinery had been in the hands of small men. The farmer's plough and harrow were made by the village blacksmith, his wagon by the village wheelwright and his threshing machine by a local millwright with his small team of craftsmen.

But the industrial revolution came, and manufacture of the main standard implements began to be concentrated in large factories. These factories provided an increasing number of the home farmers' requirements and also, up till about the middle of the nineteenth century, supplied such world demand as had then developed. McCormick with his reaper was the first foreign competitor in the field.

Typical and prominent among the great implement firms which arose in the first half of the nineteenth century were Howards of Bedford, Ransomes of Ipswich, Clayton and Shuttleworth of Lincoln, and Garrett of Leiston. Fowlers of Leeds came later, for the firm first came into prominence with John Fowler's invention of the steam plough.

John Howard, born in 1791, was apprenticed by his mother to an ironmonger in Bedford. He had inherited from his mother a mind of great activity, had been trained by her to habits of industry and taught by her to love learning and fear God.

His apprenticeship over, he first worked for an ironmonger in Olney, and later for another in Hanley. With the latter he fell out over the matter of Sunday observance and, returning to Bedford at the age of twenty-two, set up in business on his own account. He married 'a very wise woman', who bore him the three sons, James, Charles, and Frederick, who were to complete the building of the firm and of the family fortunes.

John Howard's inventive faculty was soon brought to bear on problems of tillage, and, in the first number of the *Bedford Times*, in 1845, appeared the advertisement of the Britannia Implement Works. The son, James, who inherited both his father's inventive genius and his indomitable perseverance, and who worked in the closest harmony with Frederick, kept on turning out one patent after another and extending the business until the name of the Britannia works was known all over the world.

While the father was still alive James had been sent abroad to study the requirements of various foreign countries, and he continued in his later years to travel widely. A Scottish farmer on a journey south to buy some of Charles Howard's Oxford Sheep paid a visit to the works and wrote of 'The serried ranks of ploughs, suitable for every country under the sun; Cape ploughs, Indian ploughs with heavy bent-wood beams, ploughs of iron and wood for South Russia, one-way ploughs for South America, Spain, and Turkey, double and triple ploughs of all kinds. . . .' Always in the forefront of progress, the Howards took out a patent, in 1852, for a plough with a chilled or case-hardened mould-board, twenty-five years before this particular improvement was adopted in America.

James Howard was prominent in many things apart from his business. He created a model estate and village at Clapham Park. As Mayor of Bedford his first task was to attack the urgent problem of water supply, and, like Hezekiah, he 'dug a pool, built a conduit and brought water to a city.' He addressed the Farmers' Club and the Statistical Society on a variety of subjects, from the philosophy of implements to monetary theory, and gave accounts of his foreign travels.

Nominally a Tory in politics, and latterly a Member of Parliament, Howard was a man of truly liberal ideas. We find him in 1886 taking the Chair for Mrs. Henry Fawcett at a meeting in support of women's suffrage, and working hard in the cause of education. James Howard, M.P., walking down St. James's with his thumb stuck in his waistcoat, deservedly prosperous and respected, was the same man who, as a lad of twenty, had taken his coat off to demonstrate his father's patent two-wheeled plough at the Liverpool 'Royal' in 1841.

At the first Royal Show at Oxford in 1839 the Gold Medal was awarded to Messrs. R. and J. Ransomes, who 'sent up their wagons laden with more than six tons of machinery and implements of superior manufacture.' Robert Ransome senior, the founder of the famous firm, was born in 1753, the son of a schoolmaster; he went to Norwich to seek his fortune and, like the elder Howard, was apprenticed to an ironmonger. His portrait, painted during his mature years, shows a man of high forehead, with an expression of kindliness and quiet strength. In Norwich he took up the production of brass castings and, with the backing of his bank manager, started an iron foundry. This and another small one at Cambridge seem to have been the only foundries then existing in the Eastern counties. In 1785 Ransome took out a patent for tempering cast-iron ploughshares. Four years later he moved to Ipswich, starting with a capital of £200 and taking with him a single workman who was to remain his devoted assistant throughout the remainder of his life. At Ipswich he rented and later bought an old maltings which he converted into a foundry.

Still experimenting in metallurgy he realized, in 1803, his dream of a cast-iron ploughshare that would remain sharp in use and would eliminate the expense of constant repointing which was the drawback of the standard wrought-iron share. The actual production of the first chilled-iron share seems to have resulted from an accident. Ransome had been trying various plans to secure the hardening that he wanted, when one day his molten metal burst out of the moulding frame and ran about the floor. When this metal was being broken up for remelting the master noticed that those parts which had come in contact with the cold floor were harder than the others. His patent of the Chilled Share, granted in 1803, was immediately profitable, and laid the foundation of the firm's success.

Among other patents taken out by Robert Ransome was one embodying a principle on which all subsequent ploughs have been built, viz. a construction which admits of the working parts being removed, and fresh parts substituted, in the field—i.e. without the necessity of transporting the whole implement to a forge. The case-hardening process was applied to many things other than shares, with equal success, especially perhaps in connection with railway construction.

The subsequent history of the family and the firm is too complicated for condensation. It is a story of keen and able sons and grandsons, of various partnerships, and of changing activities, ranging from railway material and the earliest cast-iron bridges to windmills and steam engines, from threshers to munitions of war; but always with the simple tools of husbandry—ploughs and harrows and cultivators—as one of the main products.

The firm was interested, among other things, in the early development of mechanical road transport, and one of their first contracts was for road 'steamers' for the Indian Government. One of these, fitted with rubber tyres, travelled the 850 miles from Ipswich to Edinburgh and back at an average speed of nearly seven miles an hour. This was in 1871. Fifteen years earlier the firm had built John Fowler's first steam plough.

Richard Garrett of Leiston, in Suffolk, did not build up a vast business organization like Howards or Ransomes; but he made some excellent scarifiers, bred some equally good Suffolk sheep and was a notable character. Like Mr. Winston Churchill he affected rather original headgear, and Albert Pell has thus immortalized his hat: 'About this time (1843) the two wonders of the [Royal] Show, to my youthful mind, were the hats of Mr. Richard Garrett of Leiston and Mr. George Turner of Barton. They have never been equalled. . . . He came to Ely, on horseback, assisted by his hat if the wind was favourable. We and others dined together and discussed implements—and splendidly constructed were his own. I have bits of them, of that date, in use now. Having given our orders, he forwarded them either by his own or hackney horses, from Leiston to Soham near Newmarket. There our cattle met them and drew the wondrous inventions to our reedy homesteads.'

THE COMING OF STEAM

When Cobbett rode through East Lothian in October, 1832, he saw much to admire as well as much to raise his anger. Among other things that met his eye were the smoke stacks of many threshing engines. 'Just at the little village of Cockburnspath we get into the county of Haddington . . . and such cornfields, and fields of turnips, such turnips in those fields, such stackyards and such a total absence of dwelling houses as never, surely, were seen in any county upon earth. You very frequently see more than a hundred stacks in one yard, each containing, on an average, from fifteen to twenty quarters of wheat or of oats; all built in the neatest manner; thatched extremely well, the thatch bound down by exterior bands, spars not being used owing to the scarcity of wood. In some of these yards the threshing-machine is worked by horses, but in the greater part by steam; and where coals are at a distance by wind or water; so that in this country of the finest land that ever was seen, all the elements seem to be pressed into the amiable service of sweeping the people from the face of the earth.' The steam engine was thus already raising the problem of rural unemployment. A few years later labourers in the south were rioting and smashing threshers in protest against the loss of their winter's work at the flail.

But as yet the steam engine had found only a very limited application on the land. It was a fixture in the buildings, a valuable power-unit on the largest class of farms; but there its usefulness ended. The next object was to set the engine on wheels and make it portable. It is true that the early 'portables' required six horses to pull them to their work—an absurd situation, as Aveling, another notable agricultural engineer, pointed out, '. . . like six sailing vessels towing a steamer . . . an insult to mechanical science'. Nevertheless these clumsy, sturdy old engines, many of which survived till recent years, solved the problem of mechanical threshing on the ordinary small or medium-sized farm which could not afford its own threshing plant. The largest makers of portables, and of the complementary portable threshers, were the great firm of Clayton and Shuttleworth of Lincoln. The demand for these reached considerable proportions just about 1850, and increased very quickly in the next few years. Claytons' output of 'portables' illustrates this:

1851	.. ..	140
1852	.. ..	242
1853	.. ..	293
1855	.. ..	491

Between 1849 and 1883—twenty-four years—the firm sold over 17,000 threshers and 19,000 portable steam engines.

The next step was for Aveling, of Aveling and Porter, to avenge his 'insult to mechanical science'.

Aveling had been a farmer on Romney Marsh, but he gave up

farming and established a small works at Rochester. In 1859 he took out his first patent for a self-propelling steam engine, and the next year exhibited, at the Canterbury 'Royal', an eight-horse engine, made to his design by Claytons and 'fitted with the Exhibitor's patent Arrangement for Locomotion and Steerage by which the whole set of machinery may be moved from farm to farm without horses'; but the judges were completely silent on its qualities. Aveling, however, was not to be suppressed, and went on showing improved models, establishing the prosperity of Aveling and Porter on the success of his engine. He got due, if somewhat belated, recognition from the 'Royal', for at the Wolverhampton meeting in 1871 his engine was awarded a fifty pound prize.

The still more important aim, in the opinion of most agricultural thinkers, was to apply steam to the ordinary operations of tillage. Indeed from the middle of last century up till the 'eighties the opinion was widely held that the application of steam power was on the point of working a complete revolution in farming, a revolution comparable to that which it had already brought about in transport and industry. The steam engine was speedy; it was tireless; it could be maintained without eating up, as the horse did, a substantial part of the product of its own labours. 'Years may yet elapse,' wrote Sir John Forbes in 1886, 'before the consummation of the process, but the "jocund team" is doomed. Changes must be made, fields squared, Companies formed, implements improved, but the silent march of events will surely bring the new power into general use.' It is perhaps still a safe prediction that the horse will one day be completely ousted from the farm by mechanical power, but it was not the steam engine that the Shires and Clydesdales and the Punches had to fear.

The first patent for a steam ploughing apparatus was taken out by Major Pratt in 1810. His system seems to have embodied the same ideas as others which later actually worked, but there is no record of its having been put in practice. Other patents followed by Thomas Tindall in 1814 and Joseph Reynolds in 1816, but there was no real practical success until John Heathcoat, M.P. for Tiverton, obtained a patent in 1832. He had been assisted with his

invention by Josiah Parkes, the famous drainage expert. Four
years later a trial of his system took place on Red Moss in Lancashire and created a good deal of stir. Heathcoat's engine was of
the caterpillar type. On each side it was supported on an endless
band, which revolved on a pair of large drums, occupying the
place of the wheels. The bands were seven and a half feet broad,
and the fore and hind drums twenty-six feet apart, giving a total
bearing area of 300 square feet. Although the weight of the engine,
carrying its full six-ton supply of coal, was no less than thirty
tons, its 'buoyancy would have enabled it to traverse much softer
soil than flow moss'. On either side of the engine at a distance of
200 yards were placed two 'auxiliary carriages' or anchored pulleys, and two ploughs were worked simultaneously, one on either
hand. The engine was moved slowly along the middle of the field,
the auxiliary carriages along the headlands and the ploughs
travelled backwards and forwards between the engine and their
respective anchor pulleys. Since wire ropes had not then been
invented, a flat ribbon of steel was used to draw the ploughs to
and fro. The ploughs themselves were of the single-furrow one-
way type, with two sets of irons set tail to tail and a double set

'Steam power has no more to do with the plough than the horse
has to do with the spade'.

FROM WREN HOSKYNS' *Chronicles of a Clay Farm.*

of stilts at either end, it having been found that one man was. unequal to the task of guidance. The total staff was nine men and a boy. The Highland Society appointed a deputation to attend the trial, who reported that the results were satisfactory in so far that the moss, which was too wet to have carried horses, was successfully ploughed. The following year, 1837, another trial was carried out at Lochar Moss near Dumfries, on the occasion of a Highland Show, and seems to have passed off successfully, though the spectators formed a crowd of unmanageable size: but history seems to relate no more.

More than a dozen more patents were granted between 1837 and 1854. Interesting among these is that of an ingenious Scotsman who had emigrated to British Guiana and who proposed to mount his engines on punts, which were to be towed along the navigable canals and to draw implements to and fro in the sugar fields between, a system that was later applied in the Mississippi delta. Other names associated with the pioneer efforts are those of Fiskin of Newcastle and the Marquess of Tweeddale; but the chief credit for bringing the development to the point of practical success belongs to John Fowler, of Leeds, and most of the subsequent improvements were due to the firm which he founded.

John Fowler (1826–64) was born at Melksham in Wiltshire. He was first engaged in the corn trade, but in 1847 he entered the works of Gilke, Wilson & Co. at Middlesbrough. He was in Ireland in 1849 and, impressed with the vast amount of bog land there, he conceived his first important idea of a mechanical system of land drainage. In 1850 he carried out some experiments in collaboration with Albert Fry at Bristol, and built his first draining plough which was drawn by horses. He took a contract for the drainage of Hainault Forest, in Essex, and used his patent implement. His extraordinarily active mind was then applied to all sorts of mechanical problems, and between 1850 and 1864 he took out, either alone or in partnership with other persons, thirty-seven different patents for ploughs and ploughing appliances, reaping machines, seed drills, horse shoes, traction engines, brick and tile-making machinery and other things. But it remained his greatest ambition to plough by steam.

Some of his experimental tackle was made by Ransomes of Ipswich, other parts by George and Robert Stephenson at Lincoln. Later he was introduced to Jeremiah Head and, working together, they produced a steam-ploughing set which fulfilled the conditions laid down by the 'Royal' for a prize of £500. This was awarded at the Chester Show in 1858. The prize had been on offer at the three previous annual meetings, but the judges had not felt justified in making the award. At Chester, however, they decided unanimously 'that Mr. Fowler was fully entitled to the prize' and their award was unanimously confirmed by the Council.

In this invention Fowler had discarded the earlier idea of a locomotive digger; a standing engine was employed, which moved the plough up and down the field by means of ropes attached to a winding drum. In 1860 Fowler made a further improvement in the shape of a double-engine tackle, the invention of which 'gave a great impetus to steam cultivation not only in Great Britain but on the Continent and in the cotton districts in Egypt.' The cost of the tackle was of course too high for the ordinary individual farmer, but contractors and steam-plough companies were set up all over the country and Fowler's factory at Leeds was, as early as 1864, giving regular employment to nine hundred hands. In the diary of Charles Hobbs of Maisey Hampton there is a note of a dividend of 15 per cent on the local co-operative steam-tackle set. This fell to 7½ per cent the following year, farmers being short of money after a disastrous harvest. But 20 per cent was recorded in 1883.

The ceaseless activity of Fowler's mind was beginning to tell on his health, and he was forced to seek some rest. He retired to Ackworth in Yorkshire and, having been advised to take outdoor exercise, he began to hunt. In November 1864 he took a toss and broke an arm—not in itself a serious matter; but tetanus ensued and he died at Ackworth in December 1864, at the age of thirty-eight. He had packed a good deal into his short life.

It scarcely needs saying that the measure of success attained with steam tillage fell short of the anticipations of the early enthusiasts. There were of course plenty who had predicted absolute failure, for there is always the ultra-conservative view:

Aye, an old wooden plough, and they say, to be sure,
As the wideawake farmer mun use 'em no more;
They mun all be of iron, and wood there's no trade for,
Why, what do the fools think as ash-trees were made for.

It is true, in fact, that in the first enthusiasm for the new power
it was often abused, land being ploughed wet because there were
no horses' feet to puddle it. It is also true that, soon after steam
tillage became a practical possibility for the farmer, severe depression set in, and much of the old arable clay, on which steam would
have found its greatest usefulness, went down to grass. But quite
apart from all this the steam engine was too cumbersome, and
lacked the flexibility of the draft horse.

For the most part the application of steam was accomplished
by the use, in modified form, of the old standard implements—of
ploughs, grubbers, drags and rollers. But quite early in the course
of the experiments the doubt was expressed whether these old
methods should not be abandoned in favour of some 'more
economical and philosophical manner' of preparing the soil. The
plough, it was argued, was at best only an imperfect substitute
for the spade, adopted merely because your horse could apply its
strength to produce only a horizontal motion. With all the possibilities of steam at command, it must be possible to devise something far more efficient, something which, as Wren Hoskyns put
it, would 'comminute, aerate and invert the soil' in one operation,
and leave the tilth, 'as fine as a new mole heap'.

Following up this line of thought, an almost countless number
of inventors have, since about 1850, applied their minds to the
design of mechanical diggers and rotary tillers in various forms,
and at least a dozen machines had reached the stage of field trials
before the end of last century. Easily the most successful of these
was the Darby Digger, a great machine weighing twelve and a half
tons. A fair number of these found, for a time, rather casual
employment on the heavy soils of Essex and elsewhere; but steam
diggers tended, on the whole, to be too heavy for the land to
carry, too expensive to build, and too cumbersome to handle.
Moreover the single heavy engine, which could in fact be detached

from the digger mechanism, was not a good general-purpose power unit. Many of these objections have been overcome by the substitution of the internal combustion for the steam engine. A fresh supply of 'mechanical and agricultural intellect' is being applied to the problem. A good many rototillers and gyrotillers are in actual use. It is possible that the old confident predictions may yet be fulfilled. But meantime the plough and the harrow remain standard equipment, and the activated digger is preferred only for special types of work, as in Professor Stapledon's gallant attacks on the Welsh mountains.

NEW HARVESTING MACHINERY

For most of the notable agricultural inventions that were made up till the middle of the nineteenth century the credit must be given to Britain. From that time onwards America and later Canada, Australia, and New Zealand began to play increasingly important parts. With broad acres of rich prairie land to exploit and with the single disadvantage of scarce and expensive labour, it was to be expected that the farming communities of the new countries would concentrate effort and skill on the invention of labour-saving appliances.

The reaper had passed through various stages of improvement since the days of Bell and McCormick. First, by a system of manual delivery, the cut corn was deposited in sheaf-lots instead of the old continuous swath. Then the manual-delivery machine was replaced by a self-delivery, and later still the side-delivery principle was worked out, which enabled the field to be cut without regard to the rate at which the sheaves could be bound and stooked. But the little heaps of loose corn stalks still had to be bound by hand, and it took five men, working hard, to keep pace with the machine.

In the early 'seventies the Americans got so far as a binder that bound the sheaves with wire, and the year 1879, remembered as perhaps the blackest in the history of British farming, was marked by the introduction of binders with the first successful string-tying devices, the Appelby and the Wood Knotters. To some farmers

1. A survival from another age. Hereford oxen ploughing in Cirencester Park

2. Speeding the plough

3. Bell's reaper
(*North British Agriculturist*)

4. M'Cormick's reaper
(*Journal of the Royal Agricultural Society*)

5. The Ivel agricultural motor, 1910

the invention of 1879 was nearly as regrettable as the weather, for it was one of the things necessary to the mass production of prairie wheat, which was to flood the home market, make bankrupt many clay-land farmers and leave many farms tenantless and derelict.

It is worth noting that England almost won the race against America for the first invention of the knotter. In 1877 the 'Royal' ran a reaper trial and offered a 'Gold Medal for an efficient sheaf-binding machine'. Two English machines—entered by Thomas Neale and H. J. H. King respectively—faced four Americans. The Judges reported that 'Mr. Neale's machine was the greatest novelty in principle, and the prettiest piece of mechanism in the yard. It is in advance of the American machines, all of which tie with wire, in the point that it ties with soft string or yarn. Its adaptability to general field work is another thing, and is greatly to be doubted owing to the mechanism being somewhat complicated.' King's machine was simpler, and also tied with string.

Oddly enough the knotter, which had proved the stumbling-block to so many would-be inventors of binders, was a complete success from the outset, and it was the other parts of the machine —the elevator canvasses, the string feed and other relatively simple parts—that went wrong. One report on an early machine says: 'Certainly there was a good deal to try the temper; occasionally indeed nothing seemed to go right except the knotter.' But gradually the minor difficulties were overcome, and wonderfully soon the demand for the older forms of reaper dwindled to quite inconsiderable volume.

Here again, however, there was another school of thought. Binder sheaves must be stooked by hand labour, and must stand in the stook at considerable risk of weather; they must be pitched on to a cart, and pitched off again; they must be built into stacks, by hand labour and with some care; the stack must usually be thatched, and later unthatched and unbuilt; the sheaf bands must be cut and the corn threshed. Surely there must be some way of telescoping all these processes and of replacing some further part of the man power by machines.

In the old days of prairie farming it often happened that the only use that could be made of the straw was as fuel for the thresher engine, and British makers had exported a good many engines with furnaces specially designed to burn straw. In Australia the straw was not required even for this purpose, since there was wood readily available. So, thought many Australians, all this affair of binders, pitchforks and carts is a sheer waste of energy. Let us harvest the grain as cheaply as possible and fall back on a box of matches as the solution of the straw problem.

The first Australian machines represented a return to the principle of the stripper, which had been in use in the great corn fields that fed the rabble of ancient Rome. The ears were simply torn from the standing stalks, collected in a box behind, and taken to the thresher to be separated from the chaff and oddments of straw. The next step was to put the threshing mechanism on wheels behind the stripper, so that clean grain could be harvested in one operation, and all the unwanted material left behind. So the early 'combine' harvester came into being. The early American machines, still drawn by vast teams of horses, were somewhat on the same lines, only the corn was cut instead of having its ears torn off. Subsequent improvements consisted of mounting an internal-combustion engine along with the thresher, and thus doing away with the unsatisfactory drive taken from the land wheels.

The first combines came to Britain in 1928, when there were still many doubts about their adaptability to our bulky crops and humid climate. The long stubbles that they left might be good cover for partridges, but they offended the eye of the tidy farmer. Moreover, the corn acreage was at a low ebb and on many farms all the available straw was needed. Again, many weeds shed their seeds before the corn was 'combine ripe', and the grain, as it came from the field, would often be too damp to store. An expensive plant to dry the grain with hot air seemed to be an essential complement to the combine. Finally, if many farmers changed over to the new machine, how could corn merchants cope with the quantities that would be thrown on the market at harvest time?

Despite these objections, some of which have proved very real, the number of combines has increased year by year until some eleven thousand went to work in 1950. Sometimes the owner has installed an elaborate dryer and has provided large storage space. Sometimes he has been content to use the machine on a restricted acreage so that he might 'pick his weather' for harvesting and so obviate the need for hot-air drying. Again, various means have been devised of drying the grain, or rather letting it dry, without artificial heat. The problem of collecting the straw has been solved by the 'pick-up' baler, which constitutes, by general consent, the best and speediest machine for collecting hay, and which, on 'combine' farms, can deal equally quickly and cheaply with the straw.

The grain harvest, once the occasion for a mass migration of workers from other industries to the land, is thus ceasing to be a season of pressure. Nowadays the peak of labour demand on many farms comes later in the year when potatoes and sugar beet have to be got out of the soil. But more than a little progress has been made towards root-harvesting machines.

THE BEGINNINGS OF THE TRACTOR

In 1859 the American production of crude oil amounted to 2,000 barrels; in 1906 the production had reached 126,993,936, and the exploitation of resources in other countries was proceeding fast.

In 1888 there appeared at the Newcastle 'Royal' a German 'Spiels' engine, based on the principle of the earlier and already well-developed gas engine, but designed to run on petroleum. 'It depends for its action upon the explosion in the cylinder of a mixture of petrol spray and oil.' It came back to the Nottingham meeting in 1889, but was not allowed to be run in the showyard on account of the danger of fire. In a very few years, however, the stationary oil engine had become a commonplace, and was being installed, as a convenient source of power for threshing, chaff-cutting and grinding, on many farms. It was no longer necessary to rise at four o'clock on threshing mornings to get the steam up for a start at seven.

It was a relatively easy step to mount the new oil engine on a chassis like that of a steam locomotive engine, and as early as 1897 we find Messrs. Hornsby producing, at the Manchester 'Royal', an 'Oil Engine Traction or Agricultural Locomotive; Hornsby-Akroyd Patent Safety; 18 Brake-Horse-Power, adapted for working threshing machinery, haulage on roads and general purposes.' This was, as far as the judges were aware, 'the first traction engine to work with common paraffin oil ever exhibited.'

The early tractor driver had, of course, all the troubles of the early motorist, but with tractors there were peculiar difficulties of design. The chief potential advantage of the internal-combustion tractor over the old steam traction engine was its much lighter weight in proportion to its power; but its lightness brought the difficulty of wheel-slip on soft or wet ground, and the early models showed an exasperating tendency to bury themselves in the soil.

Apparently the first English oil tractor to be used for ploughing was a single-cylinder machine built by Saunderson of Bedford, which was put to plough in 1897. Thirteen years later, in 1910, a new Saunderson 'Universal' oil motor, of 45–50 horse power, appeared at the Royal Agricultural Society's third Tractor Trial, held at Baldock in Hertfordshire. The late John Newman, of the Oxford Engineering Institute, related that he bought a Saunderson tractor in that year and drove it from Bedford to Pershore, a distance of 80 miles, in thirteen hours. This, he added, was the longest time that his man, who accompanied him, had ever gone without a drink. Going down a hill the brakes failed and the tractor ran away. The passenger jumped clear, but the driver sat still. His mount pecked at the hedge-and-ditch at the bottom, and the driver took a toss, but no real harm was done.

Seven entries in all, including both oil and steam machines, went through the trials. The most notable of the former was the 'Ivel' Agricultural Motor in which the weight had been reduced, from the usual figure of about four tons, to 34½ cwt. It was a three-wheeled single-speed machine and may be regarded as the first of the already long line of general-purpose farm tractors. The judges of the trials reported that 'Steam engines best fulfilled the requirements of the trials, but there can be little doubt that oil engines will ultimately best suit the farmer's requirements if the general-purpose motor tractor is to be adopted for the average farm.'

Well over a dozen makes of tractor, some home-built and some imported, were used in the efforts to increase food production in the latter stages of the first world war. Many of the machines were unreliable and many of the drivers imperfectly trained, so that, although a good deal of urgent work was accomplished, it was done at a high cost both of money and of nervous strain. An Australian 'bullocky', who had been drawn in as a farm tractor driver, reached the conclusion that an American tractor could be even more 'cussed' than an Australian ox-team, with the added disadvantage that it took no notice of the most expressive words in his abundant vocabulary.

After the war the tractor had a bad reputation to live down, and the fall in the acreage of tillage, the drop in the price of horses, and the scarcity of money all told against it. But the subsequent years have seen steady progress. The horseless farm is no longer an exception. Perhaps, as Sir John Forbes said in 1886, the 'jocund team' is indeed doomed. Whatever sentimental regrets this may occasion, the change has two important practical advantages. It has greatly increased the productivity of the man on the farm, and it has already set free, for the production of human food, more than a million acres formerly required to produce horse fodder.

NOW AND TOMORROW

The number of recent inventions and the number of ideas for future mechanical aids are a little bewildering to the older generation. On the one hand, there are new machines, more complicated, specialized and costly, appearing every year. Landowners complain that there seems to be no end to the demand for more sheds to protect them from the weather, and farmers sometimes feel that it would be better, if they had any choice in the matter, to employ more men and tie up less capital in equipment. But much remains to be done before the ultimate end is reached of reducing farm work to a purely mental exercise. In any case, the prospect of complete success, with the farmer sitting in an observation tower operating his machines by wireless controls, is not altogether attractive.

Looking back over a hundred years of progress, one cannot but be impressed by the immense ingenuity that has been directed to speeding up the operations of farming and reducing the burden of farm toil. We can feel some justifiable pride in the part played in the business by our own little country. Many of the improvements have brought small material rewards to their originators, and added but little to the farmer's profits. Most of the gain has accrued to the consumer, in the form of cheaper food.

3

SCIENCE AND THE LAND

'. . . to try how far chymistry will go in settling the principles of agriculture.'

FRANCIS HOME

It was one of the earliest discoveries in farming that one piece
of land would grow better crops than another. It was also
found that if crops were grown upon, and removed from, a
particular field, the productivity of the soil declined and the yields
grew progressively worse. The farmer's first reaction to this problem was to walk away from it. A piece of land was cultivated until
it was exhausted, when the farmer left it to revert to nature and
started afresh elsewhere. This is still the principle of the 'shifting
agriculture' that survives in many parts of the world and which,
as we are inclined to forget, died out in this country not so very
long ago. It was the system followed upon the outfields of Scottish
farms till far on in the eighteenth century, and Arthur Young
found it still widespread in Ireland.

Much earlier, however, it had been found that there did exist
ways and means of maintaining or even of raising the fertility of
the land. The fertilizing value of crop residues, in the form of
composts, dung or ashes was well known to the good farmers of
Rome. Again it was found that lime or marl would sometimes
produce remarkable effects, and that other miscellaneous things
like soot or salt or bones might sometimes benefit the soil. The
Romans, too, realized that certain crops like clover made the land
better, and not worse, for other crops like wheat or spelt.

For centuries men had pondered these facts, had speculated
about explanations and set themselves to find the underlying
principle of vegetation—something like a philosopher's stone that
should make the difference between barrenness and fertility. But

71

SCIENCE AND THE LAND

it was of no avail, for the necessary basis of chemical knowledge
did not exist. Even so clever a man as Jethro Tull could get the
story all wrong; Tull thought that the plant simply fed upon the
soil particles and that the whole secret of big crops was to prepare
the soil as a 'pabulum'. Tillage, in his view, was a true and complete substitute for manure.

Sir Humphry Davy, though he was the most distinguished
chemist of his time and is often regarded as the first of our agricultural scientists, still belonged to the old school who were
largely groping in the dark. It was the old Board of Agriculture,
under Sir John Sinclair and Arthur Young, who brought him into
the business of soil chemistry. They wanted to institute a
course of lectures on 'The connection of Chemistry with Vegetable Physiology', and they hit upon Davy, then only twenty-three,
but already known as a brilliant lecturer. The next year they made
Davy Professor of Agricultural Chemistry to the Board, at a
salary of £100 a year. He continued to lecture and to conduct
experiments for many years, and in 1813 published his lectures as
the 'Elements of Agricultural Chemistry'. The publishers paid
him a thousand pounds for the book and an extra fifty for each
subsequent edition, of which there were many.

Davy worked energetically at his experiments and won a great
reputation, was toasted by great agriculturists at the Woburn
sheep-shearings and, by his scientific colleagues, was promoted
to be President of the Royal Society. Indeed, his prestige kept
alive many of his erroneous ideas after they would otherwise have
been dead. A few examples of these may be quoted as showing
how far astray a great scientist could still go: Oils were good
manures because of the carbon and hydrogen that they contained;
Soot was good because its carbon was 'in a state in which it is
capable of being rendered soluble by the action of oxygen and
water.' Lime was useful because it dissolved hard vegetable matter,
and so on. The basis of the then accepted theory of soil fertility
was that, in the main, the living plant built up its substance from
the remains of dead plants, i.e. from the humus of the soil.

It was not an Englishman, but a German, who at last got on
the right track. Justus von Liebig was born in 1803 and became

72

Professor of Chemistry at Giessen in 1826. He was a great teacher and a brilliant laboratory worker, but it was not till about 1838 that he turned to the applications of his subject to life and living things. In 1840 he wrote a famous report to the British Association upon the state of organic chemistry which was later published as *Chemistry in its application to Agriculture and Physiology*. The plant physiologists, said Liebig, who were trying to help the farmer with his problem, were all at sea because they had omitted to learn any chemistry. 'All explanations of chemists must remain without fruit, and useless, because, even to the great leaders in physiology carbonic acid, ammonia, acids and bases are sounds without meaning, words without sense, terms of an unknown language which awake no thoughts and no associations. . . . Their experiments . . . considered by them as convincing proofs . . . are fitted only to awaken pity.' The humus theory 'corruption is the mother of vegetation' was palpable nonsense. Obviously the great bulk of the substance of a plant, of its sugar, starch, cellulose, and oil, could be and must be made from the carbonic acid of the air and the water of the soil. It was the other and smaller needs of the plants that had to be met by manuring, and these needs could be deduced from an analysis of the plant. If a plant were analysed the substances constantly found, in addition to those derived from carbonic acid and water, were ammonia compounds and the alkaline phosphates. These must form the basis of manuring.

Having thus hit a bull's-eye with his sighting shot, Liebig proceeded to make some rather mixed shooting. It was a good shot to point out that, if the plant required its manurial elements in certain definite proportions, then a surplus of lime or potash would be useless in case there were a deficiency of phosphate. It was a bad one, however, to suggest that ammonia compounds were not essential manures. Liebig arrived at the last conclusion by arguing from the special to the general. If grassland could accumulate a great store of ammonia without the application of nitrogenous manure, then clearly the plants must be collecting their nitrogen from the atmosphere. The passages in his book which had urged the necessity of ammoniacal manures were deleted from the later editions, and in the *Farmers' Magazine*, he wrote: 'If the soil be suitable, if it contain a sufficient quantity of alkalis, phosphates and sulphates, nothing will be wanting. The plants will derive their ammonia from the atmosphere as they do carbonic acid.' If man had chosen to live exclusively on beans, and to feed his beasts exclusively on clover, this statement would have been true. Unfortunately for Liebig, man also ate corn and fed his beasts on turnips. In other respects, too, Liebig pushed his theory too far. Turnips, he found by analysis, contained relatively little phosphate, and hence might be grown with manures containing little, a statement that the earlier experiments immediately belied. Worse still was in store, for Liebig had compounded his alkaline phosphates into a patent manure, which failed to work. The failure was, of course, due in part to the omission of nitrogen, but also to the fact that Liebig's process of manufacture included the fusion of the ingredients with lime and calcium phosphate, in order to make them insoluble and so prevent their being washed away in the soil drainage. The result was that the said ingredients were made unavailable to the plant. Philip Pusey could write: 'The mineral theory, too hastily adopted by Liebig, has received its death-blow from the experiments of Mr. Lawes,' and Liebig had to eat some of the hastier of his words; nevertheless, he had performed the tremendous service of stating the problem of soil fertility in scientific terms, and of setting men fairly upon the way to its solution.

What was now needed was a planned series of field experiments to discover the effects, in various forms and amounts and combinations, of the elements that the growing plant might possibly require. This was the task undertaken at Rothamsted by John Bennet Lawes.

Lawes had been born in 1814, and had succeeded to the family estate at the age of eight. He went to Eton and to Oxford, but showed little interest in classical studies. He was happier at University College, London, working in the chemical laboratory of Dr. A. T. Thomson. In 1834 he entered into occupation of Rothamsted and began to experiment with growing plants, first in pots and later in the field. One of his earlier trials with turnips showed the striking effect of applying mineral phosphate after it had been made soluble by treatment with sulphuric acid—an idea suggested by Liebig. At once he saw the importance of this discovery, and in 1842 he took out a patent for the manufacture of superphosphate. He thus laid the foundations of an important industry and incidentally of his own fortune.

Already in 1835 he had secured the services, as a collaborator, of Joseph Henry Gilbert. Gilbert was three years younger than Lawes, had been his fellow student in the London laboratory and had gone on to work for a short time with Liebig at Giessen. There, too, another association started, for among Gilbert's fellows was Augustus Voelcker, who was to become the distinguished chemist of the Royal Agricultural Society.

The association of Lawes and Gilbert at Rothamsted endured for fifty-seven years, being ended only by Lawes' death in 1900. The two worked together in everything, in planning experiments, in studying their results and in writing their reports. If Lawes had the more imagination and initiative, Gilbert was pre-eminent for industry and perseverance, as well as for his scrupulous scientific accuracy. It is difficult to imagine a better team, and results of immense importance came very fast. In a dozen years the main principles of manuring had been settled. Sir John Russell, for instance, has summed up the points that had been established by 1855.

Firstly, Liebig had been right in his contention that plants required phosphates and salts of the alkalis; but had been wrong in supposing that the composition of the ash of a particular plant was a safe guide to the quantities that should be provided. Thus, more than forty per cent of the ash found in turnips was potash, yet at Rothamsted potash produced no increase in yield. On the other hand the phosphate-content of the ash was only eight per cent, yet a dressing of superphosphate could treble the yield of roots.

Secondly, the non-leguminous crops required, in addition to what Liebig considered necessary, a supply of nitrogenous compounds. As manures, ammonium salts were about as good as nitrates. Without an adequate supply of nitrogen no increase of growth was obtained, even in the presence of abundant minerals.

Leguminous plants, however, behaved differently and could, sometimes at least, produce excellent crops without a supply of nitrogen.

Thirdly, soil fertility could be maintained, for some years at least, by means of artificial fertilizers, unaccompanied by dung or other natural manures.

Fourthly, the benefits of fallowing, long known in practice, could be largely explained as brought about by the increase, in the soil, of available nitrogen compounds.

The soil of Rothamsted continued to prove a rich mine of knowledge, though one large nugget still eluded the miners. Why did leguminous plants behave differently, in the field, from other plants? Gilbert grew clovers and such-like species in pot experiments; he burnt the soil to remove all trace of nitrogen; he added ample quantities of mineral manures and put his pots in glass cases. But here the clovers behaved like ordinary plants—languished and ultimately died if nitrogen manures were withheld, grew vigorously if these were added. And yet in the field, and even on the poorest soils, these clovers were indifferent to the amount of nitrogen supplied, producing heavy yields, with an exceptionally high nitrogen-content, under conditions where other crops would have failed.

A new science had to grow up before the riddle could be solved, and when the time came it was not Gilbert, but the Germans Hellriegel and Wilfarth, who showed that the legume's power of nitrogen fixation depended on a biological factor—the presence of the nodule-producing bacteria.

There was a long controversy about the general truth of the new theory of plant nutrition. Many farmers still believed that muck was the only source of real fertility, and that the new chemicals were no more than whips and spurs wherewith the bad farmer might urge the soil to special efforts and drive it the more rapidly to exhaustion. There was, of course, a grain of truth in the mass of prejudice—for there is more in the maintenance of soil fertility than the adding of the required amounts of nitrogen, phosphate, and potash. But Lawes lived to see the fifty-seventh successive crop of wheat, grown without natural manures, flourishing on Broadbalk field; and he could die in the assurance that he had made no very gross mistake.

The work at Rothamsted in the early days was not confined to soil and plant problems, for much of the early knowledge of animal nutrition derived from the experiments of Lawes and Gilbert. The new oil cakes were tried out as they appeared—both their effects upon the animals and the value of their manurial residues. Trials were even conducted to determine the relative economy, as meat producers, of different breeds of sheep.

Lawes was not content with bearing the growing cost of Rothamsted during his life-time, but set aside the magnificent sum of £100,000 for its permanent endowment.

The two partners in the great concern were honoured to the full by farmers, by men of science and by the King. Lawes was offered, but declined, the Presidency of the Royal Agricultural Society; was made an F.R.S.; was awarded the Society's gold medal; had honorary degrees from several Universities and was created a Baronet in 1882. Gilbert shared most of these distinctions and was knighted in 1893.

It was obviously a big task to find the right practical application of Rothamsted's work over the length and breadth of Britain, with all its diversity of soil and climate, and it required many hands. Among the more noteworthy spreaders of the gospel were Dr. Andrew Aitken and Dr. Augustus Voelcker.

Aitken was born and educated in Edinburgh and continued his training as a chemist in Germany. In 1877 he was appointed to succeed Dewar as consulting chemist to the 'Highland', and had charge of the work at the Society's experiment stations at Harelaw and Pumpherston. For a man of purely academic training he acquired a remarkable grasp of practical farm affairs, and his reports on his experiments show both a wide range of knowledge and a mastery of detail. His efforts provided Scottish farmers with the first reliable data on the use of artificial manures, and his reports in the annual 'Transactions' were eagerly read. The summary of these which he wrote in the 1886 volume made what was really a comprehensive treatise on manuring. His reports on his sheep-feeding experiments may still be read with interest.

SCIENCE AND THE LAND

Voelcker was Aitken's 'opposite number' in the 'Royal', and was a man of the same type. Born and educated in Germany, he served a short apprenticeship with Johnston in Edinburgh, and in 1849 was appointed Professor of Agricultural Chemistry at the new Royal Agricultural College at Cirencester. In 1855 he was elected chemist to the Bath and West Society, and two years later he succeeded Way in the corresponding office under the 'Royal'. Those were the days before State-supported Research Stations and Ministries of Agriculture had come into being, and when the main burden of carrying out experiments and diffusing scientific knowledge fell upon the Societies. The post of consulting chemist was therefore a most important one and the work was onerous. The 'Royal', shortly after Voelcker's appointment, decided to follow the example of the 'Highland' in instituting an experimental farm, and the responsibility for the working out of the plan fell upon Voelcker, with Lawes as his adviser. The experiments carried out at Woburn, on a hungry, lime-deficient soil, formed a very useful complement to Lawes's own, carried out on the heavy and mostly well-chalked land at Rothamsted. Voelcker died in 1883, long before Lawes and Gilbert, and was succeeded by his son, J. A. Voelcker, and he, in turn, by a grandson.

It is impossible even to mention the many others who devoted their lives to the bringing of science into the farmers' fields. Indeed, as time wore on, the old distinction between scientist and farmer faded out; a growing proportion of the pioneers were both. It is true that the synthesis of the new science and the old practice has proceeded at varying rates in the several departments of husbandry. In plough farming much progress had been made by the 'seventies, while the corresponding one in grassland husbandry had to wait another generation, and that in respect of livestock breeding is only now beginning to be achieved. The stories are told in subsequent chapters. Here, however, something must be said of others who helped to lay foundations.

The same generation that produced Lawes and Gilbert gave us a lady who became highly distinguished in agricultural science. This was Eleanor Anne Ormerod, who devoted her life to the study of the insect enemies of the farm and the garden. Miss

78

Ormerod was born in 1828 and had the ordinary upbringing of the daughter of a well-to-do gentleman of the time. She showed considerable aptitude for painting and, with her sister Georgiana, studied under Hunt. The training was to be turned to good account later, though neither sister could have expected to turn their talent to the portrayal of bot-flies and flea beetles.

In March 1852, the young blue-stocking seems to have started on Stephens, *Manual of the British Beetles*, and thereafter to have become more and more deeply absorbed in Entomology. After their father's death the two sisters lived at Isleworth, near Kew, and became close friends of Sir Joseph and Lady Hooker. In 1877 Miss Ormerod began the curious enterprise of writing, and illustrating with the help of her sister, an *Annual Report of Observations of Injurious Insects*, which ran throughout the four-and-twenty years until her death. The publication was printed entirely at Miss Ormerod's expense, and was sent to all sorts of public bodies and, as time went on, to all and sundry of her correspondents. These steadily grew in number until the sisters found themselves the Director and Deputy Director of what we should now call an International Bureau of Economic Entomology—collecting observations, providing advice and publishing an illustrated annual report.

From 1881 till 1884 Miss Ormerod lectured in her subject at the Royal Agricultural College and, in 1882, she was appointed consulting entomologist to the R.A.S.E. On the very day that she assumed the latter office she met with an accident at Waterloo Station, which left her permanently lame but did not prevent her from carrying on the work with all her old enthusiasm. Her portrait hangs in Edinburgh University as the first woman to be given the honorary degree of Doctor of Laws. Sir Ludovic Grant, in presenting her for this honour, called her 'the protectress of Agriculture and the fruits of the earth, a beneficent Demeter of the nineteenth century.' At the least she was a very remarkable woman.

The battle with the pests and diseases of farm crops has made great progress since the time when Miss Ormerod first turned to the subject. It was in 1882 that a mixture of soft soap and quassia was first used as a spray for hops. Bordeaux mixture, originally discovered as a remedy against vine mildew, proved at least a partial preventive of the potato blight, the cause of the famine in Ireland. Now the grower has an enormous armoury of chemical weapons—tar distillates, arsenic, sulphur, copper salts, derris, pyrethrum, D.D.T., benzene hexachloride, and more—against his minor enemies, and chemical methods of weed control are also making rapid progress.

The full application of science to the business of plant breeding had to wait till the time, in 1900, when a paper by the Austrian monk, Gregor Mendel, was dug out from the Proceedings of an obscure Natural History Society. But even without a complete understanding of the laws of heredity, considerable progress was made in the improvement of crop plants.

One of the most interesting of the pioneers was Patrick Shireff, who was born at Mungoswells in East Lothian, in 1789, and succeeded at an early age to the tenancy of the family farm. To anyone approaching the problem of making better strains of corn, in Shireff's day, it must have seemed that there was a choice of methods. For instance, one might have applied the method of the stock-breeder—that of continually culling the least desirable specimens of the breed, and multiplying the progeny of the best; or again one might, like Lamarck, have supposed that the effects of nurture would be inherited, and have attempted to get better varieties of wheat or oats by subjecting the strain, through several generations, to specially careful culture and abundant manuring. But Shireff had a *flair*, and seems to have arrived at the right method without having to go through the process of eliminating the wrong. The common cereals, as is now well known, are but rarely cross-pollinated, so that the great majority of individual plants breed perfectly true. The technique required, in the early stages of improvement, was therefore simply to discover the single good plant and to multiply its progeny, taking care only to prevent any admixture of the strain.

By this simple process Shireff produced 'Mungoswells' wheat from a plant selected in 1819; he followed with 'Hopetoun' oat, which was a considerable success and remained in general cultivation in Scotland for nearly a century. Here is his own account of his next success:

'When calling upon a friend in the autumn of 1832 I was struck with an ear of wheat which had been culled from one of his fields on the farm at Drem, East Lothian, and resolved to propagate from its seeds. Before coming into my possession 3 corns appeared to have been lost from the apex, and with the point of a pin I picked out 99 corns without ruffing the chaff, and the ear may still be seen in the Agricultural Museum at Stirling.

'The produce from the ear proved a new variety which has been named Hopetoun Wheat, and which was sold for the first time in 1839. After numerous trials in East Lothian for two seasons, this variety is rising in public esteem, and has been successfully grown in many parts of Scotland as well as in Gloucestershire, Kent and Buckinghamshire. . . . The grain weighed 2 lb. per bushel heavier than Chevalier, and produced 36 bushels to the acre.'

Shireff spent 1833 touring America and published, on his return, an account of his wanderings and observations. During the next twenty years he disappeared from Scotland, and farmed in England and Ireland. He returned to Haddington in 1856 and devoted his whole time to plant breeding, exploring the cornfields over a wide area for promising material. In the following year he had more than seventy pure-line plots, and these eventually yielded three varieties which were placed on the market. In 1862 he carried out a similar search for mother plants of oats, and found the parents of such successful varieties as the Early Angus and Long Fellow.

He now turned to hybridization as the next step, a method of building up new combinations of good qualities. Here again he had a measure of success, but died, at the age of 85, before this could be fully exploited.

The most successful of Shireff's successors in the pre-Mendel period was John Garton, upon whose work as a hybridist was founded the success of one of our greatest seed houses. Garton's first success was the Abundance Oat which was placed on the market in 1890, and which soon established itself, and long remained, the most widely cultivated sort in England. Other varieties of wheat, barley, and oats followed in quick succession until a great proportion of the cornfields of the country were populated with the products of the shy, retiring man with his watchmaker's eyeglass and camel's-hair brush.

In more recent times, and especially since the science of breeding was established on the work of Mendel and Johannsen, many others have entered the field. The greatest successes have been scored by the late Sir Rowland Biffen with his Yeoman and Little Joss wheats, by the late Dr. Beaven with his Plumage Archer barley, by the Swedish plant breeding station at Svalöf, by Hunter, Engledow and Bell of Cambridge, by Robb at Edinburgh, and by E. T. Jones at Aberystwyth. In recent times Stapledon and his team at the Welsh Plant Breeding Station applied modern methods to the more difficult task of improving the grasses and clovers.

It has already been said that some important scientific work on animal nutrition was done by Lawes and Gilbert in the early days at Rothamsted. But as time went on Rothamsted concentrated more and more on the soil and the plant, and animal nutrition dropped out of the programme. Aitken in Scotland and Voelcker in England continued to do useful experiments in stock-feeding, testing the new oil cakes and other materials that became available, and in other ways providing some guidance to the farmer. But all this was 'short-range' research and the difficult fundamental problems were left to other countries. Most of our knowledge of rationing is derived from the work of Wolff and Kellner in Germany, of Hansson in Denmark, and of Armsby in America.

In more recent times, however, the gap in our research organization has been closed, and Cambridge, the Rowett Institute at Aberdeen, and the Dairy Research Institutes at Ayr and Reading have played important parts in the progress of the subject. In the related field of the physiology of reproduction and growth, the brilliant researches of John Hammond have won for him an international reputation comparable with those of Lawes and Stapledon.

From far back in the eighteenth century an occasional voice had cried in the wilderness for the provision of educational facilities in agriculture, but it was not till 1790 that the first step was taken. This was the establishment of a Chair of Agriculture in Edinburgh University. It was so scantily endowed that the Professor had perforce to find some other means of support, yet a succession of three very eminent men, Andrew Coventry, David Low, and James Wilson, did valuable work in reducing the scattered knowledge of the subject to some kind of order. The fourth incumbent, Robert Wallace, succeeded in persuading the University to establish an agricultural degree and to provide some instruction in the various branches of agricultural science. Sir William Somerville was the country's first University Graduate in Agriculture.

In 1796 a professorship in Rural Economy was founded at Oxford, but the endowment was not only meagre but also insecure. It consisted of a farm, and if the tenant failed to pay his rent, or needed some draining or a new cowshed, there was no net balance for the Professor. For more than a century the professorship was a temporary appointment and the Chair was often empty. Gilbert held it for six years and scandalized some of the learned dons by delivering a course of lectures on manure. Warrington was for a period another holder of the office, but it was not till 1908, when Somerville was appointed, that the office became a whole-time one.

In 1846 the Royal Agricultural College was opened at Cirencester, and became the training ground of a large number of squires and land agents.

In 1890 T. B. Wood laid, in a dim cellar, the foundations of the Cambridge School of Agriculture and lived to see it a large and flourishing institution. University Departments, Agricultural Colleges, Dairy Schools and Farm Institutes have since followed in rapid succession, and Government scholarships have thrown these places open to increasing numbers of agricultural students.

4

SPEED THE PLOUGH

'We may still talk of what we please, of Lilies and Lions Rampant, and Spread Eagles in Fields d'Or or d'Argent; but if Heraldry were guided by reason, a Plough in a Field Arable would be the most Noble and Antient Armes.'

FRANCIS BACON

The reign of George III—'Farmer George'—and especially the middle period from about 1780 to 1813 saw the beginnings of vast changes and great improvements in British farming. Not only had there been the stimulus of high prices for the man of purely mercenary outlook—wheat stood over a hundred shillings a quarter in five of the first thirteen years of the new century—but scarcity was continually within sight and it became an obvious patriotic duty to increase the fruits of the earth. More men of education and intellect were attracted to the land than at any time before or since. When Sir John Sinclair set about his immense task of surveying the whole country he was able to find, in nearly every county, a man who combined the agricultural knowledge and the literary gifts to write a very competent account of existing farm practice and of the measures needed to raise the general standard of farming.

Great landowners set an example to those of lesser degree. In 1776 Coke of Holkham succeeded to a family estate with a rent roll of £2,200, and by 1816, largely through a bold and wise expenditure of capital, he had raised the figure nearly tenfold. Arthur Young travelled endless miles and wrote almost innumerable books, praising enterprise and skill, condemning ignorance and sloth, arguing, exhorting and instructing, and setting up a fever of enclosing, liming, draining, and improving, the like of which had never been seen. The fever reached its crisis in 1813, and within a very few years the whole edifice of prosperity came toppling down, and agriculture seemed to sink into decay. Scarcity was relieved with the coming of peace, the country went back to the gold standard and prices fell. Rents had perforce to be reduced, and the landlord, called upon to shoulder an immense burden of taxation, had no resources to invest in the land. Farmers who had formed expensive habits, and who could not change back to older and simpler ways, went bankrupt; the wise among them put on their dirty boots and lived in their kitchens. Labourers' wages were reduced to starvation level, and many could not find work, even at seven or eight shillings a week. Peace had come, and beggary.

It was long before the spirit of improvement revived. The depression indeed remained acute for more than twenty years; the land became impoverished and some clay farms were abandoned altogether. In 1830–1 the rot 'swept away two million sheep.'—'Everywhere wages were lowered and men dismissed. Work became so scarce that, in spite of the fall of prices, starvation stared the agricultural labourer in the face. Distress bred discontent and discontent disturbances which were fostered by political agitation. While the Luddites broke up machinery, gangs of rural labourers destroyed threshing machines or avenged the fancied conspiracy of farmers by burning farm-houses, stacks and ricks or wrecking the shops of butchers and bakers. In the riots of 1830–1 when "Swing" and his proselytes were at work, agrarian fires blazed from Dorsetshire to Lincolnshire.'[1]

In 1836 a Select Committee could report that prosperity was beginning to revive, but it took many years to restore confidence. Tenants had lost most of their capital and, distrusting the doubtful security of the long leases, farmed from year to year and from hand to mouth. There was little to attract the men of capital, enterprise, and ideas that the industry so sorely needed. Small wonder that an invention like Bell's reaper was still-born in such a world.

But the revival progressed, despite the setback to confidence

[1] Lord Ernle, *English Farming Past and Present.*

caused by the repeal of the corn laws. Many of the leaders in agriculture were new men, who had amassed capital in trade or manufacture, who had not lived through the long years of bitter poverty on the land, and who were prepared to take risks and to try new ways. There were indeed many new ways to try. Meat and dairy produce were in increasing demand. Bones and guano were available to speed up the process of restoring fertility to exhausted fields. There were railways and drain tiles, subsoil ploughs and scarifiers; soon there might be reapers and steam engines wherewith to fight the foreigners in the markets. And there was the new Agricultural Science that might do all kinds of things—Lawes' new superphosphate manure was a promising beginning.

Prominent among the new men were the Reverend Mr. Huxtable, Rector of Sutton Waldron in Dorset, Philip Pusey, M.P. for Berkshire, Fisher Hobbs, a great stockman as well as an able manager of land, Hewitt Davis, who revived the Coke tradition in Norfolk, and Wren Hoskyns, though he, perhaps, was more brilliant as a journalist than sound as a farmer. But the most remarkable of all, the 'Chief Leviathan', was John Joseph Mechi, whose career may serve to convey a picture, if rather an exaggerated one, of High Farming in the Golden Age.

Mechi's father was an Italian who had left France during the revolution and sought refuge in England, being given some post in Kensington Palace. John Joseph was born in London in 1802 and at sixteen became a clerk in a London house connected with the Newfoundland trade. Here he worked ten years, probably for a very small salary. He had, however, the gift of money-making, and spent a great part of his dinner-hour in selling things to his friends. By 1828 he had saved enough to set up as a cutler in Leadenhall Street. These were the days of golden opportunity in commerce, and Mechi's Magic Razor Strops became as well known to the men of London as they were profitable to their patentor and vendor. Their use extended as far as Hudson Bay and the Sandwich Islands. Unfortunately fashions, even male fashions, change. The Crimean War made beards popular, and the sales of Magic Razor Strops fell off. Mechi, however, had exceptional business acumen. Men no longer shaved, but gas lighting was just becoming an everyday affair and the effluents from the gas-lamps were causing anxiety. Mechi's patent 'for the improvement in apparatus to be applied to lamps in order to carry off heat and the products of combustion' met a need of the times, and became almost as sound a business proposition as the razor strops. In 1859 he forsook trade for high finance. He ultimately became an Alderman of the City of London, Sheriff of Middlesex and would, if success had continued without interruption, have been elected Lord Mayor.

So much for his business career. By 1840 he had made so handsome a fortune out of his razor strops that he, like others in his position, turned his thoughts to the countryside, having, as he said, 'a love of the beauties of nature, the pure air of heaven, the sports of the field, and the hospitality of our honest yeomen.' He bought a farm—170 acres only—adjoining Tiptree Heath in Essex, giving £3,400 for the land. But the little estate was to be not only his country home: it was to be his hobby and a profit-making concern as well. He knew nothing of practical farming, but by this time there was available a growing literature in the shape of the Journals of the Agricultural Societies, and Mechi studied his subject pretty thoroughly and turned his powers of observation to good account. He saw one farmer making a fortune, his neighbour losing one: he saw one field all good corn and another all weeds. So he inquired into causes and noted results, experimented in his own small garden, and decided that want of drainage, waste of manure, shallow ploughing and short leases were the curses of the country. He concluded that, so far as his individual means permitted, he would remedy them.

Perhaps Mechi's greatest contribution to agriculture was his enthusiasm. He managed to change his own farm from a barren heath, in one of the then worst-farmed counties in England, into a picture that people came far to see. No new invention or process escaped his own notice, nor, if he could help it, the notice of anybody else. He became a well-known figure at the discussions of the various farmers' clubs which were springing up, and gave them all, without diffidence, the benefit of his experience and ideas. His farm soon became, in effect, a National Experimental Farm on which new implements, new theories, and new ideas were tried out. He was always open to invest capital in the land, though always with a business eye to profit.

The days were gone when the 'long clay pipe, the somewhat boisterous stave, and the "hot-stopping"' were the only inducements that brought farmers together. Farmers had much to learn. Agricultural practice must move forward to meet the new free-trade conditions and meetings everywhere were concerned to discuss new practices. In 1849 we find a prominent Norfolk tenant-farmer acknowledging at such a meeting that the farmers of England all knew that, in the agricultural press and on the land, there were three 'great Leviathans'—Mr. Mechi, Mr. Hewitt Davis, and Mr. Huxtable. These three had become the foremost exponents of the new High Farming.

At this same meeting Mechi was 'accused' of having sunk no less than £33,500 in his farm, and he himself confessed to having a landlord's investment of £60 an acre and a 'working capital'—the equivalent to tenant's capital—of £14 an acre. And this at a time when he estimated the average farmer's capital to be £4 and the owner's capital something like £25 an acre.

A few years after Mechi had taken Tiptree Hall, Rothamsted Experimental Station was founded, and Lawes' and Gilbert's feeding and manuring experiments were followed by none more eagerly than by Mechi. Liebig published his book on agricultural chemistry. The first Royal Show was held at Oxford. The Royal Agricultural College at Cirencester, with its model farm, was founded, and Mechi became one of the five members of its Board. 'We should have more model farms like Cirencester,' said Mechi. Farmers' sons ought to attend the courses, 'to be taught not only to top and tail turnips but also the elements of geology and agricultural chemistry. We want an Agricultural College in every county.' The indifference of landed proprietors, of the Government and even the new Royal Agricultural Society of England to this, the only institution of its kind, galled him exceedingly. 'If knowledge is power,' he said, 'ignorance must be weakness, agricultural as in other matters.' In short, he threw all his energy into the fight for better farming: 'If my exertions in the cause of agricultural progression make some impression on agricultural lethargy and disbelief, my object will have been accomplished.'

The farming of Essex, with its dry eastern climate, was mainly dependent on corn, with cattle less for profit than for manure. In spite of its proximity to London markets, and the object lessons to be seen in Suffolk and Norfolk, its standard of cultivation was low. The soil at Tiptree was clay, and clay farmers were in a bad way. Essex landlords were in the main an indifferent lot, encumbered with debts and mortgages, jealous of their hedgerow timber and little inclined to encourage tenants in good farming. Farm buildings were of wood and thatch. Many of the inhabitants of the heath district were poor and wretched squatters. Through the troublous 'thirties, during the labourers' revolts and the exploits of 'Captain Swing', Essex had suffered in a special degree from incendiarism and lawlessness. The Laws of Settlement, two hundred years old but still operating, had led to the peopling of the heath with undeserving poor; in times when 'every parish of settlement was a prison and every other parish a fortress', any district where the Lords of the Manors allowed the building of a rude mud hut and the enclosing of a patch of barren heath, attracted many such outcasts. When Mechi bought his farm, poaching and pilfering were rampant. Men hung around the beer shops with nothing to do, while the land cried out for their labour.

Mechi had not been long at work before his improvements began to attract attention, and visitors came flocking to Tiptree Hall. Every year in July, following the example of Coke and the Duke of Bedford at Holkham and Woburn, Mechi had a meeting. Farmers, city acquaintances, noblemen and gentlemen interested in agriculture, statesmen and distinguished foreigners all met as his guests. Thus, too, he made the acquaintance of the foremost improvers and learnt from James Smith and Josiah Parkes about the new discoveries in drainage and subsoiling. As early as 1847 he was assailing the doubters and inviting them to come and see what drainage had done for him. Land formerly unproductive, 'a heavy clay with a strong yellow subsoil in a state between bird lime and putty, mixed with a hodge-podge of stones, with a pan worn hard by the plough sole'; land that had been so cold and wet that the former tenant had been able to breed but never fatten a lamb; this land had been altered out of recognition by laying 80 or 90 miles of drains. You could see for yourself how the much-talked-of 1 inch-bore pipes functioned. As to subsoiling, the necessary sequel to draining, Mechi's land suffered what his labourers called a 'little earthquake' under a Deanston great plough drawn by six straining horses. His crops never forgot it. The whole farm was worked thereafter like a garden.

So, too, in 1851, when the American reaping machines were brought over, they were given a public trial on Tiptree farm and Mechi at once adopted their use.

Later still, when other agricultural improvers were talking of steam culture as 'yet a venture' it was with Mechi already an established practice. In 1853 he introduced to the Society of Arts a model of Romaine's steam cultivator which, he thought, 'was about to introduce a new economy in British agriculture'. It had been consigned to him by the Agricultural Department of the Canadian Government and, fearing it would be lost to agriculture, Mechi had found the necessary capital to patent and manufacture it. 'If it does not supersede the plough,' he said, 'it will limit its operations. When once the steam cultivator is shown to answer, no doubt many others will appear, and I venture to predict that, within seven years, steam will become the grand motive cultivating power.' Three years later in fact Mr. Fowler's new steam plough, with subsoiler attached, demonstrated its efficiency on his clover lea—watched by seven hundred of his guests, including Mr. Fowler himself. Mechi had heard clay-land farmers sighing for 'horses without feet'—here they were! Why did they still hesitate?

There were four cardinal points in the new clay-farming practice—deep drainage, deeper cultivation, more manure, and therefore more stock housed in covered yards. Very soon Mechi arrived at the conclusion that what really mattered on a farm was the quantity of meat produced to the acre. The more meat you produced the more manure you had, and the more corn you could grow. So he set himself to show his neighbours how to start the expanding circle. He had no doubts that, even if the population of the country should rise to sixty or seventy millions, the potential fertility of the country was equal to supplying all its needs.

The great need of farmers was manure. The new 'portable' or artificial manures had just been discovered when Mechi bought his farm. Nitrate of soda was being used experimentally by a few progressive farmers; Peruvian guano was growing rapidly in popularity. Since 1835, when the first small consignment of the latter was landed on English shores, its benefits had been so widely recognized that in a few years so much as 80,000 to 100,000 tons came into the country annually; in 1847, 220,000 tons were imported. Fears grew that the supply of this valuable ferlizer would soon be exhausted; and it was dear—as much as £10 a ton in some seasons. Science was busy with the chemical properties of soils, and experimenting with new artificials. In 1843 Sir John Lawes, then Mr. Lawes of Rothamsted Park, commenced to make superphosphate of lime at Bow. But bones, of which extraordinary quantities were used, and dung, were still the cheapest and most widely used forms of manure. There was at that time 'nothing like muck' to maintain the fertility of the land, and the faith of all farmers centred upon it.

At first Mechi thought that the use of artificial manures was profitable, and he did not hestitate to take advantage of the new discoveries. It was not long, however, before he was practising and preaching as the more important means of improvement the purchase of feeding stuffs for stock bred on the farm, combined, of course, with the complete conservation and utilization of the manure thus obtained.

In Norfolk and Lincolnshire farmers were doing much the same thing. When Mechi, being a young farmer, new to the job, looked round to examples of good farming he found his fellow 'Leviathan', Hewitt Davis, one of the keenest tenant farmers in Norfolk, spending on his 1,200 acres at the rate of £200 a year on artificials and nearly £3,000 a year on oil cake; and we can hardly be surprised that his once poor rabbit-warren of a farm had now become highly fertile, 'profitable to the tenant and producing a largely increased rental to the landlord.' It was truly said of those Norfolk farmers that they had no thoughts but of stall-feeding and that their muck heaps were like little cities. But the corn stacks more than paid for this costly method of feeding the soil.

This generous system might pay on the free-working loams of Norfolk and the silts of Lincolnshire but would it do on cold poor clay of Essex? Mechi had no doubt about it. He seldom produced less than 10 to 13 score pounds of meat per acre over his whole farm. This was the key to good farming. His land was cropped half in wheat and half in clover, tares, mangolds, and beans. Although it was cropped with wheat every second year for ten years and 'otherwise hard worked' its fertility increased year by year.

'No permanent grass can keep so much stock per acre as turnip culture and green crops, folded or fed in stalls.' 'The scythe is the farmer's greatest enemy; cut off your green crops with sheeps' teeth.' 'Pork at 6d. a lb. will pay for barley at 36s. a quarter, and, at 4d., for barley at 24s. a quarter, over and above manure.' So Mechi lectured, wrote, and practised, inviting all and sundry to come and see for themselves.

Visitors would remark the lay-out. All the old timber trees, those 'villainous stumps', had gone, as had the crooked fences, wide hedgerows and open ditches. New roads led to all corners of the farm. A continuous range of farm buildings, built solidly of brick and slate, replaced the former Essex board and thatch. The labourer's cottages, which had been ill-kempt and unhealthy, were replaced with comfortable, dry, and well-designed houses. It was a new extravagance to spend good money in this way, but the motive was not purely philanthropic; the money was invested to bring a return in contented and efficient service. Farm-houses, too, thought Mechi, should be 'genteel and substantial residences, with all requisites for domestic comfort and economy, residences worthy of a more intelligent and more capitalled tenantry, rejoicing in pianos and libraries.' This advice, at least, was easy to follow, and the rich farmer of the Golden Age housed himself magnificently, drank claret instead of small beer, and discarded his smock-frock for smartly tailored hunting clothes. This, according to Mechi, was only right and proper—a farmer who follows hounds and dresses respectably will be considered quite as likely to farm well and make as good a member of society as one who imitates in every respect one of his labourers.' He himself liked a day over the stubbles, but not over his own, for he could not 'afford' to keep stubbles as game preserves.

Rising over the roofs of the farm was a great shaft, and below it a fixed steam engine, busily employed in thrashing and dressing corn, working chaff cutters, cake crushers, root pulpers, millstones, and irrigating pumps. On the subject of steam Mechi was a visionary, and was accustomed to entertain his visitors with a pæan of praise of the new power—'mighty steam . . . that marvellous and almost invisible power which brooks no opposition: which never tires. Scouring the plains, piercing the hills, threading the valleys and ploughing the wide ocean; mastering with indolent ease time and space, wind, water, and season. . . . Can agriculture escape its influence? It must and will feed as well as clothe the people cheaply. . . . Scarcely any article used by the farmer but is indebted to the new discovery. His very loaf is now no longer dependent on wind or water, but is secured by steam. And yet we hear the miserable flail tapping the barn door and see the exhausted and haggard thrasher evidencing alike the misery and miscalculation of making man a mere automaton. . . . Honour to that departed philosopher whose sagacity and perception, under Divine Providence, applied the bubbling resistance of our tea-kettles to the most noble and useful purposes of humanity.' Again he would tilt against the 'barbarous Midland practice of ploughing with four horses in a line and two drivers.' He might regret that 'no longer on a tranquil May morning would he be amused to hear the ploughman objuring his horses, "Boxer, Wiolett", "Worrie" and "Hike, come hither" in the morning air,' but his engine gave him a greater pleasure. He employed an intelligent farm labourer as his engine man, and thought him worthy of a wage of 10s. a week, with double pay at harvest.

As to livestock, Mechi was no fancier. He knew what pleased him—'handsome well bred creatures. Plenty of length, breadth and depth in fore and hind quarters, large above the knee and hock, and small below; a little head with full intelligent and contented eye, a neat horn, a firm but yielding coat that fills the palm, and an outline level and pleasant to the eye—in fact a sort of rotund squareness.' Sheep, lambs, calves, bullocks, cows, and pigs were housed on Mr. Huxtable's system of sparred floors, all within doors, in accordance with the latest theory of warmth and dryness as a substitute for fodder. 'Let us keep our cattle warm and dry and well fed and we shall seldom feel the cramp in our pockets.' What did he do with the straw?—'Eat it, that was let the cattle eat it, and I can keep four times as much stock.'

If, while he tapped the thermometer that registered the exact temperature within the cattle house, he confessed that he never liked the look of his animals so well on the boards as on a little mountain of clean straw or on a green pasture, he would add that it was not a question of fancy but of profit, which would lead him round again to the all-important question of muck. Every bit of the precious manure fell through the spars on to the floor, where were spread sawdust and burnt clay; fat stock made fat crops; lean stock, lean crops.

One of the other two Leviathans, Mr. Huxtable, the Rector of Sutton Waldron, and another self-taught farmer, had installed an irrigation system for the cheap distribution of liquid manure from barn and yard, and Mechi adopted the same process. A powerful jet, 'of a thousand scrubbing-brush power', was directed into the house. The 'pudding' flowed in a lazy stream to the subterranean iron pipes which fed the great reservoir tank, large as a chapel. From this tank, after dilution with water, the gruel made in this way was pumped to the fields and sprayed over the crops.

By these means it was sought to reduce the tremendous bills for bones and other 'portables'. Few farmers indeed could face an expenditure of £4 an acre on an irrigation system, but many applied the lesson as far as they could, and liquid manure tanks were built on many farms.

Besides the irrigation of the crops, the visitor to Tiptree could note the use of Suffolk drills instead of broadcasting, of Garrett's horse-hoe replacing much hand hoeing; of thin sowing—as taught by the Reverend Smith of Lois Weedon—instead of thick sowing; of the one-horse carts—introduced by Henry Hannam of Berkshire in 1828—instead of the cumbrous Essex wagons; and of the two-horse plough instead of the four-horse plough.

So the Leviathans farmed, with apparently Inexhaustible purses. They found imitators, but also they incurred unpopularity. One tenant farmer, having heard of the thousands of pounds spent on the farms, said that he thanked God he had not got the money to spend, or he too might be fooling it away. The great men were accused of influencing statesmen who turned their experience to political purposes, for how could one hope for protection again if these fools kept boasting about profits? Landlords, seeking higher rents, asked their tenants why they did not grow such crops as Mr. Mechi and company. But when Mechi's book, *How to Farm Profitably*, was published in 1857 it had a good reception, ran through three editions, and sold ten thousand copies.

Although they might very justly be accused of extravagance, the example of Mechi and his fellows certainly helped to raise the general level of farming. Caird, summarizing the progress of agriculture from 1770 to 1851, noted the important advances that had already been made. The yield of wheat had gone up from 23 bushels to $26\frac{1}{2}$. Turnips and mangolds were grown on land which had previously been thought unfit for them. Bare fallows were becoming unnecessary, and green crops and leguminous crops enabled the stock-carrying capacity to be increased enormously. At the same time higher livestock prices had led to great improvements in the breeds.

In September 1857, eighty gentlemen sat down to a splendid dinner at the London Tavern. The occasion was the presentation to Mechi of a 'Superb piece of plate, in very rich design in the Renaissance style. A fine piece of silverwork, 3 feet 6 inches high, weighing 500 ounces, and costing between £500 and £600.' Figures on the plate represented Agriculture, Commerce, Peace and Plenty, and below were scenes of a farmyard, a group of agricultural implements, Mechi's arms and an inscription: 'Presented to John Joseph Mechi, Esq., F.S.A., of Tiptree Hall, Sheriff of London and Middlesex, by 420 of his friends in token of their appreciation of his continuous efforts to promote the interests of agriculture, 1857.'

SPEED THE PLOUGH

The Chairman, Thomas Bateson of Coombe Down, Bath, in his address acknowledged the indebtedness of farmers throughout the length and breadth of England to Mr. Mechi for allowing theoretical ideas to be put into practice and thereby showing them what was good and what experiments did not produce the results expected.

This was the zenith of Mechi's star, and his subsequent career, reflecting the vicissitudes of the times both in the City and on the farm, makes sad reading. As always in farming, depression came on the heels of prosperity and by the middle 'sixties the gilt had already begun to wear thin. Industrial collapse set in first. Mechi was a Governor of the Unity Stock Bank, and its failure in 1866 hit him very hard. Another loss in connection with the Unity Fire and General Life Assurance Office caused him to resign his Aldermanic gown instead of becoming Lord Mayor of London. His means were very much restricted.

Tiptree Hall also fell on evil times. The year 1864–5 was a famine winter for stock. The droughty summers of 1868 and 1870 left turnip and root crops scarce. There was the rinderpest in 1865–6, and the early 'seventies were wet and brought poor wheat crops. Of the disastrous harvest of 1873 it was reported from Essex that 'heavy rains followed the wheat sowings, beating down the land as if a roller had passed over it. The wheat has not been threshed out, but it is believed there will be no head corn at all— nothing but chickens' food: the straw is of bad colour, very much mildewed and breaking easily.'

The bad seasons told on the balance sheets at Tiptree, and outside sources of money had dried up. Mechi was already a poor man in 1879, when the disastrous harvest of that year brought the end. His affairs were put into liquidation, and Mechi was broken in health and heart. In that year he had a second presentation, a few contributing to give the old man a pony and carriage. He died on 20th December 1880, at which time those who 'recognized the integrity of his personal character' were contemplating a subscription to provide for the wants of his old age. The project did not materialize in time for Mechi himself, but the moneys raised were devoted to the support of his widow and daughters.

SPEED THE PLOUGH

His end was like that of many another who had shared his aspirations and vied with him in enterprise.

The Tiptree Hall Visitors' Book, which had been signed by so many great and illustrious visitors, is now in the British Museum.

THE FENTON BARNS SAGA

For a truer picture of the progressive farming of Mechi's time we may turn to one of his contemporaries who lived and farmed in a widely distant part of the country. East Lothian has been to Scotland what Norfolk has been to England—the pioneer county of the agricultural revolution and the model of all that was admirable in farming right up till the great days of the 'sixties. And the greatest figure among the tenant farmers of his time in East Lothian was George Hope of Fenton Barns. The farm stands a little way from the sea and looks south across a flat valley where now the main railway line runs by the little junction of Drem.

To go back to early days, it was not till near the end of the eighteenth century that the general run of Scottish farmers began to depart from their old ways—their infield and outfield, their high-backed rigs and weedy cornfields. Even in East Lothian, as late as 1780 there was 'little appearance of amendment'. Only the more progressive men were growing turnips and clover; potatoes, which ultimately became so important a crop, were grown on a field scale only near the towns. Great areas still required draining and liming before they would grow even moderate crops of wheat.

But, for one reason and another, the agricultural revolution in Eastern Scotland was accomplished with quite exceptional speed. For one thing there had been no complex system of open fields and commons to sweep away, and there was no need for tiresome and costly enclosure acts. Steam coasting vessels opened up new markets in the south and a good many Scots, having saved money in trade or manufactures or the country's service, came back prepared to invest their money in Scottish land. In a generation great stretches of country-side were changed almost beyond recognition.

At first the profits of the Napoleonic times were put back into the soil, but even Scottish heads were turned by the false prosperity of the last few years before the peace. The younger generation in East Lothian took to riding, 'began to keep greyhounds, to be members of coursing clubs . . . and yelped the same note of folly as their betters in birth, their equals in extravagance and vice.' But 1815 came, 'the smart young farmers no longer galloped along the road . . . and the greyhounds were hanged.'

George Hope was born too late to be spoilt by fortune, for he had just started at Dirleton Village School, at the age of three and a half, in the year of Waterloo and the greyhound hangings. In any case his family, though tenants of 670 English acres, were far from prosperous. Grandfather Hope, who had started life in extreme poverty on a small farm near Edinburgh, picking up a few shillings by carting coals for the neighbours when farm work was not pressing, had moved in the seventeen-seventies to the farm of Ferrygate in East Lothian; in 1796, with more courage than discretion, he took a lease of the large double holding of Fenton and Fenton Barns. Prices might be good, but a vast deal of improvement was wanted before the new farms would grow crops to justify their rent; and Hope's capital was quite unequal to the claims upon it. A large part of the land was a 'moorish sand, covered in great part by furze bushes'. This had to be cleared and limed and was in fact soon and fairly successfully brought under crop. The rest, however, was cold, ill-drained, sticky land, which responded very slowly to management that was short of means. Grandfather Hope died in 1801, at the age of fifty-two, broken in health and spirit by his five years' struggle with the unkind soil.

The holding was now divided, the eldest son Robert taking over the lease of Fenton and his younger half-brother that of Fenton Barns. Prices were good, and some part of the dead-weight of debt seems to have been lifted in the last years of the war. By great ill luck, however, the old lease was coming to an end with the good times. A new lease was arranged in 1814, in the vain expectation that prices would keep up, at the enormous rent of £1,710. So Robert was left with a dear bargain, and the family had to tighten their belts. They ate meat but once or twice a week and spent the winter evenings by the light of a single tallow candle. Mrs. Hope slaved at her cooking and baking as hard as her husband worked out of doors, but they made no headway, sinking indeed deeper in debt year by year. At last Robert, seeing himself on the very verge of bankruptcy, decided to throw in his hand and emigrate to America. But next Haddington Market day he must have had a heart-to-heart talk with the factor, for he came home with the news that the landlord was prepared for the future to take a corn rent instead of a fixed cash sum. This made an important difference, for it meant not only an immediate remission but an insurance against a further fall in prices. So they took new heart and tried again.

In 1820 the half-brother at Fenton Barns died, and the factor persuaded Robert, rather against his judgment, to take over the complete double holding with which his father had started. But what had been too much for the father's resources was too much for the son's. Year after year they struggled along, often at their wits' end to pay a paltry tradesman's bill, and never able to give the land the full measure of generous treatment for which it cried out.

Meanwhile George had left the village school, put in a year or two at another in Haddington, gone into a lawyer's office there at the age of fourteen and carried on with his education at the night school. He seems to have made no great impression on his dominies, having a poor memory for words and being slow at his Latin. But Mr. Donaldson, the lawyer, thought well of him.

George had no particular ambition to farm—he knew too much about farming—but to please his parents he went home at the age of eighteen, after four years in the office. As bailiff at Fenton Barns he soon showed the stuff he was made of. For years he rose at five every week-day to see the men to their work. The farm staff liked him, for he treated them with respect and understanding and they worked well together. On the days when he had to be at Edinburgh cattle market he rose at two in the morning and rode the twenty miles before six. When he was twenty he had an offer of a good post in Australia and would fain have gone, but his mother persuaded him to stay. In these early days he was continually disappointed at the slow response of the farm to his labours. Riding here and there in the surrounding country he saw crops nearly always better than those at home, and he was discontented. The farm, in fact, was still largely undrained, though his father had now started his own tile works, and was taking out the profits in the form of drain tiles for his own fields. As yet there was no guano or nitrate of soda to whip the land into activity.

At this time there was little but the yearly round of farming, but George has recorded that he went to a meeting of Cobbett's, in October 1832, and 'returned much gratified', for already he was an ardent Liberal and reformer. He was indeed a grave and serious young man, thinking deeply on politics and religion in the intervals of farm work. About this time, too, he revolted against the Calvinist dogmas that he had endured in the Parish Church, and after much heart-searching, and to his mother's great grief, left the Kirk and became a Unitarian.

At last there were definite signs of improvement at the bank. As mile after mile of drain pipes were buried in the fields the corn yields began to improve, and the cattle and sheep were leaving a balance of cash profit besides their manure. In 1836 Robert Hope, now regarded as one of the leading men in the country, went to London to give evidence before the Select Committee to inquire into the State of Agriculture. The farm now employed seventeen men and six women workers in winter, and another eighteen women and boys in summer, besides the gang of shearers in harvest time. It still grew few turnips, and only enough potatoes for the farm folk. But for the last four years the wheat, of which 175 acres were grown, had averaged nearly 28 bushels. The landlord had rebuilt the farm offices, there was not much land remaining to be drained, and Robert 'was now doing tolerably well'—thanks to his corn rent. He told the Committee that he thought corn rents might save other tenants from the fate that had so nearly been his own. Two years later, in 1838, he achieved the ambition of his life, 'got up his bond of obligation' and was 'now free and clear of all claims and encumbrances.'

The task had taken forty-two years; it had killed Grandfather Hope and also George's mother who, although she had enjoyed a few last years of ordinary comfort and peace, did not live to see the bond brought home. Robert Hope himself became a speechless (though not a helpless) invalid a very few years later, and more and more of the burden of affairs fell upon the shoulders of his son.

There were various ups and downs on the farm. Foot-and-mouth broke out in 1840, but it was a mild type and caused little loss. In 1842 the crops on Fenton Barns were the finest ever seen and indeed could 'hold up their heads with any in the country'. The farm indeed was now coming to be regarded as a model of good management, and in 1841 Robert Hope wrote to one of his other sons: 'We are expecting soon Mr. Mace, a young man from Kent, to learn our system of husbandry.' This Mr. Mace seems to have been the first of the great army of pupils who were to learn farming at Fenton Barns in the subsequent thirty years. They came from all over Britain, and from Denmark, Germany, Sweden, and many other countries.

If George Hope had consulted his own pleasure he might now, with a well-stocked farm and money in the bank, have led a very comfortable life—might even have gone back to the smart breeches, the well-groomed hacks, and the greyhounds. We must not indeed give him overmuch credit for continuing to live laborious days, for he was a bad shot, and never developed a taste for the ordinary country recreations. Also he seems to have been plagued by swarms of bankrupt uncles, impecunious cousins and widowed aunts, and to have had so strong a sense of family duty that he was kept continually worried by their affairs. All the time he was thinking deeply about politics, reading all the literature of Cobden's Anti-Corn Law League and becoming a thoroughly convinced free-trader.

In 1842 the League offered three prizes for essays on the Repeal of the Corn Laws, and George decided to try his hand at 'exposing the impolicy and injustice of the Bread-tax'. His essay was awarded a thirty guinea prize and he woke one morning to find himself famous. Cobden wrote him in the warmest terms—as indeed he might, for here was indeed an ally from among the ranks of the Philistines. Cobden and John Bright came and spent a day at Fenton Barns. Hope was invited to sit on the platform at League meetings, and to make speeches. There were of course other farmers, and more particularly landowners, who called him traitor, but his neighbours in East Lothian, for the most part, took the affair very well. They knew that Hope was entirely

A Sketch by Richard Doyle from 'Early Victorian England'
(Oxford University Press)

The Repeal of the Corn Laws—Disraeli 'Impressing on the Agricultural Interest that it is Ruined'.

sincere, and they agreed with him at least in part—that the tenant farmer had more to gain from other things than from corn laws: security of tenure, abolition of the game laws, and a general curtailment of the landowner's power would be more than a fair exchange for protection. It is difficult for us now to realize the power which the landlord of those days had over his tenants. To shoot a rabbit that was eating up his young turnips or to vote the wrong way at an election(and there was then no secret ballot) might, with some landlords, mean the end of a farmer's tenancy. And often there was not even a pretence at compensation for the improvements which the tenant had made. Hope himself was later to suffer what amounted to eviction for his political views.

This rather solemn and perhaps slightly priggish young man, who was full of elevated sentiments and high principles, had long considered in the abstract the problem of matrimony; the choice of a spouse was obviously a matter for grave and prolonged consideration. But George, like a common mortal, fell suddenly in love upon an April day, and was married between the haysel and the harvest of the same year. The lady was the daughter of an Edinburgh solicitor, and the pair remained completely devoted to each other until Hope's death. They had troubles to share, for one young child died of scarlet fever and later two more were taken, within a week, by diphtheria. Apart from this, Hope's home life was completely happy and he became mellowed and humanized as the years went by.

The farming at Fenton Barns, in the main, went from good to better. There was fairly severe loss in '47 from pleuro-pneumonia and a general setback with poor crops and poor prices in '49. On the other hand the farm had the good fortune to escape the terrible rinderpest in the winter of '65–'66, which elsewhere carried off so many cattle.[1] In 1851 Hope went to the great Exhibition and saw the American reapers; went to Mechi's shop and bought a razor strop which, four years later, was looked at with the gravest suspicion by a French customs officer; went to Windsor for the Royal Show; journeyed out to Tiptree for the trial of McCormick's and Hussey's reapers, where he shuddered at the sight of Mr. Mechi's green wheat being sacrificed in the cause of science; and passed on to Norfolk, to shake his head over farmers who bred pheasants and rode to hounds.

The main farming development of the late 'forties, in Hope's district, had been the increasing cultivation of potatoes; and the East Lothian six-course rotation, with a full 'break' of potatoes and another of turnips and swedes, was becoming established.

[1] The writer's grandfather had seventy head and buried them all but one old cow.

The rotation went with a very heavy winter stock of both cattle and sheep, and a high bill for oil cake. But the stock would often leave a cash profit besides the mountains of muck which were turned into profitable sale crops. Hope made a special feature of his potatoes and nothing gave him greater pleasure than to see his hundred and odd acres level over the rows.

George Hope was not a pioneer in the sense that he attempted to be first with every innovation, but he was continually watching developments and went ahead as soon as he was satisfied that a thing was a practical success. He turned over from hand-reaping to machines some time in the 'fifties, and bought steam tackle in 1863. He early took an interest in the new agricultural science, and was awarded a medal by the Highland Society in 1853 for some experiments in cattle feeding. In 1856 he was one of the 'Highland' Directors who had the responsibility of taking the Scottish live-stock to the Paris Exhibition. He had charge of the stock from Edinburgh to Lowestoft, and thence by steamer to Dunkirk, where the Secretary and another Director, who had gone before as the advance party, met him. There were various adventures. One bull died at Lowestoft and another jumped into the harbour and was drowned. But in the main the enterprise was carried through very successfully. Hope's own Leicesters, which formed part of the exhibit, were awarded a third prize.

Hope expanded his farming enterprises considerably as time went on. The first venture was to lease another hundred acres of rough grazing at Dirleton Common. This was soon brought under cultivation, largely by carting on thousands of cartloads of clay wherewith to give some semblance of body to a soil that was practically blowing sand. Later he bought a farm of 600 acres in Berwickshire, a hill grazing in Peebles and still later the low-ground farm of Bordlands, of 480 acres, in the same county. He had not in fact the money to pay for these purchases, but he had infinite faith in land as an investment, and cheerfully signed his mortgages. He had once been tempted to other forms of invest-ment—had tried a gamble in railway shares during the boom— and had burnt his fingers. Thereafter he put all his capital into land with the one exception that he invested some in an ultra-conservative Scottish insurance company, of which he was later made a director.

Later, when his son and his excellent grieve Hugh Bertram had been trained to see to the details at Fenton Barns, Hope did a great deal of work as a valuer and arbiter, and made a great reputation for knowledge and judgement and the absolute fairness of his decisions. No man in Scotland enjoyed the more complete trust of the farming community. He wrote, too, a good many agricultural articles and was continually consulted by Russell of the *Scotsman*, who would come out to Fenton Barns of a Sunday and compose his leaders on Agricultural Policy with Hope at his elbow.

A. G. Bradley, who was one of the great many pupils who went to Fenton Barns to 'learn the system of husbandry', has written[1] a vivid account of the farm and the district in the heyday of the 'sixties. The whole of the low-ground land of the county was like a garden, paying a rent of from three to five pounds an acre. A fine new house of red sandstone had recently been built at Fenton Barns. The old one was occupied by the faithful steward Hugh Bertram, then sixty-five years old, and it was here that the pupils lived, fed and were ruled over by Hugh's managing daughter. Hugh himself, who had started behind the plough, had no book learning except the Holy Script, but was a man of great ability and consuming energy with a voice that could carry nearly across to Fife. From the farm-house windows could be seen a wide view of great rectangular fields, bounded by closely trimmed hedges that showed up as thin seams in the vast chequered counterpane of crops. There was hardly a tree or a thicket or a patch of waste land in the whole of the nearer landscape.

The farming at Fenton Barns 'almost reached the sublime'. The great organization went like clockwork. 'No wildrose or old-man's-beard rambled in the hedgerows, no May or Blackthorn blossom lit them up, neither did the violet nor the primrose find a lodging beneath their shade.' There was no permanent grass, but only the rye-grass and clover of the six-course rotation. The potato crops—the old Regent sort for the most part—were

[1] *When Squires and Farmers Thrived*, by A. G. Bradley, 1925.

wonderful to behold, as well they might be with forty loads of cake-fed muck and 8 cwt. of artificial fertilizer under every acre. Fine pairs of hard-trained, hard-fed Clydesdales with brisk hinds in the plough stilts shared the ploughing with the farm 'steamer' which was one of half a dozen that could be seen at work in the plain below the farm.

The men labourers lacked the manners of the south country sort that Bradley knew. There was no touching of caps and no 'Sirring', even of the master. But they were skilful and willing, strong and loyal. The women workers or 'bondagers' were almost as numerous as the men. There were a dozen or so of ploughmen's wives, sisters, and daughters, and about as many more immigrants from the Highlands, who came for about half the year and lodged in bothies. The Amazons did nearly every kind of work except where horses were concerned. 'In threshing-time they ran up ladders with sacks of wheat that would have broken the back of a Rugby forward. They wore a uniform costume of straw bonnet, a pink neckerchief, blue blouse, linsey-wolsey skirt to the knees, woollen stockings and hobnailed boots.'

Harvest was still a time of busy scenes. The sickle and scythe had ceased to be the chief tools, but a hundred thousand sheaves had still to be bound by men's hands, and a gang of Irishmen came over each year for the work. The whole force, home and alien, had their porridge provided for them, cooked in a great boiler and stirred with the wooden granary spade.

Haddington, six miles away, was the leading grain market in all the north country and to it flocked, each Friday, old farmers in their broughams or waggonettes and young farmers in smart gigs. After the sales came the 'Ordinary' at 'The George', where farmers and their pupils—English Squire's sons, Danish and Swedish Counts—crowded the well-plenished tables. None of these cheerful, competent, prosperous men dreamt of the fate that was hanging over them. Only a dozen years later the grain from the prairies burst upon the country like a flood, in which none but the strongest could live. Nor were those who sank always the less competent or the less careful. As in Essex and many other of the arable counties those who went under could often have saved themselves if they had been prepared to jettison their faith and forget their duty to the land.

What would have been George Hope's reaction to the crisis it is difficult to say; he had a wise head indeed, but his faith in high farming was a like a second religion; as it happened he never had to face the problem.

Hope devoted the last years of his life to public work. He still kept pegging away at his favourite subjects in agricultural politics —more security for the improving tenant; abolition of the game laws; repeal of the Scottish Law of Hypothec which gave the landlord first claim upon the estate of an insolvent farmer, and thus restricted credit to farmers in general—better housing for agricultural workers, the abolition of the bothy system and so forth. In general politics he was still the advanced liberal, pleading for an extension of the franchise, the ballot, women's suffrage, and universal education.

In 1865 he was persuaded by his friends, almost at the last minute, to come forward as parliamentary candidate for his native county. It is clear that he had no personal ambitions in the business and he could hardly expect to win the seat, for the sitting member was Lord Elcho, heir to the Earldom of Wemyss, and thus one of the leading members of the county aristocracy. The land-owners would be solid for Hope's opponent, and many of the farmers and miscellaneous small fry would certainly never bring themselves, whatever their opinions, to vote against their lairds. However, it was put to Hope that there was a chance of success and that, once in Parliament, he would be able to help forward the various reforms that he so ardently wished to see. In fact he polled a number of votes that was surprisingly large under the circum-stances. Elcho and his friends took the affair very ill and Hope's landlord shared the view that this was really too much. Mr. Hope might be an excellent grower of turnips, but it was a piece of incredible presumption that he should think of opposing a man of Lord Elcho's standing. Moreover, he was a tiresome, mis-chievous fellow, with his constant harping about game laws and security. What was the country coming to if the owner of land could not do as he liked with it? The Fenton Barns lease was not due to expire for eight more years, but the affair was not forgotten. When the time came Mr. Hope was informed that his application for renewal would not receive consideration.

Hope had all along seen that this might happen, and he took the blow with complete tranquillity. There is no sign of anger even in the private letters that he wrote to his brothers. There was indeed a widespread agitation in Scotland, and there were letters in the Press from men like the President of the Royal Danish Agricultural Society, who had been a pupil. Even Tory landlords tried to use their private influence to have the decision reversed, for they saw that the step was calculated to win a great deal of sympathy for all Hope's subversive doctrines. But the landlord was stubborn, and in May 1873, the Hope family bade farewell to what represented the life-work of three generations. 'Hughie' Bertram, the Bailiff, went too, joined a son in Canada, and spent the evening of his life in pouring derision upon the prairie farmers and all their ways.

Hope moved to his Peeblesshire farm of Bordlands and carried on serenely with his various remaining concerns, finding time, too, for a little fishing. He was still in full vigour of body and mind, in spite of his sixty-four strenuous years, when, in 1875, he was again invited to stand for Parliament. This time it was Aberdeenshire, and the rival candidate was again a leading county man, the uncle of the Earl of Aberdeen. Hope's personal feelings in the business were exactly as they had been ten years before. He would come up to Aberdeen and tell the electors plainly and frankly what he stood for; if they chose to elect him, good and well.

But such a guileless mode of attack was hardly calculated to defeat the prestige of birth, backed up by an elaborate party organization, influence, and money. Hope, in fact, was too honest for this world—at least for the political world of his time. In Aberdeenshire it was his religious views that chiefly weighed against him, for to the old full-blooded Calvinist a Unitarian was barely to be distinguished from an Atheist. The ministers prayed in their pulpits that his soul might be saved, but this was not helpful to his immediate prospects. He polled a very respectable number of votes, 1,568 against his opponent's 1,903, and went home quite undisturbed and perhaps actually relieved in mind.

There was one minor ambition that he never realized for himself; it was to farm, even if it were but a few acres for a few years, some of the famous Dunbar Red Land on which, and only on which, perfection could be attained in the culture of potatoes. In his last year Hope had, however, the satisfaction of seeing his son settled on Oxwell Mains, in the land of his dreams.

Returning from Aberdeen in his usual health, he soon after developed symptoms that alarmed his family and told himself plainly that his days were now to be few. He spent the remaining few months quietly arranging his various affairs, seeing his son settled in his new home, and met his end peacefully at Bordlands in December 1876.

THE CHAMBERLAIN SYSTEM

During the depression which lasted from the late 'seventies till 1939 (with the brief interlude at the end of the first world war) there was a progressive decline in tillage farming over most of the country. To many it seemed that the only hope of survival was to put away plough-land to grass. Wheat, which had been the most important crop, fell in price earlier and faster and farther than any other farm product. Corn prices in general dropped more than those of beef and mutton, while milk—one of the few commodities that could not well be imported—was in steadily improving demand. Moreover, as it became clear that less and less money was coming in, expenses had to be cut by one means or another; and they could, in the last resort, be reduced to the annual depreciation on a dog and a stick.

There were, indeed, some noteworthy exceptions. Farmers on the silts of Lincoln and Norfolk made the discovery that they had the near-perfect conditions for potato-growing, and they ploughed up while others laid down. The turnip-and-barley men in Bedfordshire, with the coming of the railway, sold their flocks and turned their farms into kitchen gardens, relying on London's stables for the essential supply of manure. Fruit growing expanded in the traditional orchard counties like Kent and Evesham and spread into Essex and Cambridgeshire. But in general it was a time of up horn and down corn.

Probably the most difficult problem was presented by the poor light four-course arable, where the folded flock, fed heavily on oil cake, had served to maintain soil fertility at a level that could support moderate yields of corn. The folded flock was expensive, and could not stand on its own legs in competition with New Zealand frozen lamb; and the loss on the sheep could no longer be balanced by profits from wheat and barley. On many of the farms on the Downs and Wolds, on the Cotswolds and Lincoln Heath, in West Norfolk and elsewhere—which had been the last to be brought under the plough—an alternative system was hard to find. The expense of fencing, and of the laying-on of water to the fields, was prohibitive, and the only available types of clover and grass—what are now called the 'commercial strains'— dwindled away after a year or two and gave place to weeds. The land 'would not carry grass'. Rents fell to nominal figures, or to nothing; indeed, there were instances where the landlord, with indomitable faith in the future, paid his tenant to carry on. In the less extreme cases, the situation slowly drifted from bad to worse. When the banker's patience was exhausted, part of the flock would be sold in order to reduce the overdraft, and outlying fields, one by one, reverted to scrubby waste.

Long ago, of course, Prout of Sawbridgeworth in Hertford- shire had read what he took to be the lesson of Broadbalk field at Rothamsted—that land could be farmed, and corn could be grown, without muck. He continued for a score of years to grow little but cereals—and mostly wheat—with no more dung than could be produced by his work horses and an odd cow. According to Prout, if only you were prepared to buy enough fertilizer, and could contrive to control weeds, you might grow corn as often as you pleased for as long as you pleased. But Prout was farming on heavy land in good times, and it did not seem that his experi- ence could apply, with corn at half its former price, to chalk Down or Cotswold brash or Norfolk sand.

In the latter part of the century, however, George Baylis began farming on what was essentially Prout's system on the Berkshire Downs and, adding one unwanted farm to another until his total holding ran to many thousands of acres, he continued to make profits until the 'thirties. Even then it was not that his land was worn out or that his yields dwindled; the fact was that he could not, working his land with innumerable horse teams, get his costs down to the new low level of corn prices that followed on the country's return to the gold standard and the breaking of the Western Canadian prairie. Full-scale mechanization, with crawler and combine, was too great an adventure for a man of his age.

One of the first small band of pioneers to enter upon this adventure was Mr. F. P. Chamberlain of Crowmarsh Battle Farm, near Benson in Oxfordshire. Not all of his fellows succeeded. To some of them it seemed that the American engineers had produced the complete answer to the problems of low-cost corn growing and that, given full and efficient mechanization, there was little else that mattered. In fact, it proved easier for the farmer to turn engineer than for an engineer to turn farmer. In any case, Chamberlain learnt his agriculture first. The son of a farmer in the Marlborough country, he 'took to' Crowmarsh Battle in 1894, the year when wheat touched its lowest price for a century— 22s. 10d. a quarter. Crowmarsh Battle farm lies next door to that on which Jethro Tull began his first experiments in farm mechanization fully two centuries ago, and in the heart of a wide stretch of corn land.

Like many others at that time, the farm had seen better days, as can still be inferred from its spacious farmhouse and substantial buildings. The old family, after rising fairly high in the social scale, had failed, like many more, to adjust themselves to the changed conditions. Their vacant places were being taken by incomers—mainly from the south-west and mostly stock breeders and dairymen—who lived in the kitchens of the great houses and worked all the hours there were.

The original farm, extending to 550 acres, had been increased by other leases to nine hundred. It is bounded on one side by the Thames and stretches up the north-westerly slope of the Chilterns —valley gravel along the low ground, heavy loam on the lower slope and a thinner soil, on chalk, towards the top. It had long been farmed on the typical system of the locality—corn growing, bullock feeding and a folded flock.

When Chamberlain took over he set up a dairy herd of some fifty or sixty Shorthorns, and later planted up 65 acres with apples and plums. He kept no sheep and no livestock except his cows and ten horses. Steam tackle was hired to help the tillage.

For a time Battle Farm was managed as two complementary units—a dairy farm below and a corn farm on the hill. But the cost of the long uphill haul of cow dung to the ploughland proved to be prohibitive, and the decision was reached that the crops must make do with artificials alone. In fact, practically all the produce—corn, straw, and hay—was sold.

One of Chamberlain's views being that 'So far as possible a farmer should be a chemist and a botanist, but above all should be an accountant', he compared income and expenditure on his two enterprises and reached the conclusion that, while the hill was making a profit, the returns from the dairy section were negligible. He therefore sold his dairy herd, and, apart from a few grazing cattle on some twenty acres of pasture and a few head of poultry, livestock has since played no part in his scheme.

The first tractor was bought in 1927 and, according to the books, showed a saving, as compared with horse work, of some fifty pounds a year. Gradually the process of mechanization was completed—tractors, combine harvester, grain drier and combine drill.

There has been no fixed rotation; on the original arable block the proportion under wheat and barley has been, on average, over two-thirds, the remainder being one year ley (which is mown for hay) and a very little bare fallow. The chief means of weed control is the bastard fallow after early-cut hay. The proportion between wheat and barley has varied widely according to the relative price prospects. Far from there having been a progressive decline in yields, records show a rise—from 8 sacks in the five years 1929–33 to over 9¼ in the period 1941–5.

In recent times numbers of other farms, faced with similar problems, have moved faster and quite as far as Chamberlain along the road to specialized and mechanized corn production. Some of these have encountered difficulties. One has been the loss of 'body' from the soil by reason of the slow fall in its humus content. Another has been increasing damage, especially to winter corn, from a soil-borne disease of wheat and barley that modern science ascribes to the fungus *Ophiobolus* and to which farmers long ago gave the ominous name of 'Take-all'. Chamberlain seems to have hit upon a simple prescription for both these troubles. A large proportion of his corn is undersown with Italian ryegrass and trefoil to provide green manure, a cheap substitute for the folded flock or the dung cart. Its operation against *Ophiobolus* is more subtle; the fungus can live on stubble during the autumn and winter if it can secure also a supply of soil nitrate; but the growing plants use up this nitrate and so starve and weaken the enemy; moreover, the green manure, decaying with the return of spring, strengthens the young corn to repel the attack.

Chamberlain's 'system' is by no means the only guide to profitable farming on the sort of land where the sheep fold, the bullock yard and the four-course rotation were wont to be regarded as the means to the end of bread and ale. In particular, where fencing and water can be provided, the modern ley system is perhaps a better one. But Chamberlain's contribution to progress is a notable one.

5

IN PASTURES GREEN

Since the very beginnings of farming in these Islands (which archaeologists date about 2500 B.C.) grasslands and grazing animals have played a big part in our economy. Julius Caesar reported that, though some of the tribes grew wheat and barley, most depended for their living chiefly on their herds and flocks. Roman Britain, indeed, helped to feed Rome; but a thousand years were to pass before there was any considerable export of farm produce, and the trade was then in wool, produced mainly on the natural pastures of our downs, wolds and hills. To-day, as has often been remarked, grass is our most important crop. It would therefore have been strange if the grass field had been overlooked by our improvers.

Two circumstances, however, combined to delay progress. On the one hand, the country's most pressing need, during the century that began in 1760, was for more bread, and the chief preoccupation of the pioneers was with plough farming. On the other, pasture presents more complex and more difficult problems than the field of corn or roots, and progress has been interrupted by many long-maintained controversies.

Since ancient traditional ways have some bearing even on yesterday's history, it is worth noting that, from very early times, there have been two schools of thought about the way to fit together plough-land and pasture into a farming scheme. The Saxons divided their village lands, as Caesar divided Gaul, into three parts. One—originally small but steadily growing as more mouths had to be fed—was kept continuously under the plough, growing wheat and rye, barley and oats, peas and beans. A second was mown every summer, and provided, after haysel, common grazing for the village livestock. The third—the common or 'waste'—yielded turf, firewood, and perhaps timber, but also provided most of the grazing during a large part of the year. The Celts, by and large, worked on a different plan. They were accustomed to grow corn, on a particular piece of land, year after year until the harvest no longer gave a tolerable return for seed and labour, and thereafter to abandon the piece, for an indefinite period, to nature. The arable land weeds were then gradually ousted by grasses and other perennials. When this tumble-down ley had gathered a tolerable sward and the soil was deemed to have had a reasonable spell of rest, it was broken up for another round of cropping. Sometimes, during its last year under grass, a piece would be enclosed to form a night paddock for the livestock, so that it might be fortified with manure for the ordeal that was to come. Thus in the North and West ley farming, of a sort, goes back to remote antiquity.

A grassland surveyor of two centuries ago would have mapped a high proportion of our pastures as bad or indifferent. The commons of the Midland clay country were infested with brambles and briars, dotted with anthills and interspersed with marshy places that harboured the water-snail and explained the prevalence of 'the rot' in sheep. The downlands and wolds, having supplied the bone-making minerals to scores of generations of sheep without any attempt at replacement, would have been diagnosed as extremely deficient in phosphate. The cheese pastures of Cheshire and the Wiltshire Vale were probably in little better case while, on the sandy heaths of Norfolk, the proverbial two rabbits fought for every blade of grass. The Scottish 'outfields' with their tumble-down leys provided a varied but scanty diet. But perhaps the mountain grazings of the Scottish Highlands and Wales, lightly stocked with well-balanced numbers of sheep and cattle, their bracken regularly mown to provide litter for the winter, may have been in better case than they are to-day. Here and there, too, the surveyor would have found an old enclosure of rich deep soil, long used for fattening beasts and managed with skill and care, that carried a Class I sward of indigenous ryegrass and white clover. Of such Hilgard, a Northampton squire, wrote in 1814:

'There is some extraordinarily good grazing land in Leicestershire, Yorkshire, Lincolnshire and in some of the fens; the best
I ever saw is in the Vale of Aylesbury. These superior pastures
will feed one large ox, and one large wether sheep or a ewe and
lamb, per acre.'

Up till the seventeenth century pastures were made either by
letting nature have her way or else by scattering about on the land
the sweepings of the farmer's hay-loft. The first step of progress
was the introduction, from France and Flanders, of the 'artificial
grasses'. The list, as given by the early writers, included Sainfoin,
Lucerne, Red Clover, White Clover, Trefoil and Ryegrass. By
the time of Jethro Tull these were being sown by the experi-
mentally-minded in many parts of Southern and Eastern England.
Tull himself, apart from being the pioneer of the Drill Husbandry,
was an enthusiastic cultivator of Sainfoin. But the 'book farmers'
of those times, in their desire to stir up a spirit of improvement
among their practical brethren, too often made the mistake of
overstating the merits of their new improvements. Even James
Adam, who ordinarily wrote with proper caution, could say of
Sainfoin, as late as 1789:[1]

'An acre of land when improved by this grass will maintain
four cows very well from the first of April to the end of November; and afford besides enough of hay to make part of their food
the following four months.'

Sainfoin, in the end, won its place in particular districts—
mostly on the chalks and limestones—from Dorset and the Vale
of Glamorgan to Cambridgeshire and Essex; but it has remained
a stranger to the great majority of British farmers. Lucerne, where
it could be persuaded to grow, astounded everybody with its
powers of drought-resistance, but it often failed. England, indeed,
was the end of the plant's long trek from its home in Asia Minor
or Turkestan, and it is small wonder that it took a poor view of
the British climate. Even to-day few farmers will lay odds on the
success of their sowings. At all events, lucerne was not destined
to play a major role in the Agricultural Revolution.

Red Clover (what we now call 'Broad' red) proved to be of

[1] *Practical Essays on Agriculture.*

immense value, but its importance was greatest in the arable country and especially as one of the key crops in the Norfolk four-course rotation. In the early days it throve amazingly along all the drier side of the country from Lothian to Wiltshire and Dorset wherever the land either was sweet by nature or had been marled or limed. But even here it was short-lived—rarely better than a biennial. In the North and West it was less reliable from the outset. Moreover, even in places where at first it seemed to be completely happy it began, after a few rounds of the four-course, to be less dependable—the land became 'clover sick'—and the interval between successive sowings had to be stretched to eight years. It was in such cases that the farmer fell back upon trefoil, which was immune from the trouble. As time passed a variety of types of red clover, under a confusing variety of not too specific names, came into being—Marlgrasses, Cowgrasses, Single-cuts, and more. Some were doubtless evolved by a process of semi-natural selection, the surviving forms being those best adapted to particular local conditions. Others may have arisen from crosses with the native wild type. However this may be, the sorting out of types was a difficult task for subsequent generations.

It was the two remaining 'artificial grasses'—ryegrass and white clover—that were to play the major roles in the making of better pastures. Both species are natives, but it happened that it was in Flanders and the Netherlands that farmers first learnt the rather difficult art of cultivating herbage plants for their seeds. They had been doing this for many years while their neighbours still relied on the sweepings of their hay-lofts.

We now recognize that clover and grass species are composed of a great variety of forms which constantly intercross. It is easily to be imagined that if we repeatedly harvest seed from fresh sowings, we shall end with a preponderence of those types that develop quickly and produce seed freely; such types tend also to be short-lived, early-flowering and stemmy.

How far had this process of deterioration gone when ryegrass and white clover seed began to be imported? In the first, evidently a long way. James Adam, for instance, remarks that ryegrass produced early spring feed but that 'unless it be cut early for hay it becomes hard and wiry; for this grass has few leaves and runs all to stalk'. This could not have been said of the plant that provided the bulk of the famous pasturage of Leicestershire or the Vale of Aylesbury. The ryegrass of commerce then, apart from being an alien, must already have become 'artificial' in a real sense. More than a century was to pass before the full significance of the point came to be appreciated, and, in the meantime, a vast quantity of paper was to be used in arguing the merits and demerits of the plant. But the artificial or (as we now call it) 'commercial' ryegrass was of real use for certain purposes and in particular areas. In the cooler and moister areas, and on the moister and more fertile soils elsewhere, the plant's urge to seed production was somewhat restrained, and its life was long enough for the relatively short ley.

One of the earliest references to the plant is in Plot's *Oxfordshire*, where we read:

'They have lately sown Ray-grass or the *Gramen Loliacium* by which they improve their cold, sour, weeping grounds, for which it is best; but also for dry upland grounds, especially light stony or sandy land which is unfit for Saintfoin. It was first sown in the Chiltern parts of Oxfordshire and since brought nearer Oxford by one Eustace, an ingenious husbandman of Islip who, though at first laughed at, has since been followed by those very persons who scorned his experiments.'

Later on the 'artificiality' of ryegrass became more pronounced. In Lawson's pamphlet on the Cultivated Grasses (1843) we read:

'The repeated saving of seeds from first crops by the early growers resulted, towards the end of the last century, in the prevalence of a short-lived variety, afterwards termed Annual Ryegrass and unfit in many cases for the laying down of lands to two or more years' pasture; which naturally directed attention to the selection of a more lasting variety. Accordingly we find that this desideratum was then supplied by Mr. Peacy [Pacey] of North Leach, Wiltshire [actually Northleach, Glos.], whose perennial ryegrass, as it is still called, soon became known throughout both Scotland and England. Mr. Peacy's example was followed by many other cultivators, each of whom discovered, or fancied he had discovered, a variety possessing new or additional merits so that, prior to the publication of the *Hortus Gramineus* in 1824, Dickson's, Ruck's, Russel's, etc., had been introduced. Since that period names of many other particular growers have been added to the list; so that it now requires no little discrimination to fix on what are really the most deserving of cultivation.'

It is worth noting that Lawson describes the common ryegrass of commerce as 'biennial, triennial, or quarennial duration' though he does not say whether, as he supposed, it was the strain or the environment that determined the length of life.

Perhaps the white clover that constituted the early importations was less 'artificial' than its companion ryegrass. Some of the early descriptions of the imported plant would be rather more applicable to the native 'wild' white than to the modern 'Dutch'. But the differences to the eye, between the two, are not very clear cut. Indeed, as late as 1915 so good a botanist as M'Alpine, writing in the Highland *Transactions*, could cast doubt upon the growing belief that there was a difference, important in practice, between the two—the difference that the one continued to live long after the other was dead—or perhaps, as we should now say, that Dutch white consists mainly of short-lived and wild white mainly of long-lived strains. As M'Alpine pointed out, white clover of sorts was to be found in pastures of some age where none but 'Dutch' had been sown. Were these plants derived from the sown seed, or were they wildings that had found their own way into the sward? Who could say? but M'Alpine had maintained his attitude of scientific doubt somewhat too long. Cockle Park had already convinced its farmer visitors that, however botanists might argue, wild white and Dutch were, for practical purposes, very different plants.

An interesting probability is that the native white clover had been harvested, here and there in England, before the Dutch type began to be imported. One of the interesting *Observations on Husbandry* of Edward Lisle (published in 1756, but written some time before 1722) is that a Hampshire neighbour had 'Sowed the wild white clover, which holds the ground and decays not', the seeds of which he had from Sussex, where its culture was then practised.

For long years the only herbage seeds sown in quantity, in most parts of the country, were those of the 'artificial' grasses. Of Berwickshire, for example—which was a highly progressive county—Kerr wrote in 1809:

'There are hardly any instances of the seeds of natural grasses, as they are called, being sown; at least none have come to the notice of the reporter.'

Bad farmers might still resort to their hay-lofts, but the good farmer's prescription, when he laid away a field for a period of years, was 'a bushel of clean ryegrass, six to ten pounds of white clover, four to six pounds of red clover, two pounds of trefoil and frequently a pound or two of narrow-leaved plantain, here called ribgrass'.

WILLIAM CURTIS

Some of our early naturalists, especially Benjamin Stillingfleet, made beginnings in the task of sorting out our native grasses. But the first specialist in the subject was the eminent botanist William Curtis who, in 1790, published his *Practical Observations on the British Grasses best adapted to the laying down of Meadows and Pastures*. There were several editions, the last in 1854.

The subject was a forbidding one, for the number of reasonably distinct forms is vast and their identification and classification far from easy; indeed modern Agrostologists still argue about the species, sub-species and varieties that make up common genera like the bents and fescues. Moreover, it was one thing to classify and describe, and quite another to make a selection of those best deserving to be cultivated under particular conditions of soil and climate. One of Curtis's fears was that, if he played for safety by including a large number in his select list, such confusion would be created in the mind of the plain farmer that he would end by using none.

As time was to show, Curtis had no great luck in choosing a team from the embarrassing abundance of material. His first six included Sweet Vernal (which long continued to have an entirely undeserved place in grass seed prescriptions); Meadow Foxtail (which, with all its merits, is too difficult to grow from seed); Smooth-stalked Meadow grass (which under the name of Kentucky bluegrass was already winning fame and favour in America, but was to play no notable part in its native land); its better but still unimportant relative of the rough stalk; Meadow Fescue (about which Curtis's judgement was, in the end, to be vindicated); and Crested Dogstail, which, as Curtis properly observed, was 'the fittest for poor dry land'.

The reserve list included Cocksfoot—'coarse but exceedingly hardy'; Timothy—'productive but coarse and late'; with a motley collection of what are now regarded as weeds.

Curtis was prepared to supply what we should now call 'mother seed' of the six grasses of his choice. The six packets were to be sown separately, each on a small plot of carefully cleaned ground, and the product was to be blended, with the addition of white and red clover, for field sowing. Incidentally, the red clover was to be of the native wild type rather than the 'broad clover of the shops'.

GEORGE SINCLAIR

Before the last edition of Curtis's book was published there appeared another and more exhaustive treatise on the same subject. This was the famous *Hortus Gramineus Woburnensis* of George Sinclair, gardener to John, Sixth Duke of Bedford.

Like many of the master gardeners of his time, Sinclair was a Scot. Born at Mellerstane in Berwickshire in 1785 and descended from a long line of gardeners he was in the service of the Gordon family when, in 1803, Lady Georgina Gordon married Duke John. Shortly afterwards Sinclair went to Woburn, where he remained seventeen years. About 1824 he went into partnership with Messrs. Cormack & Sons, of New Cross, who were nurserymen and seedsmen. He died in 1834.

The first edition of the *Hortus* is a sumptuous folio with dried specimens of the grasses in lieu of illustrations. The second (1825) is illustrated with fine plates and contains, besides accurate botanical descriptions of all the known grasses, a mass of data on the seasonal growth, total yield and chemical composition of the produce of each species grown in pure culture. Sir Humphrey Davy advised about the recording, and carried out the analyses. Truth compels us to say, however, that the chemical work was worse than useless. Davy may probably have been aware that the best available methods of analysis were far from likely to give any real indication of nutritive values; but his figures, some of which were palpably absurd, continued to be quoted as the findings of the leading authority on the subject. For instance, as late as 1882 Mr. Faunce de Laune, anxious as he was to prove that ryegrass was a pernicious weed, could hardly bring himself to believe those of Davy's figures which he nevertheless quoted: 'Let the produce and nutritive powers of rye-grass be compared with the cocksfoot grass, and it will be found inferior in the proportion of nearly 5 to 18.'

In the preface to his second edition Sinclair remarks that, apart from ryegrass, no perennial grasses had been sown until about 1775, when Timothy had begun to be used in a small way. More recently the use of Cocksfoot had 'considerably extended so as to supersede ryegrass in some districts, through the successful practice of Mr. Coke of Norfolk. Thus out of 215 distinct species of grass which are capable of being cultivated in this climate . . . only two have been cultivated separately to any extent.'

Sinclair's first approach was to get a close-up picture of some of the richest old pastures in Devonshire, Lincolnshire, and the Vale of Aylesbury. Of these he says:

'When once broken up for a course of crops they cannot for a great length of time be again brought into so good a sward; and this opinion is based on the best of grounds—experience. The cause why those grasses cannot be renewed in as great perfection . . . must either be that these plants require many years to attain productiveness; or that the soil has been too much deteriorated by the course of grain crops' . . . or lastly, that the seeds sown must have been of species other than those composing the original sward 'whether to one or to all these points the want of success is to be imputed it is of importance to enquire.'

The good old pastures were therefore explored at various times during the growing season, and the widely prevalent species were listed. These included a score of grasses, four legumes and the 'herbs' yarrow and ribgrass. Buttercups and sorrel were common but, since neither seemed to be grazed from choice, they were left out of the list. A second catalogue was drawn up of the pasture plants of dry, elevated and sandy soils, and a third for moist or boggy grazings.

When the individual species had been observed and recorded in the Woburn plots, and when a great mass of figures had been accumulated, Sinclair proceeded to draw up seed prescriptions for permanent awards on various soil types, and also for alternate husbandry. These mixtures, though they included a number of plants that have since been discarded, leave out none that, according to our modern ideas, deserves a place.

Especially interesting is the selection for temporary pasture. If one species were to be singled out, says Sinclair, it must be Cocksfoot; but because it was ordinarily the farmer's objective to provide a continuous supply of nutritious herbage throughout the season, it was vain to suppose that any single species would suffice. Cocksfoot might, however, form about three-fourths of the grass component, the remainder to consist of meadow and hard fescues, rough-stalked meadow grass, tall oatgrass, timothy and ryegrass. These, with white clover, were the materials for the ley.

Curtis's work was slow to influence the practice of the general run of farmers. The demand for the seeds of the natural grasses was small, and it seemed hardly worthwhile for the seedsman to organize a supply, or to instal the machinery that would have been needed to produce samples of reasonable purity. The provision of ryegrass and clover seeds was a business proposition; to organize the supply of a much wider variety of wares seemed to the ordinary country trader to be a doubtful adventure. The adventurer, in the person of Charles Lawson, was already in the field, but few had yet heard of him. Meantime another and different step of progress was to be made.

THE DONCASTER REPORT

'At the annual meeting of the Doncaster Agricultural Association in 1828, a resolution was passed that it was desirable to extend the enquiries of the Association to other subjects of general interest besides cattle, and a Committee was appointed to make enquiries, and report the results of these, on the use and advantages of Bones as a Manure.' The following year saw the publication of the famous report.

This set out that the earliest use of bones as a manure, of which any member had information, was in 1775, when Colonel St. Leger, then of Warmsworth, had used some. But it was not until about 1815, when the practice of grinding was introduced, that bone manures had begun to excite general attention in the district; this date, it may be recalled, preceded by a generation the work of Liebig and Lawes, who first recognized that phosphate was an important plant nutrient and that bones had a high phosphate content.

The Committee's object was to make sense of the varied experiences and observations of their members; and they did, indeed, make a lot of sense of them. Under a wide range of circumstances crushed bone was 'a famous manure for turnips'. Moreover, if only a full crop of turnips could be grown, more corn and better clover would follow. The Committee was inclined to attribute the beneficial results upon the succeeding crops to the abundant manuring that resulted from folding sheep upon a good crop of roots; and they seem to have overlooked the possibility that the response was, at least in part, a residual effect of the bone manure itself. But this, perhaps, was regarded as a matter of academic interest only.

In some cases there had been trials between bones and other manures. Where the comparison was with dung, guano or rape-cake, the results (as we should expect) were conflicting; but it did emerge that bones had a more lasting effect than rape-cake. Mr. Littlewood had convinced himself that bones were not a complete plant food, for 'a mixed tillage consisting of bones, rape-dust, burnt earth, dove manure, etc., is more certain of producing a good crop of turnips than any one of these manures alone.' There were some puzzling failures of bones on gravelly soils—due perhaps, as we may suspect, to their deficiency in potash.

The Committee devoted most of their researches to arable crops, but they also concluded that 'bones might be laid on grass-land with great good effect'. This, indeed, was beginning to be realized elsewhere, particularly on cheese farms. Mercer[1] has recorded one case that was typical of Cheshire. Thomas Leech, in 1828, became tenant of Brine Pits Farm, Nantwich—a heavy wet farm of 200 acres, for which he paid a rent of £270. His landlord, like many another in those days, allowed rent remissions as his contribution to lasting improvements—drainage, liming, and now also 'boning'. In 1833–4 Leech had a remission of £100, in 1835–6 of £132, and in 1839–40 of no less than £200. Since bones could then be bought for 90s. a ton, the quantities spread on Leech's 200 acres must have been prodigious. There is evidence from other sources of dressings of a ton and even of two tons to the acre. But Leech knew what he was about, for his annual sales of cheese rose from about 88 cwt. in the first four years of his tenancy to 120 cwt. for the years 1834–8 and to 135 cwt. in 1849–51.

Bone manures were 'the grand improvement' during the second quarter of last century, but three others are worth mention.

The early 'thirties saw the introduction of two more 'artificial grasses'. The one, Italian ryegrass, if it was even shorter-lived than its relative, and too prone to elbow-out its bedfellows, was highly productive and very leafy. The other, Alsike clover, named after the little Swedish village where it was first grown, was not the equal of red clover, but proved a better second string, where the sickness was feared, than trefoil.

The second was perhaps a revival of a former practice. It represented a compromise between two schools of thought about the best procedure in sowing grass seeds. Many writers from the early years of last century maintained that the surest way of establishing a sward was to sow without a 'nurse crop' of corn. For instance, John Wilson[2] remarks:

[1] *R.A.S.E. Journal*, Vol. 98, 1937.   [2] *British Farming*, 1862.

'When it is intended to lay down arable land to grass, or to restore it to permanent pasture or meadow, it is always advisable to sow the seeds without a corn crop. This doubtless involves an additional cost at the outset, but it is usually more than repaid by the enhanced value of the pasture so obtained.'

On the other hand, seeds for a short ley should probably be sown under corn, since the ultimate benefit could not compensate for the loss of a crop. The compromise, devised by some unknown farmer in the Scottish Borderland, and probably in the eighteen-forties, is thus expressed by Macdonald:[1]

'In addition to the varieties and quantities of clovers and grasses usually sown . . . 2 lb. of rapeseed per acre is allowed for the twofold purpose of protecting the young clovers and affording valuable fattening food for sheep. Grasses thus sown are ready, in ordinary seasons, for pasturing stock in the last week of June and, up to the end of October, usually fatten from eight to twelve sheep per acre. The value thus obtained from such pasture the first season far exceeds, even with moderate prices for stock, that which a full crop of oats yields. Nor are the advantages limited to the first season; for the grasses, being strong and vigorous in a firmly compressed soil, are not easily injured by drought and frosts . . . and yield more the second season also.'

This indeed was not the earliest recorded use of rape as a 'nurse' for grass seeds: Arthur Young had favoured the idea. But it seems that the technique was now first worked out in detail.

The other Scottish innovation, which came fully a decade later, was the Timothy meadow. This originated in the upland district of Kyle in Ayrshire, where the soil is a cold boulder clay unsuited to the culture of turnips and where oats, ripening in the wet and often boisterous weather of autumn, can make no reliable provision of winter fodder. Here timothy was found to grow vigorously and, when regularly and heavily manured, to last for seven or more years and to yield heavy crops of hay that was relatively easy to cure. The early practice was to sow a stone of the seed, with two or three pounds each of rapeseed and Alsike clover.

[1] D. G. S. Macdonald, *Hints on Farming*, 10th Edn. 1868.

The practice later spread to the fertile Carse of Stirling where, under the more congenial conditions and with intensive use of fertilizers, immense crops of hay have ever since been grown.

CHARLES LAWSON

By the eighteen-thirties, with bone manures abundantly available, and with Sinclair's *Hortus* as a guide to the necessary plant material, it might have seemed that the stage was set for rapid progress in pasture making. It is true that, for the next generation, the emphasis was to be on plough farming, for there was almost constant anxiety about the people's bread; and it is true that, over a large part of England, farmers' interest was confined to one-year leys and to the improvement of permanent swards; but in Scotland and the Border Country, and to a less extent in Wales and the South-West, ley farming was normal practice. Two things, however, remained to be done. The one was to organize the supply of seeds of the known good herbage plants and to provide these reasonably true to name and free from weeds. The other was to educate farmers to the new ways.

The most successful of the pioneers in these tasks was Charles Lawson. He was the son of Peter, who had come to Edinburgh towards the end of the eighteenth century and had set up in the seed and nursery trade. Charles, born in 1794, joined his father as soon as he was of age, and the business was carried on under the name of Peter Lawson & Son. The firm throve from the start, and in 1843, after the death of its first head, moved into a handsome new building in George IV Bridge, which it long shared with the Highland and Agricultural Society.

Charles Lawson had a very wide range both of botanical knowledge and business interests. To many he may be best known as an arboriculturist, for he introduced into Scotland the Austrian and the Swiss Stone Pines and the Spanish and Russian Silver Firs. His name is immortalized in the elegant and useful *Cupressus Lawsoniana*. He made a special study of the conifers and began that great work, the *Pinetum Britannicum*, which was completed, after his death, by other hands. His botanical interest covered the whole range of cultivated plants—flowers and vegetables, trees and shrubs, roots, potatoes and grain; but above all grasses and clovers.

Peter Lawson & Son grew into a prodigious organization, with connections spread over a great part of the world. The firm's annual catalogue offered almost every kind of seed or plant that the florist or fruit grower, forester or farmer might want. At the height of its prosperity and at the peak of the seed season, deliveries from its warehouses often passed fifty tons in a day. There were five nurseries in and around Edinburgh and there was a branch office in London.

On grasses and pastures Charles wrote an admirable handbook under the title of *Agrostographia, or Treatise on the Cultivated Grasses,* which ran through many editions, the last published four years after his death. For the plain farmer he gave, in his *Agriculturist's Manual,* an account, sufficient for practical purposes, of the kinds that he considered most worth sowing. His prescriptions of seeds mixtures for temporary and permanent pastures were quoted in all the books of the day.

Among his various plant introductions the most important, for the farmer, was Italian ryegrass. A trial importation was made in 1831 from Northern Italy. By 1850 sales were running at about 25,000 bushels annually, and at that point the firm began to organize production by home growers. Lawson's own description of the new grass may be quoted as illustrating the precision of his observation:

'Compared with any varieties of common ryegrass, the *L. Italicum* affords a stronger braird (first shoot), arrives sooner at maturity, has a greater abundance of foliage, which is of a lighter or more lively green colour. It grows considerably taller, is more upright or less inclined to spread on the ground; its spikes are longer; spikelets more thinly set . . . the seed has the awn adhering to it. . . . It is preferred by cattle to any of the common sorts . . . while it yields early, bulky and quickly-succeeding herbage which renders it an invaluable grass for alternate husbandry. Its comparatively limited duration fits it well for sowing in mixture with other grasses intended to form a permanent sward, as it dies out

IN PASTURES GREEN

and gives place to the weak or slowly maturing perennial species which are destined ultimately to fill the ground.'

Charles Lawson rose high in the world. He was on terms of the closest intimacy with M. Vilmorin, his great contemporary in France. He was consulted by Queen Victoria and by Napoleon III. He was Lord Provost of Edinburgh in 1863, when he had the honour of entertaining the Prince of Wales (King Edward VII).

In 1852 he bought the estate of Borthwick Hall in Midlothian, and as time went on devoted himself increasingly to his botanical studies and to the adornment of his grounds, leaving the management of the business more and more to his three sons. Under their guidance the firm spread itself to cover oilcakes and the new potash manures from Germany, and—unfortunately—plunged deeply into the highly speculative business of exploiting the guano deposits of the various 'bird islands' of the Pacific. It seems that large sums were paid for guano deposits which existed mainly in the imagination of the sellers. In any case the adventure was disastrous, and Peter Lawson & Son broke. The seed business was refinanced and carried on. But Charles Lawson was left almost penniless and depended, in his latter years, on an annuity provided by some of his personal friends. He died in 1873 at Borthwick Hall, where the noble trees that he planted still stand as his memorial.

Meanwhile, although much unsatisfactory material continued to be sold to farmers as 'seeds mixtures', a number of great seed houses, some of which continue to flourish, were built up on the same foundations of expert knowledge and business integrity that Charles Lawson had laid.

THE CLIFTON PARK SYSTEM

One of the 'grasslanders' whose work attracted interest about the turn of the century was Robert H. Elliot of Clifton Park, a place that lies north of the Border but south of Tweed, a few miles from Kelso. It is true that Elliot found among his contemporaries few farmers, and only one important seedsman, who were prepared to go all the way with him; but his work has proved an inspiration to his successors.

Elliot was a younger son who, like many more of his generation, went out into the world to seek his fortune. He relates how, in 1855, at the age of eighteen, with 'a trifling capital, and that firm belief in my own capabilities which is common in youth' he took ship for Bombay, proceeded down the coast in a native salt boat and turned up, with a letter of introduction, at an isolated coffee plantation in Mysore. After a bare year's apprenticeship he got a grant of a block of jungle, pitched his tent in a glade, built a house of sun-dried clay and thatch and, by the end of another year, had eighty acres planted with coffee. This adventure succeeded well, and the two books that he wrote about it leave the impression that his success was well merited. They contain, besides accounts of shooting expeditions—tiger, bear, and bison—and the story of the development of his estate, a good many ideas and speculations on the future of India, about which he had, for his time, very advanced ideas. In any case he won the loyal devotion of his native staff, the respect of the Indian community, became a close friend of the Maharaja and was the first chairman of the first-elected Assembly of the State.

In the early 'eighties, by which time he had built up a considerable fortune, he bought the Clifton Estate, where he spent the remainder of his life, except for periodic visits to India. In 1887 he took in hand the farm of Clifton-on-Beaumont, extending to 1,250 acres and, until his death in 1914, found his main interest in grassland experiments.

Elliot read widely both in contemporary books and journals and in the English farming classics—Arthur Young, Sinclair and more. One paper that particularly excited his interest had appeared in the Journal of the 'Royal' for 1882. It was 'On the Laying Down of Land to Permanent Pasture', by Mr. C. De Laune Faunce de Laune of Sparsted Court, Sittingbourne, Kent.

Mr. Faunce De Laune combined with his Norman blood a simple faith in respect of the farming policy appropriate to the times, and on the methods by which it should be brought into effect. The prevalent system of heavy-land farming, with wheat its key crop, had seen its day: it could not survive in competition with the product of the prairies, where farmers were now equipped with the string binder. Much English land must go to grass—and that quickly, for otherwise there would be no money left to buy grass seeds and livestock.

But, according to Faunce De Laune, the general run of farmers knew little or nothing of this business of pasture making, and it was useless to suggest that they should follow the advice of their seedsmen. The ordinary country seedsman did not know one seed from another, and his main concern was to undercut his competitors in seeking the custom of the hard-pressed farmer. The gospel according to Sinclair was gospel indeed, but was still a closed book to most. At the best the 'mixed seeds' supplied by many dealers were very imperfectly cleaned of weeds and, at the worst, were heavily adulterated. Moreover, the proportion of ryegrass in such mixtures was invariably excessive, partly because ryegrass seed was very cheap and partly because ryegrass was the easiest of all herbage plants to establish from sowings. But ryegrass, considered as material for a lasting sward, was itself no better than a weed. Sinclair had found it to be a low producer of poor nutritive quality; moreover it grew, like most weeds, so vigorously that it crowded out the more delicate but more desirable plants; and finally it was an annual.

De Laune did not mean, by the last statement, precisely what he wrote. If he had been a modern experimenter, reporting with proper scientific caution, he would have said that, under the conditions of his experiments, the ryegrass seed of commerce produced a preponderance of monocarpic types—i.e. of plants that died soon after they had first been allowed to run to seed.

Faunce De Laune's paper started a long and rather barren controversy. Some could confirm his observations while others could point to the fact that ryegrass was the commonest constituent of many of the choicest old pastures in the country. But of course the two sides were talking about two different plants. The compilers of text books and of seed catalogues generally added to their list of prescriptions 'Mr. Faunce De Laune's mixture for permanent pasture—(no ryegrass)' and left it at that.

Elliot dedicated the first edition of his book *Agricultural Changes Required by the Times* to Faunce De Laune. He agreed that the times necessitated a cut in expenses and therefore a plan to produce more and better grass, and he agreed, too, that there was an ample choice of plants that must be preferred to ryegrass. But he saw salvation in ley farming rather than in once-for-all grassing down.

It was no new idea, sixty years ago, that the ley could be used as an instrument for building up the fertility of the soil. Perhaps the clearest of the earlier statements in this sense is to be found in an article by John Boswell in the *Quarterly Journal of Agriculture* and reprinted in *The Agricultural and Horticultural Gleaner* in 1836:

'I maintain that, except a few favoured spots such as banks of rivers, etc., no ground can, without loss, be left long in pasture; that it appears to me four or five years is, generally speaking, the longest period land should be allowed to lie in grass; that if pasture be the object, at the end of that time the ground should be broken up and returned to grass again. I maintain that, *without grass*, severely cropped land cannot be restored to full fertility; and *without cropping* grass cannot be made to continue at the maximum point of verdure and utility. Lastly, I maintain, no land under any circumstances ought to be cut for hay if intended to remain some years in pasture; and if cut for hay every kind of land should be directly ploughed and put again through the rotation.'

Elliot—or indeed Stapledon—could hardly have put the point more clearly. But Elliot amplified Boswell's statement with a more precise explanation of the beneficial effect of the ploughed-in turf:

'The cheapest and best form of manure is a good turf, for the decaying sod not only supplies the plant with food but, what is nearly as important, and some might say of even greater importance, produces a good nest or, in other words, good physical conditions in the soil . . . so that, after being disintegrated, it may not rapidly run together again.'

This statement has been amply confirmed by modern investigations. Whether the object be to prevent soil erosion (by making the soil more highly absorbent of rain) or to hold moisture in a period of drought, the crumb structure that is created by the growing roots of grass is more perfect than can be attained by any other known means.

On the optimum duration of the ley—that which combined maximum output of herbage with the cheapest manure for the land—Elliot's experiments led him to agree with Boswell. Four years was his answer. Moreover, in that time, vigorously growing plants would 'extinguish' couch and save the farmer many laborious grubbings and draggings.

After many trials Elliot produced a grass-seed prescription which included firstly Cocksfoot, Meadow and Tall Fescues and Tall Oatgrass, all deep-rooted and drought-resistant grasses; secondly, as legumes (since unfortunately he did not live to welcome Wild White Clover), Late-flowering Red Clover and Kidney Vetch; and lastly, partly again for their drought-resistant powers but also in the belief that they supplied some nutrient that was lacking in a grass and clover sward, Chicory, Burnet, and Yarrow.

While he paid tribute to Charles Lawson's work in providing reliable supplies of seed, he thought that Lawson should have followed Sinclair more closely. Lawson had compromised—had sacrificed the prime object of producing a good and lasting sward to commercial considerations. The chief of these was to offer something cheap that would quickly produce a sward of sorts, and this could be achieved only by including an undue proportion of ryegrass.

In one respect too, Elliot overstretched his argument about the fertilizing value of turf. He thought that, with deep roots to till the soil and to reach down to the depths of the subsoil in search of food, and with a proportion of leguminous plants, he would be able to dispense altogether with fertilizers. This contention, perhaps, was supportable in relation to potash and nitrogen; but he should have realized that the hundreds of lambs that left Clifton-on-Beaumont each summer must have carried away in their bones something that could not be replenished from the subsoil.

Elliot argued strongly for the establishment of local experimental farms, and thought that each county should be provided with one. He was, however, strongly critical of the work being done at nearby Cockle Park, where the main emphasis of the grassland experiments, in their early years, was on the improvement of old pasture swards by the use of fertilizers alone. Elliot did not deny the lesson of the Tree Field plots—that it was profitable to apply basic slag to bad old grass; but this, he submitted, was the wrong approach, since the main objective, or at least the first step, should be to replace the wrong plant species with the right ones. The fact is that Clifton and Cockle Park were each telling half the story—which is that both good plants and a high level of fertility are essential to the making of productive grass.

Elliot was fortunate in winning the wholehearted support of a leading seedsman, James Hunter of Chester. Hunter 'featured' the Clifton Park seeds mixtures in his catalogues, and built up a considerable trade in them. But it was unfortunate that he should have been the only 'whole hogger', for there was some suspicion —entirely unfounded in fact—that Hunter and Elliot were working in collusion with the aim of exploiting the system for profit.

In his early days at Clifton-on-Beaumont Elliot was known locally as 'the Daft Laird'—partly, of course, by reason of his heretical notions about farming but also because, as it seemed to his canny tenants struggling with the difficult times, he had no proper sense of the value of money. Later he was just 'the Old Laird', and he is still remembered as a fine figure of a man, tall and white-haired, courteous and kind.

In his old age, and especially in years when the 'take' of grass seeds was poor, Elliot spent a lot of time, after harvest and again in spring, 'mending' his swards with a garden rake and a little bag of seeds. In one particular year, after a wet summer that brought much 'lodged' corn, there was a deal of patching to be done; and every afternoon, for two or three weeks on end, the Old Laird, with his equipment, was driven in the family coach the four miles from the Park to the farm. Mrs. Elliot went with him for the airing. But presently the lady protested that she had her social duties to think of: she must have the use of the carriage to make a round of calls. Very well; her dutiful husband would be content to stay at home, or go walking in the afternoons.

Twice, in the following weeks, Mrs. Elliot related how she had passed on the road a closed carriage belonging to the local post-master, with its blinds closely drawn—very mysterious indeed. . . . But among the household bills at month's end was one that Mr. Elliot had failed to intercept. It was from the local postmaster for 'Carriage Hire, Clifton Park to Clifton-on-Beaumont and Return', with many 'ditto dittoes'. Social duties had been done, but also the sward had been well and truly 'mended'.

COCKLE PARK

In the latter 'eighties a new sort of animal—a University Graduate in Agriculture—appeared upon the farming scene. It was Robert Wallace who, going from the old Royal Agricultural College to Edinburgh as the fourth holder of the long-established chair of Agriculture and Rural Economy, first succeeded in per-suading a University Governing body that Husbandry, with the natural sciences upon which its practice should be based, provided suitable material for a full course of academic study.

Among the early graduates were three who, one after the other, occupied the chair of agriculture at Armstrong College (now King's College), Newcastle-on-Tyne; and each of whom in turn became honorary director of the experimental farm that had been set up at Cockle Park, near Morpeth, by the Northumberland County Council.

The first, William Somerville, son of a Lanarkshire farmer and the first B.Sc. (Agric.), was distinguished both as a forester and as a 'grasslander'. He shortly moved to Cambridge as the first Draper's Professor and, after a brief spell at the Board of Agri-culture, became the first full-time occupant of the old-established chair at Oxford. He maintained his pastoral interests throughout his whole career and he re-wrote the lesson of Tree Field on Sussex downland, on Cotswold hillsides, and on Oxfordshire clay. The second, Thomas Hunt Middleton, followed Somerville to Cam-bridge and to the Board. He had a brilliant career as an administra-tor, and it is to him that we are mainly indebted for our modern network of research and advisory services. The third was Douglas

Weston Gilchrist, who was appointed in 1902 and whose term lasted for twenty years.

When Somerville took over in the 'nineties the depression had almost reached its nadir. Having, as an orphan lad, struggled with adversity on the family domain in Lanarkshire, he recognized that, for the time being, only the least expensive improvements were likely to interest the general run of farmers. His general approach to the problems of the time was therefore to show a way to some increase in output at very small cost.

His 'classical' experiment was on Tree Field which—with its cold boulder-clay soil and its matted sward of bent in which stray plants of white clover barely managed to survive—was typical of much land that, thirty years earlier, had been under the plough. The immediate question to which an answer was sought was whether with mutton at sevenpence a pound such land could be profitably improved.

The Tree Field plots were stocked with sheep, and the effects of the various treatments were measured in terms of live-weight increase. It soon emerged that, although the soil of Tree Field was rather acid and though liming raised the output of mutton, the balance of the profit-and-loss account was on the wrong side. Another plot showed that the traditional method of fertilizing the grass through the animal—by feeding oil cake—was fairly effective and moderately profitable. Superphosphate alone gave a good and profitable return; with potash or nitrogen there was little additional gain. Superphosphate and lime together gave excellent results; but the same yield of mutton could be secured much more cheaply by the use of basic slag. This last material, a by-product of steel-making, had until a few years before been piling up in mountains round the works, because chemists had been unable to suggest a treatment that would release its stores of phosphate. At last it had been shown that no chemical treatment was needed—it was sufficient to grind the material into a superfine dust.

The Tree Field results became more widely known than those of any other farm experiment, largely by reason of Somerville's method of presentation, which is reproduced on the opposite page.

NORTHUMBERLAND COUNTY COUNCIL FARM
COCKLE PARK

DURHAM COLLEGE OF SCIENCE, NEWCASTLE·ON·TYNE

*Influence of Manures on Feeding
Value of Tree Field Pasture*

Soil - poor stiff boulder clay　　　*Plots 3 1/20 acre in area*

No manure
L.W.I. 246 ℔s.

PLOT 6 — 246 ℔

4 tons Lime 1897
Cost 52/-
L.W.I. 312 ℔s.
Loss 31/-

PLOT 2 — 246 ℔ | 66 ℔ | 99 ℔ 31/- loss

**5 1/2 cwt. Dec. Cotton
Cake fed to sheep
1897-8 : cost 32/- L.W.I.
532 ℔s. Profit 57/-**

PLOT 1 — 246 ℔ | 102 ℔ | 184 ℔

**10 cwt. Basic Slag in
1897 Cost 22/-
L.W.I. 822 ℔s.
Profit 158/-**

PLOT 3 — 246 ℔ | 70 ℔ | 506 ℔

**5 cwt. Basic Slag in
1897 and same 1900
Cost 22/- L.W.I 662
℔s.   Profit 108/-**

PLOT 4 — 246 ℔ | 70 ℔ | 346 ℔

**7 cwt. Super in 1897
and 1900. Cost 36/-
L.W.I. 642 ℔s.
Profit 88/-**

PLOT 5 — 246 ℔ | 115 ℔ | 281 ℔

**Same as Plot 5 and 1 1/2
cwt. Sulphate of Pot-
ash in 1897 and 1899.
Cost 52/-   L.W.I.
685 ℔s. Profit 85/-**

PLOT 7 — 246 ℔ | 166 ℔ | 273 ℔

**Same as Plot 5 and 1/2-
ton Ground Lime in
1897 & 1899. Cost 56/-
L.W.I. 769 ℔s.
Profit 107/-**

PLOT 8 — 246 ℔ | 179 ℔ | 344 ℔

**Same as Plot 5 and 97 ℔.
Sulphate of Ammonia in
1897, 70 ℔. in 1899, 84
℔. in 1900. Cost 59/-
L.W.I. 628 ℔. Profit 60/-**

PLOT 9 — 246 ℔ | 189 ℔ | 193 ℔

Six seasons' (1897-1902) results per acre

*Live weight increase (L.W.I.) of sheep fed on plots is
represented by area of outline of sheep.   Where
divided, fore-part shows increase on original pasture (246 ℔s), the middle the cost of manures, and
the remainder, the profit. L.W.I. is valued at 3 3/4 ᴰ pr. ℔.*

It was Tree Field that first won fame for Cockle Park, but it was destined to become even better known for its prescription of grass and clover seeds for ley. This was largely Gilchrist's invention, and was the outcome of a long process of trial and error. Gilchrist and his team were indeed not the sole experimenters interested in the problem. In particular there was William Findlay who, on his tiny experimental plots at Craibstone (Aberdeen) was asking himself the same questions and getting very much the same answers. The Cockle Park and Craibstone mixtures, for one year's hay and two year's grazing, proved to be widely adaptable and, with relatively minor modifications, are in wide use to-day from Devonshire to the Orkney Isles.

These prescriptions were based upon a number of findings, each arrived at in oft-repeated trials. The first was that the native late-flowering strains were by far the most valuable sorts of red clover for the three-year ley. It was not only that they were longer-lived than the broad reds. They were also far hardier, and could be relied upon in areas where most of the imported red clovers perished in infancy.

Second was the fact that many of the 'natural' grasses could not tolerate the competition of perennial ryegrass and late-flowering red clover. Only two—cocksfoot and timothy—combined this toleration with other desirable qualities.

Thirdly, the only leguminous plant which could be relied upon to stay the course of a three-year ley was the native wild-white clover, harvested from old English pastures.

Thus, at least in one particular context, a simple and easily understandable answer had been found to a problem over which a great deal of ink had been spilt by four generations of agrostologists.

Douglas Gilchrist died in the spring of 1927, shortly after he had intimated his intention to retire at the end of the academic year. A week before his passing he delivered in Perth the last of his innumerable lectures on 'Some Lessons from Cockle Park'. He was a genial, friendly man, not very effective as a classroom teacher but very much in his element on his experimental farm, armed with a spud and a whistle and surrounded by a party of seedsmen or farmers. The spud was used to show the effect of long-continued fertilizer treatments on the physical and biological characteristics of the sward; the whistle was employed to assemble his audience and to command silence for the next lesson.

ABERYSTWYTH AND AFTER

The time has not yet come to tell the rest of the story. It is a story of a remarkable young Englishman who, gathering round him a devoted body of Welsh disciples, started out to breed herbage plants. It was commonly supposed that the practical difficulties were insuperable. How does one assess the merits of an individual grass or clover plant, as eaten off the ground by a cow? How does one improve, by selection, plants that are pollinated by the wind or the humble bee, and that refuse to be self-fertilized in the same way as more reasonable species like oats or wheat? How does one 'fix' desirable characters in a necessarily heterogeneous population? Nothing of that has proved impossible; but there was much more.

The next stage was to study not only the value of the plant—or rather the plant association—to the grazing animal but, conversely, to explore the influence of the grazing animal upon the sward. Again, there was the difficult problem of competition, in a mixed sward, between one species and another and, conversely, the mutual benefits of association between plant and plant; which species tolerate or benefit from the presence of which others, and which species are suppressed by which? There was too the problem of preventing the intrusion of wild native plants, whose seeds are blown hither and thither, into a crop which can neither be hoed nor scarified nor given a fresh start, on clean ground, each year. The answer again depended upon a full understanding of the reactions of each species to soil, climate, fertilizers, and grazing treatment.

It is not too much to say that Stapledon and his school have shown that there are still vast possibilities of progress in pastoral farming, not only in our own small island but wherever grass can grow.

6

CATTLE AND CATTLE BREEDERS

'At the heart of the secret of civilization lies the domestication of animals, training man unconsciously in the ways of government and control, adding a new tenderness and regard for life to his nature, guiding him from barbarism to civilization and impelling him along the ascending pathway of humanity with a force he has been slow to recognize and acknowledge.'

JAMES RITCHIE, *Animal Life in Scotland*

The debt which the world owes to British livestock breeders is widely recognized. Indeed, of the twenty or more breeds of cattle, horses, sheep, and pigs whose merit are widely acknowledged throughout the world only three—the Friesian cow, the Percheron horse, and the Merino sheep—originated elsewhere than in our small islands.

The leading position of this country, in this particular art, has sometimes been explained by supposing that the aptitude for stock breeding—the breeder's eye— is a gift of Providence that has been vouchsafed to the inhabitants of this island in somewhat uncommon measure; and it does seem that a 'bad beast'—in the sense of one that is of relatively little use—offends our eye perhaps more violently than it offends the eye of a 'foreigner'. For instance, it is told of Mr. Fisher Hobbs that he had a Cuyp landscape with a cow in it which was a standing offence to his ideals of bovine symmetry—'the brute was deformed, no ribs, no anything.' He could not bear the sight of the beast over his breakfast. So he got Davis of Chelsea down to paint out the offending image and replace it with a straight-backed blocky Hereford.

But there is another and perhaps a more rational explanation. It was here in England that the Industrial Revolution created the first considerable market for meat and milk and butter, and it was here therefore that farmers had the first opportunity of turning

140

their farms into factories of these commodities. To create better breeds of stock—more efficient machines for their particular purposes—became an object of fairly obvious importance.

It will easily be seen that livestock improvement had, in the main, to await the advent of better farming in other directions. An early maturing breed of sheep is of no particular use until we have a pasture that is capable of making lambs fat; a deep-milking cow is no asset until we are in a position to feed her for her high production. It is not surprising therefore that no Bakewell appeared until the middle of the eighteenth century, when the new turnips and new clover had arrived to supplement the meagre resources of the older animal husbandry. It is not surprising that it was after the great fever of draining, liming and enclosing (which marked the end of the eighteenth century) that Culley wrote 'a laudable spirit for the breeding of good stock everywhere prevails.' Since those days many of the old local types of farm livestock have disappeared, defeated in the keen race for public favour. Many others have been changed almost out of recognition.

Bakewell's own famous breed of cattle, the Longhorn, has come perilously near to extinction. In Bakewell's own time it spread widely—as far north as Westmorland and as far south as Wiltshire and Gloucester, where the richness of its milk helped to increase the reputation of Double Gloucester Cheese. But it was driven from one county after another by the more mellow-fleshed Shorthorn from the north-east of England, and it had disappeared from the Royal Showyard before the end of last century. Since that time there has been a minor revival. The Longhorn's influence on the cattle stock of the country to-day is, however, negligible. Bakewell's more lasting contribution to livestock improvement was the New Leicester sheep.

The literature about Shorthorn Cattle, even if we exclude the hundred and odd volumes of Coates's Herd Book, would fill a small library, and includes items as various as fat volumes of history, scientific papers on heredity, and poems from *Punch*. The reason is that the breed is not only the most important, numerically, in the British Isles, but is the most widely distributed breed of cattle in the world. Moreover, most of the record prices, since Colling's Comet brought a thousand guineas in 1810, have been made by Shorthorns.

'When you come to that fine country on both banks of the River Tees,' says Culley, 'you are then in the midst of the Short horned breed of cattle'; indeed, nearly all the famous early breeders like Charles and Robert Colling, Thomas Bates, and the earlier generations of Booths attended Darlington market.

Thomas Bates, whose name will be for ever associated with the milking strain of Shorthorn, is generally recognized as one of the most interesting characters in the history of stock breeding. He was an undergraduate at Edinburgh University, where he combined the study of Agriculture and Divinity. He was an enthusiastic genealogist and applied himself to the study of cattle pedigrees.

> I was here stopped by a call from a gentleman who has come from Sydney he was here 15 months ago & took out stock and says to buy the Duke of North- or Short-tail, but I told him he could have neither, he wanted an offer if I ever sold him (the Duke) but this I could not grant, as many had asked the same.
>
> I beg my kindest regards, & shall be obliged by your early answer whether you would wish to have any of the three bulls & remain
>
> Dear Sir
> Yours truly
> Thomas Bates

From a Letter by Thomas Bates.

He had very particular and personal views about the qualities to be desired in a Shorthorn beast and he succeeded, to a rather remarkable extent, in embodying these qualities in his own cattle. But since nobody else, at first, had the same ideals in mind, Bates became rather like the soldier who maintained that everybody else was out of step. In the end a large section of the breeders followed his type, and twenty years after Bates's death (i.e. in the 'seventies) there was a widespread view that the future of the whole breed depended on the few cattle of pure unadulterated Kirklevington blood. Such cattle made enormous prices—a number, for instance, were brought back from the United States in 1876 at four-figure prices. As commonly happens when fashion runs mad, the taste shortly swung in just the opposite direction, and by the 'nineties, cattle of Bates's blood were hardly thought worthy of registration. In fact, the middle view ultimately prevailed, viz., that Bates had some good notions and some meaningless fads in connection with cattle breeding, and that his cattle were neither perfect nor worthless, but were in fact useful dual-purpose animals with certain points of weakness that had to be corrected by a subsequent mingling of outside blood.

At the first Royal Show in 1839 Bates won all the first prizes in the Shorthorn classes, with specimens of the breed which had been taken round by sea to London, thence by barge to Aylesbury, and had walked the final 23 miles to the Oxford showyard. The following year Bates showed again, but was smitten hip and thigh by his near neighbours and hated rivals, the Booths. The Booth cattle had a long period of success, and the rivalry between the two types lasted till nearly the end of last century. It came indeed in the end to be fairly generally admitted that the Booth and Bates types were both good in their several ways and that they were not so very different—the Bates cattle having somewhat more milk and rather more style, while the Booth were more fleshy and perhaps more robust. But for long each of the two sects worshipped its own idol and missed no opportunity of trying to cast down the other. In both cases, but perhaps especially among Bates's followers, there was a tendency to over-emphasize pedigree and to neglect individual merit, a tendency that is generally fatal to further progress. Fortunately the plain farmer has the final say in the matter, and a long recorded lineage does not fill the milk pail or tip the weighbridge.

Another great chapter in the Shorthorn story fell to be written in the north-east of Scotland. The man who began to make this piece of history was Captain Barclay of Ury, near Stonehaven. Barclay was the son of one of the notable early 'improvers' who 'trenched and drained, blasted and limed' until, with immense labour, he turned his niggard patrimony into a fine estate. He himself was in general more famous as a sportsman than as a farmer. His physical strength is still a tradition in his own district. He boxed and he hunted, he loved cock-fighting and, with his friend Hugh Watson of Keillor (famous as a cattle breeder also) he drove the Defiance Coach 'in a green coat, with big yellow buttons, always rolling a quid in his mouth before he spoke.' His most famous exploit was to walk, for a wager, a thousand miles in a thousand hours—as he did with a wide margin to spare. Perhaps naturally, it happened that Barclay was sometimes temporarily in a state of opulence and sometimes in rather dire financial straits. When in the former state he seems to have gone to England to buy Shorthorns and when in the latter he felt constrained to sell the cattle for a supply of ready cash. And so it happened that he achieved more good than many a man of more constant good intentions.

But the man who created the Aberdeenshire or Scotch Shorthorn was of quite the opposite type. Amos Cruickshank was a canny man of few words, a devout Quaker, and a bachelor who went soberly about his business throughout a long and useful life. His brother Anthony was prospering in his hosier's business in Aberdeen when, in 1837, the two brothers became joint tenants of the farm of Sittyton, about 15 miles from Aberdeen. Sittyton consisted of 170 acres of improved land and 50 acres of waste; the curious inquirer will find in the *Transactions* of the Highland and Agricultural Society for 1841 Amos's account of the reclamation of this waste and his precise account of the expense of the operation, amounting to £776 8s.

The two brothers worked in unbroken harmony, although

6. Holderness cow

From an engraving by Ward of a painting by Garrad, by courtesy of the late G. H. Parsons

7. Francis Quartly with his favourite Devon cow

From a presentation portrait of 1850

8. North Devon ox bred at Holkham by Thomas Coke

9. Wonder, grey cart stallion
From a print of 1830 in the collection of the late G. H. Parsons

they did not always agree about cattle. Anthony knew the value of publicity and understood that, with cattle as with gloves or hose, it was an advantage to keep in the fashion, however wayward that fashion might be. 'Anthony blamed me greatly,' related Amos, 'for not buying some of the Duchess family at Thomas Bates's sale.' But the final decision on any point in connection with the cattle seems always to have lain with Amos. He knew what he wanted, and he pursued his way regardless of controversies and fashions. He was not so careless about pedigrees and bloodlines as has sometime been suggested, but no pedigree carried any weight with him unless it belonged to a good beast. And merit, with him, was judged by no arbitrary standards. It meant usefulness to the farmer and the butcher—a robust constitution, a wealth of good beef, and a capacity to reach finished butcher's condition at an early age. Again in his own words: 'The Sittyton herd has always depended upon the demand for young bulls from tenant farmers who feed beef for the London market, and hence the plan of breeding has been at once brought to a practical test. If a mistake was made—no matter how straight the pedigree—the rent-paying farmer would have nothing to do with the produce.'

Nobody is disposed to deny that Amos Cruickshank had all the qualities that go to the making of a great constructive breeder of livestock. He had a very definite ideal type clearly in mind. He stuck to his own notions with quiet but stubborn persistence, listening to other men's opinions, arguing rarely for his own, but going, in the end, his own way. He was patient of unsuccess and unworried by the absence of recognition. He seems indeed to have been mildly surprised when everybody suddenly came round to the view that he had been right all along.

Amos Cruickshank waited more than twenty years for his real stroke of luck. But at last he bred a bull calf that seemed to him to embody the qualities that he had long regarded as the essentials of a beef Shorthorn. The breeding of this calf, Champion of England, was as nearly an accident as anything could be in a well-managed pedigree herd. In 1858 Cruickshank was in need of a stock bull and, after a futile search for what he wanted in a number of English herds, he went home with the vacancy still unfilled.

Then he bethought him to write to his friend Wilkinson of Lenton in Nottinghamshire whose herd he admired and whose judgement he trusted, to see whether Wilkinson could help in the matter. The answer was that Wilkinson himself had a useful old bull (he was in fact eight years old) that might fill the gap until something else could be found, and if Amos cared the bull could be put on rail at the modest price of thirty guineas. This bull, 'Lancaster Comet', bought unseen, was turned out to grass with a group of cows, was left out too long in the bleak Aberdeenshire autumn weather, developed rheumatism and had to be destroyed. But in the meantime he had begotten 'Champion of England'.

This calf, whose descendants were destined to populate the plains of both the Americas, was not, according to the then prevailing opinion among Shorthorn men, a specially good specimen of the breed. He lacked refinement and style. Even to Cruickshank's own ideas (and despite the hopes that he expressed when he christened the calf) Champion of England was not the perfect specimen. But here was growth and wealth of flesh; here was early

From a Letter by Anthony Cruickshank.

maturity and constitution; here was a type of beast that would load the tables of those Londoners with great joints of honest beef. So Cruickshank set about the second part of his task, which was to stamp the qualities of his bull upon the whole Sittyton herd. The task was relatively easy, for Champion of England was a singularly impressive sire and his progeny had such a wealth of vigour that they could be inbred as closely as was required without loss of breeding powers. Patiently and systematically the work went on, the best sons and grandsons of the 'Champion' taking their places in succession as stock bulls. Meantime, in the 'seventies, Booth and Bates cattle were selling for many hundreds of pounds apiece while most of Cruickshank's bull calves were still going to his neighbours as crossing bulls—though at gradually rising prices as their value became more generally realized. Then American buyers gave the new type a trial; it throve on the prairies, and the buyers came back for more, and then for more again. Meantime new herds, destined to be almost as famous as the Sittyton one itself, were being built up with Cruickshank blood in Aberdeenshire—by Marr of Uppermill, Duthie of Collynie, and many others.

Anthony was dead, Amos was getting old and the lease of Sittyton was running out. 'I am in my eighty-second year', he wrote in 1889, 'and from a serious illness I had last year I am not now able to give the cattle that attention I used to do and which it is essentially necessary to continue.' So, in the early summer he sold his whole herd of 153 animals for shipment to Argentina. The exporters said in their catalogue which they printed for their South American customers: 'We have taken away the fine old herd in its entirety and there is now only one opportunity of securing a share of its treasures.'

There was very natural consternation among the North-country breeders, who had come to look upon Sittyton as the never-failing fountain of pure Shorthorn blood. But the exporters had spoken too soon. A financial crisis in the Argentine ruined the prospect of selling even Sittyton cattle at a profit, and in fact only one small section of the herd crossed the water. Part of the cattle found a new home on the Wiltshire pastures of Mr. Deane Willis, while the others went to enrich the already famous herd of William Duthie at Collynie.

In 1894, when the 'Highland' Show visited Aberdeen, Amos Cruickshank was presented to his late Majesty King George V, then Duke of York. The following year the sober old Quaker died in peace at Sittyton which he had tenanted for 'three nineteens'. He had lived to see a few of the notable triumphs, both in the showyard and in the sale-ring, of the new type that he had created; and he saw his gift to the world safely deposited in the hands of very competent trustees. The wave of popularity of the Cruickshank strain did not reach its height until the 'daft days' that followed the First World War. In 1920 at the annual sale of bull calves from Collynie, 24 head reached the astonishing average price of £1,400. If the shade of Amos attended he must have shaken his head over the foolish extravagance of the bidders.

The Aberdeen Shorthorn was created in order to produce Aberdeen beef and was largely responsible for the high reputation of this commodity on Smithfield market. The type was also what was wanted, in those days, by Ireland (for her store cattle trade) and by the United States (still a beef exporter) and Argentina. But it was definitely a beef strain of the breed with enough (but usually no more than enough) milk for the full nourishment of a lusty calf. But if all Shorthorns were to be beef Shorthorns, what should we do for milk?

One answer was that there were dairy breeds—the Ayrshire and the Friesian, the Jersey and the Guernsey. But the old type of milk-and-beef Shorthorn, though suffering from neglect by the pedigree men, was still the farmers' cow of England. Many of the old pedigree herds of this type had been 'topped' with Scotch bulls to the serious detriment of their milking propensities, and the ordinary milk producer could no longer find a pedigree sire on which he could rely for the production of milking stock. And so a few men began to urge that the old dual-purpose strain of Shorthorns must be revived, not as the rival to, but as the necessary complement to the Cruickshank Shorthorn. First came the voice of Mr. Richard Stratton, like one crying in the wilderness. Writing in 1897, he says: 'The dairymen of this country should

be the best and most numerous customers for pure Shorthorns
... if the foreigners fail us, as they probably will some day, where
will be the outlet for our bulls?' He urged his view in season and
out of season; he incurred the censure of the Shorthorn Society
when he himself was its President; but he could not be suppressed.
In 1901, chiefly through his efforts, the Society instituted prizes
at county shows for 'Pedigree Shorthorn Cows of Milking
Characteristics.' In 1905 the Dairy Shorthorn (Coates's Herd
Book) Society was formed to promote the interests of the other
type of cattle.

Up till this time the breeders of registered Shorthorns who had
been keeping milk records could have been counted on the fingers
of one hand. There was, most notable of all in the degree of his
achievement, George Taylor of Cranford in Middlesex, and there
were Robert Hobbs of Kelmscot and Lord Henry Bentinck of
Underley, also belonging to the older generation. Three other
notable herds, that were later to make history, were founded in
the 'nineties—at Babraham by Mr. Charles Adeane, at Iford by
Mr. Robinson, and at Tring by Lord Rothschild, under the
management of Mr. Richardson Carr.

The new Association, with Lord Rothschild as President and
Mr. Fred. Webb, the Agent at Babraham, as Secretary, was
formed at a time when the increasing imports of chilled beef were
hitting the home beef-producer hard and when, to quote Charles
Hobbs, 'The British farmer was looking to milk to help him turn
the corner,' and the Dairy Shorthorn was quickly revived. Fortunately the regulations of Coates's Herd Book permitted the
registration, as foundation animals, of approved cows whose
ancestry had not been recorded, and increasing numbers of farmers
began to grade up their herds by the use of pedigree bulls and in
time joined the ranks of pedigree breeders. Thirty years ago the
Dairy Shorthorn ring at the 'Royal' contained few cattle and
drew only a handful of spectators. It has since often been the
largest feature in the cattle section.

The arguments that have been advanced for and against the
dual-purpose cow would fill most of this book. There is no doubt
that it is easier, and therefore makes for quicker progress, to go

for a single object—beef or milk as the case many be. To keep a balance between the two considerations, to improve the two different tendencies simultaneously, and to produce a true-breeding strain with the desired combination of qualities, is as hard a task as any breeder can set himself. It requires probably more skill and at least twice the amount of patience. But it is far from being proved that the Dairy Shorthorn or the Red Poll breeders have undertaken an impossible task.

If, on a day in or about the year 1822, there had been seen, coming over the ridge into Wharfedale an old man on a white horse, it might have been George Coates, with his satchel full of calf records and bull pedigrees. He would have been making his way, very likely, to Greenholm, near Otley, where lived Jonas Whittaker and where some fine Shorthorn cattle had a home in the difficult and hard-up times that followed upon the Napoleonic wars. Since 1812 the breeders of Shorthorns had been urging the obvious need of published pedigree records and Coates undertook the work of compiling the Herd Book. It meant many long journeys on his white cob, and many long spells away from his own beasts. There were several original guarantors, but one after another died, and at last the whole responsibility rested on Whittaker; without his help there would never have appeared Volume I of the *Shorthorn Herd Book*, printed at the Wharfedale Stanhope Press, top of the Market Place, Otley, with drawings on Stone of Miranda and Maria by James Ward, R.A.' Coates's *Herd Book* was the first book of its kind excepting only the *General Stud Book* of Thoroughbred horses. It was carried on by George Coates with the help of his son, and was then taken over by Mr. Strafford, the famous live-stock auctioneer. He owned and edited the book until 1872, when it passed into the keeping of the Shorthorn Society.

In some cases a modern breed of cattle has been built up on a single old local type, as the Improved Shorthorn was made from the old Teeswater. In other cases a dash of the blood of an already improved breed has been used to introduce some desirable quality that the local breed lacked; so, for instance, the modern Suffolk sheep was made from a foundation of the old Norfolk Horned breed, with a dash of Southdown. Sometimes again the process has been to bring together two old strains with different merits and different faults and work for the best possible combination of good qualities. This last was the process by which the Red Poll came to be. The old cow of Suffolk, in Arthur Young's time, was a dun-coloured, hornless, milky animal, whose butter, according to Young, was 'justly considered the pleasantest in England'. Even in those days Norfolk beef was esteemed, and although some of it was produced by fattening the droves of Scottish cattle that were assembled every autumn at Falkirk Tryst, some, too, was the produce of the local breed 'blood red with a mottled face, a Hereford in miniature'. These two breeds were for long kept apart, but early in the nineteenth century two Norfolk yeomen began to make the blend of beef and butter that constitutes the Red Poll. The men were Richard England of Binham and John Reeves, a tenant on the famous Holkham estate. When Reeves retired from farming in 1828 his sale catalogue included 'eleven matchless blood-red cows and a two-year-old bull, one of the most perfect animals in the Kingdom.' At this time England's herd included thirty-nine cows, all also red and polled. Although Low in 1845 prophesied its early extinction, the breed continued to spread in its native East Anglia and in 1862 was recognized by the Royal Agricultural Society. From the first successful experiment, by careful selection and a certain amount of inbreeding, the dual-purpose character of the breed has been maintained, and other skilful breeders like Powell and Pond have carried on the good work. Henry Euren and the Rev. George Gilbert applied their learning and their skill in genealogy to the task of registration, and a complete and accurate herd book was the result.

The notion of producing highly specialized types of cattle for the dairy or for the butcher, is a comparatively modern one. The Hereford, the Devon, and the Sussex, although they were never noted for their milking propensities, started as dual-purpose breeds—for labour and for meat. Thus the Turners, yeoman farmers of Kelmscott in the early nineteenth century, when they wanted to stock their Thames meadows, would ride the seventy-odd miles to Hereford to buy their stores, great beasts 'with athletic frames and limbs sufficiently clean for the purpose of travelling' which had probably taken their places in plough teams for four or five years before they left for the richer grazings, to be fattened for the Christmas market.

But long before this time, before even the days of Bakewell, some cattle breeders in the West Country foresaw the time when beef would be a commonplace dish, instead of an occasional luxury, on the tables of the ordinary citizen. These men, notably the Tomkins of Kings Pyon, William Galliers of Wigmore Grange, John Price of Ryall, William Hewer, and the Jefferies of Lyonshall, worked together with a common object. The story of the Tomkins family has scarcely received the attention it deserves from agricultural historians. In 1720 Richard Tomkins, the yeoman descendant of an impoverished Royalist family, was gathered to his fathers and left, by his last will and testament, to his son Benjamin, 'one cow called Silver and her calf.' From then until 1859, when Richard's great-grandaughters finally dispersed the herd, there was continuous careful selection for those qualities that made the Hereford famous.

Up to a point the breeds of each group are rivals and competitors one of another. As beef cattle the Herefords are to some extent then rivals of the Shorthorn and the Aberdeen Angus, the Galloway, the Sussex, and the Devon; and rivalry is doubtless an excellent stimulus. But it is also true that each breed, apart altogether from the unessential things like colour and horns, has its own place in the economy of agriculture. And the special merit of the Hereford is its combination of the power of quick fattening with a real will to live under difficult conditions. It is on the richer estancias of South America that Cruickshank's Shorthorns have found their best environment; it is in satisfying the requirements of the ultra-fastidious beef-eater that the Angus has found its chief use. It is on the poorer and drier ranges of Texas and Australia that the Hereford has found its place. The cattle are great 'rustlers'. They cheerfully travel long miles every day from water to grass and from grass to water; they are stout-hearted in times of drought and famine.

With this eminently sane ideal before them, of a hardy fleshy beast, it must seem a little odd that an older generation of Hereford breeders should have quarrelled bitterly on a mere question of colour, to wit on the point whether a true Hereford must have a completely white face, or whether a mottled face might be allowed to pass. The question has sometimes been compared to that which so bitterly divided Swift's Big-endians from the Little-endians, but there was something more in it than that. The fact is that if you go and invent a superior article you may as well stamp it with your trade mark, and the 'white-facians', who ultimately won the day, can claim that the modern Hereford is not only an honest beast, but shows his character and breeding in his face.

The Hereford has penetrated long distances into the hill country of Wales, and the Dairy Shorthorn now occupies a good many of the richer pastures along the coasts of the Principality. But the higher mountain grazings still belong to the native Welsh breed. The old Welsh cattle included white animals, probably related to the White Park cattle that are still preserved in various parts of the country. But the modern breed is black, and breeders have set themselves the difficult task of combining milking propensities and beef quality with the hardihood necessary in any animal that is to survive, with but a scanty ration of hay, the cold and wet of the upland winters. Welsh 'Runts' are still fattened for London Market on the rich pastures of Leicestershire, but the store breeders of Wales were hard hit by economic conditions during the twenty years that ended with the Second World War. It was better to sell milk than to rear calves wherever the pastures were good, and more profitable to breed sheep than cattle where they were poor. Only since 1947 has there been a notable revival.

Among the interesting survivals of ancient breeds, apart from the Park cattle mentioned above, is the Gloucestershire, with its remarkable colour pattern—a white band along the back of a black ground colour. It has been saved from extinction by local patriotism and is still to be found decorating the glades of Badminton.

In Devon the ox-team also survived long, cheered on by the

ploughboy's song. Although the Pilgrim Fathers took no cattle in the *Mayflower*, some must have followed soon after, for it is recorded that 'the plough which turned the first furrow line in the soil of New England was drawn by a Devon ox.' Actually the cattle of Devon are of two breeds. The Devon proper belongs to the hilly country in the north-west round Barnstaple and Bampton and extend into the west of Somerset by Wiveliscombe and Minehead. Neatly built and blocky, yet active and hardy, with thick, red, curly coats that provide a fine protection against the wet and cold of the country round Exmoor, the Devon must be regarded as a breed very perfectly adapted to its particular environment.

Quartley, Davy, and Turner are the great names associated with this breed. The time of the American and Napoleonic wars was one of 'up corn' and might have been one of 'down horn' in North Devon, but for the foresight of Francis Quartley. He was to be seen in many a market over many a year, outbidding the butchers for any heifer of real merit; to his herd so collected he applied the Bakewellian system of rigorous selection and inbreeding, and brought the Champion cattle to perfection. Under his two nephews the herd's fame was spread abroad, and it provided the most important and valuable blood lines in the breed. The Davys bred Devons at Rose Ash for a century and a half and the representative of the third generation compiled and edited the first volume of the *Herd Book* in 1851. George Turner of Barton was not only a very eminent breeder from about 1840 onwards, but a famous character. At the age of eighty-four he could still ride a hard ten-mile point to the death of a stag, and had scarcely a grey hair in his head. 'What hair dye is it that does so well with you?' asked a noble neighbour. 'Temperance, my Lord; you just try it.' These old yeomen families still go on, cultivating the same farms for generations and cherishing their herds of Ruby Reds.

The South Devon cow, bigger by far than her northern neighbour and a trifle ungainly in build, makes up for any lack of feminine charm by providing the material for the making of Devonshire cream. South Devon bulls, when fattened out at mature age, have reached the greatest weights ever recorded for any sort of cattle. Live weights of well over 30 cwt. are not unknown. Unfortunately great size is no longer regarded by the butcher as a merit, for he has now difficulty in finding customers for the great joints that an older, heartier and more prolific generation of Englishmen liked to see on their sideboards. But, in any case, the tendency of the South Devon breeders is to adopt milk recording and other scientific measures with the end of making their breed still more useful for the dairy, and to be content with a more moderate size.

The ancient red cattle of Sussex, which possibly immigrated with the Saxon invaders, were used for centuries, and until almost the other day, to plough the heavy Wealden clays; ox teams were used too, in the days of the old iron industry, to haul the great loads of timber to the bloomeries through soft miry ways in the partially cleared forests. They thus developed immense powers of draft. When these oxen had finished their working careers they took a year to fatten for Smithfield Market, being then perhaps seven or eight years old. But in spite of the views of people like Arthur Young, who thought the ox was destined to replace the horse as the draft animal of the farm, all this was changed. Sussex cattle must now go, as many have gone, to places like South Africa if they are to find a place in a draft team. At home they have had to be fined down and adapted for earlier fattening. The men who transformed the Sussex into a modern beef breed, with quality of flesh and a very fair measure of early maturity were Ellman—a name famous in another connection—Willsher and Smith. In doing so they managed to preserve the old thriftiness and ability to live on the poorer sorts of pasture.

We must now return to the north-east corner of Scotland where, as we have already seen, an important beef industry sprang up in the early part of the nineteenth century. The reasons were complex. For one thing the farmers of Lothian and East Anglia, who had bought the great droves of Scottish store cattle, were now concentrating more on corn, for wheat especially was running up to prices like five and six pounds a quarter in the latter years of the Napoleonic wars. For another the farms in the north-east of Scotland were being improved at great speed. Barren moors and hill-sides, which were capable of doing little more than maintaining life in the beasts that grazed them, were transformed by lime and bone dust and an immense amount of back-breaking toil into fine fields of oats, turnips and grass. Then the steamship arrived, and it became possible to send fresh beef from Aberdeen to London by sea. As M'Combie, the great Aberdeenshire cattle breeder said: 'bone dust and steam revolutionized the cattle trade', and 'Prime Scotch' beef established its place in Smithfield Market—the unquestioned first place that it has since maintained.

But Amos Cruickshank and his friends were not to have it all their own way. Shorthorn blood was in fact rapidly permeating the cattle stock of the district, but a considerable number of breeders believed that another and perhaps a better way to exploit the new market would be to make a breed out of the native strains. Most of these cattle were black and many were hornless, and it was these breed characters which were chosen as the marks of the new improved type. The first great breeder was Hugh Watson of Keillor, a large farm in Strathmore on the border between the counties of Perth and Angus. Watson set up in his farm in 1810 with half a dozen of his father's 'best and blackest cows and one bull', a foundation that he strengthened by a purchase of 'ten best heifers and one best bull' at the famous Trinity Market at Brechin. Watson was a close friend of many of the leading Shorthorn breeders, and studied and copied their methods while preserving a rather different notion about the ideal type. He began showing in 1820, and in 1829 sent on, from Perth Show to Smithfield, a great black polled ox that created something of a sensation; and also a fat heifer 'with a foreleg as fine as a roe-deer's' that so delighted Earl Spencer's eye that he had a medal struck bearing her image. Soon there was no herd of the new breed which was not indebted to Keillor blood—especially to that of 'Old Grannie' who lived to be thirty-five and a half years old and produced twenty-five calves. She had won many honours in life and had the posthumous one of being entered as No. 1 in the Herd Book of her breed.

If the real foundations of the breed were laid by Watson, the main credit for building upon these must go to William M'Combie.

His family had migrated from Glenisla in Angus northwards to Aberdeenshire, and had there prospered for two generations as dealers in the old store-cattle trade. They travelled as far afield as Caithness and the Western Isles to buy for the feeders of Lothian and Norfolk and often presented as many as fifteen hundred head at Falkirk Tryst. William was a laird's son, and went (unwillingly) to college. But he persuaded his father to let him go home to Tillyfour, to work with the farm men, to share their brose and porridge, to cut two harvests and to tend the cattle. Then he took his place in the family business. To quote from his own book: 'The life of a dealer in those days was a fascinating one—buying up the stock, driving them home feeding by the way, sometimes swimming the Spey with the cattle —full of risk and the excitement which youth loves.' In later years he could hold an audience spellbound with reminiscences of his early life and of the men, like Thom and Adam Bogue, John Rennie of Phantassie in Lothian, Brodie and Kerr and many others who were his friends and business rivals.

After his father's death M'Combie carried on in the store trade but gradually built up, with his many opportunities for selection, a herd of pure black polls. His luckiest purchase was 'Queen Mother' from Fullerton's herd in Angus. For a time she refused to live up to her name and was put to work in the wood cart and the plough team, whereupon she mended her ways, became a matron and the foundress of famous families.

It was, oddly enough, an English Shorthorn breeder, William Torr of Aylesby, who confirmed M'Combie in his resolve to go on with 'The Blacks'. Torr was judging at Aberdeen Show in 1856, and at the dinner after the Show urged the local breeders 'to give their attention to the breed of black cattle, the native breed of the county.' Three years later, at Glasgow, Mr. Torr prophesied that 'Scotchmen would ere long beat the best English beasts with the fine Polled Angus he had seen that day.' M'Combie was not only to see that prophecy fulfilled, but was to beat the world. He showed at Birmingham and went on to Smithfield, where in 1867 he exhibited Black Prince, which created such a sensation that he had to be taken to Windsor, by Royal Command, for Queen

Victoria to see. John Benzies, the herdsman, when asked about the steer's diet, answered: 'Just heather bloom, heather bloom.'

In 1878 came the big victory at the International Show at Paris, where the Tillyfour group of Angus won the grand championship for foreign-bred cattle and also that for beef-producing animals of any country, the voting of the jury being 24 to 7. The Ballindalloch herd of the same breed, destined to win a great place in later days, stood second for both awards. M'Combie was well called 'a menace to vegetarians'.

The third of the great triumvirate was Sir George Macpherson Grant of Ballindalloch, in Speyside. As Queen Mother and the bull Hanton (which M'Combie had bought from the Keillor herd) had laid the foundation of the Tillyfour herd, so the cow Erica, of Keillor breeding, and the bull Trojan from Tillyfour, made the Ballindalloch herd. Grant's importunity to the R.A.S.E. directors probably induced them at last to admit 'those polled cattle' to the prize list of the Royal Show, though it was not until 1894 that regular classes were provided.

In the meantime, especially in 1865–6, the herds of the north-east were devastated by rinderpest, some being completely wiped out. But despite this severe setback the breed has spread and prospered. It has been favoured by the change in the consumer's taste towards smaller joints of more tender meat, with a lower proportion of fat to lean, and it has now long been the exception for any but an Angus beast, or an Angus cross, to win supreme honours at Smithfield Show.

In the early days of pedigree registration the Angus shared with the Galloway a common *Herd Book of Polled Cattle*, but the partnership was never a real one. It is true that there are common characteristics—both breeds being black and polled and noted for the quality of their meat rather than for great size or 'an extreme propensity to make fat'. But while the one is at home in the cold and largely arable district of the north-east the other has adapted itself to the wet climate and the moors and hills of the south-west of Scotland. The spirit of the Galloway country-side is well caught in Stevenson's lines:

CATTLE AND CATTLE BREEDERS

Grey recumbent stones of the dead desert places,
Standing stones on the vacant wine-red moor;
Hills of sheep and the howes of the silent vanished races,
And winds austere and pure.

The strange-sounding names like Carsphairn, Borgue and Minnigaff are all that remain to recall an ancient Celtic kingdom. At the beginning of the eighteenth century it was 'Galloway for woo' '—from the little old soft-woolled sheep. It was black-faced sheep from the southern uplands of Scotland that dis-possessed the Highlander of his croft, but it was herds of cattle that drove out the old smallholders of the south-west. The drov-ing trade in store cattle, between Scotland and the Eastern Coun-ties of England, sprang up quickly after 1603, and the eviction of tenants to make way for cattle caused intense feeling and even led to an uprising of levellers. The sheep, except a very few, were banished to the hills.

The drovers who bought the cattle for English customers pre-ferred them hornless, so the farmers 'bred off the horns'. The cattle were bred on the moors and grazed, till they were four or five years old, on the better pastures near the sea. They 'left their native home, to the number of about 30,000 each year, shod for the three weeks' trek into Norfolk', where, after the name of the great fair where most were sold, they were given the name of St. Faith's Cattle. Even in those days the Galloways had a great reputation with the butchers, being 'such nice cutters-up, and laying the fat on the most valuable parts, that it is no uncommon thing in this refined market to see one of these little bullocks out-sell a coarse Lincolnshire ox, though the latter may be heavier by several stones weight.' The 'refined market' has been the market for Galloways ever since.

By the end of the eighteenth century the breed had developed the characteristics which were described by Aiton in 1810 and which again constituted the standard of points laid down by the Council of the Galloway Society in recent times. The Galloway was destined to lose a big stretch of its original country to the Ayrshire because, in the nineteenth century, milk selling or cheese manufacture became a more profitable venture, on the better and middling sort of land, than cattle breeding for beef. On the other hand the breed has invaded the northern counties of England, groups of black cows with black or blue-grey (Shorthorn cross) calves being now a common sight on the hills of Cumberland and Northumberland.

Another change that occurred was that from store raising to the production of finished beef. This of course became possible with the introduction of turnips, the improvement of permanent grass by the use of lime and bones, and the sowing of grass and clover seeds. Not a few of the enterprising landlords—Herons and Maxwells, Selkirks and Murrays, Cathcarts and Stewarts—followed a practice which was started by Sir James Graham of Netherby, of giving, in place of a medal or money premium, a bull calf from his own improved herd to the tenant who could show the best group of yearlings or two-year-olds. There was no single breeder who took a place, in Galloway circles, comparable to that of Bakewell or Colling with their respective breeds. For one thing there was no intensive inbreeding, the view being taken that this would result in a dangerous loss of vigour and constitution. George Graham of Riggfoot, across the border, called by 'The Druid' 'the Black Booth of Cumberland', may perhaps be singled out. By Sproats famous bull, 'Cumberland Willie', he bred numbers of calves that went as sires to many of the leading herds at the time, and most good specimens of the breed have now a strong strain of this blood.

It was about 1840 that the Ayrshire invasion became alarming. The dairy breed made a rapid conquest of Wigtownshire and began to permeate the Stewartry of Kirkcudbright. A show and sale of breeding stock, started at Lockerbie in 1851, did something towards preserving the native breed. Four years later another select annual sale was organized at Castle Douglas, and the Galloway Agricultural Society was started. The breed also owed a great debt to the Very Reverend John Gillespie of Mousewald, who was largely responsible for starting the Herd Book. Gillespie was a man of real eminence in the Scottish Kirk, who took the widest view of his pastoral functions—his flock included not only mankind, but the lower animals as well. He had moreover a vast force of personality and a shrewd head, so that he won a position of leadership in the Highland Society and indeed in the whole field of Scottish agriculture.

Despite M'Combie's assertion that the Galloways of his time were 'sad, sluggish dogs to feed', the breed has continued to make headway both at home and abroad. It can withstand the most rigorous climates and has been found to thrive high up the slopes of the Rocky Mountains of America and as far north as Alaska. In recent years it has shared with the Aberdeen Angus a good many of the highest honours at Smithfield.

The Galloway proper is now black, but this was not always true; and two of the colour variations, the Dun and the 'Beltie', are still preserved.

The West Highland or Kyloe is well known as part of the decorative scheme in many English parks and is still more pleasing to the eye when seen against its proper background of mountain and loch. Before the great sheep invasion of the Highlands, which began about 1760 and brought all the misery of the clearances in its wake, the Kyloe was the chief farm animal of the West Highlands and the Isles. The cows and calves ran together by day, but at nights were kept in separate folds. In the morning a calf and a milkmaid made a simultaneous onslaught on the cow, which was usually too wild to be milked in the absence of the calf. The scene, where the herd was a large one, was one of pandemonium.

The whole organization—cattle, herds, dairymaids, and dairy equipment—often migrated in summer from the hamlet in the valley to an upland shieling, the people living in rough huts and making their store of butter and cheese. Store cattle were sold to pay the rent and for the rest the people depended on the produce of their fields and mountain-sides—on oatmeal and barley bread, on buttermilk, butter, cheese, fish, and game.

Eleven years before Dr. Johnson set out on his adventurous tour of the Hebrides a certain Mr. Moorhouse from Craven, in Yorkshire, ventured into these unknown wilds to buy cattle. He tells how he slept in the same bed that had seventeen years earlier received Prince Charles. He went on from Skye to Raasey with

Flora MacDonald's husband, and, 'on a fine harvest evening, bargained with him for a thousand cattle at two guineas a head to be delivered free of charge at Falkirk.' This was but one of the many droves that were ferried over from the Isles and travelled the long green road by Badenoch, Lochaber, and Balquidder to Falkirk Tryst, where, up till the middle of last century, as many as five or six thousand Highland Cattle were sold to Midland graziers or other south-country buyers. Improvement had already begun in the eighteenth century, mainly by the Island landowers—McNeils of Barra, Macdonalds of Balranald, and McKinnons of Skye. The great folds on the mainland—of Blair Atholl, Breadalbane, Argyle and Glenlyon—were formed later.

From Portalloch in Skye came the famous couple that went with the rest of the Scottish contingent to the Paris Exhibition of 1856, and that were borrowed as models by Rosa Bonheur.

That England owes a good deal to successive incursions of foreigners is as true of her cattle as of her people. Culley thought the old Shorthorn owed a good deal to Dutch importations; there are stories of an Alderney cross being used in the improvement of the Ayrshire, while the Friesian and the Kerry have come in recent times and in opposite directions over the water.

Imports of Channel Island cattle upon a large scale began in the early years of the nineteenth century. A certain young Yorkshireman had settled at Little Bushey Farm in Herts and set up in business as a cow dealer. One day on his way to Barnet Fair he passed on the road a man leading a neat little cow of a kind he had not seen before. Thinking to please his young bride with an unusual gift he bid the man ten pounds, which was refused. Later on, at the Fair, however, the man found his little beast an object of derision, and had to take her away unsold. He was again overtaken on the road by Mr. Fowler and, being sadder and wiser, accepted seven pounds, and five shillings for his own fee. The little cow freshened in due course, and for seventeen successive weeks presented Mrs. Fowler with enough cream to make more than a stone of butter. Fowler discovered the origin of his valuable acquisition as the Channel Islands, and he entered upon the trade of importing 'Alderneys' as the cattle of all the islands were then indiscriminately called. He and his four sons brought over droves of forty or fifty at a time, shod the beasts with thin iron plates, and walked them to their destinations in and around London. Then the Fowlers began supplying cattle to America and Australia, and the breeds rapidly spread over the temperate regions of the world. A hundred years ago only a few 'Alderneys' were to be found 'as appendages to gentlemen's parks or rural villas, useful to supporting the luxury of the tea-table', or in a few of the butter dairies of Dorset and Hampshire. Now the Jersey and the Guernsey have each their own Herd Book in England as well as in the United States. New Zealand has provided another home for the Jersey, and other countries have taken many more. It is a very remarkable thing that the little Island of Jersey, capable of supporting but a few thousand head of cattle, should have been able to stock so large a proportion of the world's dairy farms. Twice indeed the drain seemed likely to be more than she well could bear. On the first occasion the situation was saved mainly by Colonel le Couteur, who in 1834 started the Jersey Agricultural Society and urged upon farmers the importance of retaining a proportion at least of their best stock. In 1866 the Herd Book was founded by another Grand Old Man, Colonel le Cornu. The next crisis arose about 1880, when the exports were again mounting too high—in 1787 over two thousand cattle left the Island, largely by the persuasion of long-pursed Americans. This time restriction of exports had to be enforced. Both times, however, a proportion of breeders refused to be tempted, and enough good cattle remained.

The present position of the Jersey in Great Britain is largely due to the influence of three men. Dauncey of Horwood and Dr. Watney of Buckhold were the leading English breeders, and both took the view that strong constitution and a big butter yield were the main objects to be sought—rather, that is to say, than the deer-like refinement of the Island stock. John Thornton, the auctioneer, collected and collated the pedigrees for the earlier volumes of the English Herd Book and is known as the historian of the breed.

The Guernsey cow has, in the opinion of most judges of feminine charm, hardly the good looks of her sister. Also, according to the chemist with his Gerber test, her milk is hardly as rich, though the mere consumer usually inclines to the opposite view. Anyway, she makes up for any exterior plainness by many solid virtues, being less exacting in the matter of food, bearing more exposure in cold and wet climates and filling a rather larger size in pails. For these sound reasons she is often preferred by the business milk-producer, both in England and across the Atlantic.

An Irishwoman's lament for her Kerry Cow runs:

> *And when the Shorthorn calved at May*
> *Of corn and cake she got a skinful,*
> *And may I never sin if she*
> *Gave at a milking half a tinful.*
> *Och wirrastrue; my Drimindhu,*
> *You neither needed cake nor corn;*
> *On just dry hay, three times a day,*
> *You gave a canful night and morn.*

This little black 'poor man's cow', coming from the far south-west of County Cork, which (it has been said) 'if you were to put green spectacles upon her, would feed off the main road,' is now well-known in England, and has been found to give, for so small a beast, a very creditable yield of milk. Her still smaller, squatly built relative the Dexter is always a source of interest at our big shows.

The one and only non-British breed of cattle that has been adopted in Britain, or indeed in any important stock country of the world, is the Friesian, coming from the rich polder grazings beyond what used to be the Zuider Zee. Before the days when British ports were closed, as a precaution against disease, to Continental cattle, considerable numbers of Dutch black-and-whites were brought over to replenish our town dairies. Between 1889 and 1892 especially, a fair number of pure-bred Friesians arrived and several herds were formed. The cattle were found, on the more fertile sort of farms and with the necessary intensive feeding, to produce very abundant yields of not very rich milk. Later on, in 1914, an importation of sixty-nine specially chosen specimens from Holland was made by special governmental licence; later importations followed from South Africa, which had long adopted the breed of its parent country; and still later Canada has contributed to our herds. Perhaps naturally, under the circumstances, the merits of the breed are enthusiastically extolled by some, its failings ruthlessly criticized by others. It is true, of course, that the Friesian holds all the world's records for output of milk—it is not unusual for a single cow to produce two hundred guineas' worth in a lactation. Some later writer will have an interesting tale to tell of the men who, in these last forty years, have built so fast, and apparently so well, upon what seemed an all too slight foundation.

The Ayrshire began life on the small dairy farms of South-West Scotland. Its emergence as a type of some note may be dated by the fact that Mrs. Dunlop, the friend of Robert Burns, presented the poet with a pair of cows of the new breed when he went to set up in Ellisland Farm. This was in 1790. In the small old herds of Ayrshire the individual animals got very careful attention for, if the farmer reared and fed them, his wife or daughter did the milking.

Mr. Adam Montgomerie of Lessnessock describes from his own recollection the duties of a West-Country farmer's wife in the old days when farm life was really hard. She was out to milk as early as three or four o'clock in the morning, she did her housework and cooking in the intervals of her cheese-making, besides sometimes taking a turn at feeding the cattle and cleaning the byre. The wife of even a comparatively large-scale farmer might be seen stirring the cheese-vat, a baby on her arm and a couple of other small children running round the kitchen. Long before the days of accurate butter-fat testing the women used to sample each cow's milk and set the samples in glass tubes to show the depth of the cream layer. Thus early were the cattle selected for the quality as well as the quantity of their milk.

The farmers in the Kilmarnock district, as early as 1793, formed themselves into a club, and fifteen years later organized a cattle show. Descendants of some of the early prize-winners—both cattle and owners—still occupy the ancestral farms. In 1814 the

Highland and Agricultural Society gave local premiums for the cattle in the Kyle district of Ayrshire, and in 1834 provided classes at their Show.

As mines and ironworks and cotton mills increased in the Midland of Scotland, and as Glasgow flourished, the demand for milk and cheese, butter and buttermilk, grew rapidly, and dairying and Ayrshire cattle spread as far as Argyle, West Lothian, Wigtown, and Kirkcudbright. Then grew up a trade in older cows for London milk sheds; one dealer, Burrell, often taking as many as seven or eight score at a time down to Essex, where Ayrshire men as well as Ayrshire cows were already seeking new homes. But the greatest of all the dealers was Mistress Jane Dunlop, who drove up and down the country in a gig for most of the week and showed her collection, of sometimes as many as a hundred and seventy head, each Wednesday in Glasgow.

Stimulated by the Highland Society's offer of prizes for the best imitations of Cheshire and Gloucestershire cheese, the Ayrshire men, about 1850, set about copying the technique of the best English makers. James Caird of Baldoon sent his dairyman south to learn the art. Mr. Robert McAdam persuaded the Agricultural Association to send two special commissioners to visit all the chief English cheese districts, the men when they returned reporting in favour of the Cheddar system. The next step was to invite Mr. and Mrs. Joseph Harding up from Somerset and to set them up as itinerant instructors. It was a strange language that they spoke, but most of the process could be demonstrated practically, and farmers and their wives and dairymaids flocked to the classes. The Scots were apt pupils, and in 1856, when the first Kilmarnock cheese show was held, some of the produce was taken to England for sale.

The farmer of the West of Scotland is an incorrigible showman, and Ayrshire has probably more agricultural shows than any other area of its size in the world. Whether it is stock or produce there is intensely keen competition, and immense trouble is taken, and high artistry used, to make the exhibits appear at their best. There was indeed one period when a foolish fad for small teats and 'tight', highly carried udders came near to doing serious harm to the Ayrshire cattle, but fortunately many of the breeders were too shrewd to allow themselves to be carried away. But the long-continued selection under the hard-to-please eyes of the breeders has made for a quite extraordinary and uniform symmetry of form.

Ayrshires have been exported in large numbers to Sweden, to Canada, the United States and many other dairy countries. One has seen bulls from Lessnessock looking equally at home in a wintry Ontario landscape and on the Mua hills of Kenya.

The breeding of cattle is now rapidly becoming a highly scientific affair. A milk record, before it is accepted, must have a variety of corrections applied to it, taking account of all the various circumstances under which it has been made. Even bulls have (hypothetical) milk records allotted to them. It was in fact the Danes who first instituted official schemes of milk recording, but they found their first British disciples among the Ayrshire men. The inception of the Scottish Scheme was brought about largely through the efforts of John Speir of Newton, near Glasgow. Speir was an experimenter and a pioneer by nature; and possessing, besides his other qualities, a persuasive tongue and a ready pen, he soon had a wide sphere of influence. He became a Director of the Highland and Agricultural Society and gave his fellow members of the Board no peace until, in 1903, they agreed to inaugurate a scheme of recording and butter-fat testing on the Danish model. In the first year three local Societies were registered and the numbers grew until, in 1914, there were thirty-six.

Speir was a man of immense energy and strong convictions and undertook an immense burden of public work in connection with agriculture. He was a pioneer lecturer in agriculture. He played an important part in the establishment of the West of Scotland College of Agriculture. His articles in the Highland and Agricultural Society's *Transactions*, and in the farming press, covered a wide range of subjects, though the problems of milk production received most attention. Many of his articles were records of his own observations and experiments.

It is true of the milk industry, as of many others, that there have been men in it who lived before their time. Among the dim old volumes in second-hand bookshops it is not very uncommon to find a copy of *The Harleian Dairy System; and an account of the various methods of Dairy Husbandry pursued by the Dutch*. The book was published in 1829. Its author was William Harley, who some years before the book was written had established a dairy herd of nearly three hundred cows at Willowbank on the outskirts of Glasgow. In his book, Harley describes his methods, which were designed 'to supply the people of Glasgow with milk of reliable quality.' These methods included a weekly weighing, morning and evening, of the milk given by each cow; a method, of a sort, for testing the proportion of cream, and a system, not always easy to enforce, designed to produce order and cleanliness.

Up till about the middle of last century the greater part of the milk output from farms—i.e. excluding that from city dairies— was still manufactured on the farm into butter and cheese. But the rise in the town population and increasing prosperity made for a steady increase in the demand for fresh liquid milk. Seventy years ago every town drew its supplies from its own immediate neigh- bourhood, the producer being generally also the retailer. Where the town was large the cattle were mostly kept in it rather than round it, being fed partly on farm produce carted in and partly on brewers' grains, oil cake, bran, and other by-products. Even up till 1864 practically the whole of London's supply came from within a radius of some seventeen miles from the City. But these London cowsheds were nearly emptied by the Cattle Plague of 1865–6, and a great impetus was given to a change which had already begun.

In 1850 a business had been set up by Mr. George Barham, who initiated the method of cooling the milk before its despatch. The development of the railways and the speeding-up of train services greatly increased the possibilities of the new trade. In 1865 only three million gallons of country milk were brought to London. In a year the quantity had doubled. The present figure exceeds a hundred and fifty million gallons.

In recent years no branch of agriculture has advanced more rapidly than milk production. The scientific principles of ration- ing, first worked out by Kellner in Germany and Hansson and his associates in Denmark, have been developed and applied by Crowther, Mackintosh, and others for our home conditions. The milk-recording movement has spread, though not as widely or as rapidly as many would wish. The application of hygienic methods in the cowshed has made very rapid strides, control of once dreaded diseases, such as contagious abortion and mastitis, is steadily improving, and artificial insemination is placing the best males at the disposal of the small men.

The farmer has sometimes been blamed for his reluctance to adopt the methods of hygiene necessary to make his milk a safe as well as a nutritious food; but the blame must be laid in equal measure upon the consumer, who was long inclined to regard the whole affair as a fad and who has been reluctant to realize that to equip the farm with hygienic buildings and sterilizing plant, to clip and groom and wash cows, and to do the many other things that must be done, costs the producer money which ought as a matter of ordinary business to give some return. More than a generation ago there were already pioneer farmers like Mr. Titus Barham of Sudbury and Mr. Wilfred Buckley of Moundsmere, who were producing on lines that had already been adopted for American Certified Milk; through his retail shops in London Lord Rayleigh was already selling milk from tuberculin-tested cows; in 1914 Robert Hobbs of Kelmscott opened the first private farmer's shop to sell milk of a standard equivalent to that of the modern Certified Grade. But there was still no attempt to organize the production of clean milk on a national basis. The first effort in this direction was made during the First World War. In 1917, when the price of milk, like that of many other foods, was brought under Government control, Mr. Wilfred Buckley was working at the Ministry of Food and succeeded in having instituted a system of special licences enabling the producer of high-grade milk to charge a higher than the standard price. Since then the Government and the people have taken a growing interest in the subject and a great mass of legislation has been passed.

The great leader of the campaign which was to carry the new ideas into the cowshed and the dairy was Robert Stenhouse Williams, a physician and bacteriologist, who became the first

Director of the new National Institute for Dairy Research at Reading. With but poor equipment and a minute but devoted staff, he succeeded in convincing a number of progressive producers. In his spotless white hospital coat, he showed how to groom and wash and sterilize; and he argued away the prejudices of the cowmen, in homely unassuming talk, with unfailing kindness and patience.

Stenhouse Williams' object was to free the dairy cattle of the country from tuberculosis, and otherwise to ensure that fresh raw milk could be consumed with safety. He believed that pasteurization lessened the food value of milk and that it must be regarded as a necessary evil. A passage from a speech of his, delivered in 1919, reads as if it might have been spoken twenty years later: 'If our milk supply be considered as a national problem it is clear that our first function is to ensure that milk be available for our children in the most nutritious possible form and at a reasonable price, since it is quite probable that efficient nutrition is the most important single factor in the development of a nation.'

Knowing the variety of people concerned in the production and handling of milk, he urged the necessity for widespread education for the farmer and his workers, for the distributor, the dairy instructor, the sanitary inspector and the Medical Officer of Health.

For twenty years he laboured for this cause with an enthusiasm which only increased with opposition. He lived to see the task at least well begun, his Institute somewhat more adequately equipped and endowed, and the general public awakening to the importance of the milk question. The words inscribed in the library of the Shinfield Institute, erected to his memory, give the key to his success. 'He had the gift of winning friends and of earning the affection of his fellow workers. He held fast to his purpose through difficulties that persisted for years and must have daunted a man of less heart. This Institute is his monument.'

While Stenhouse Williams, with the support of a growing number of milk producers, laboured at the problems of dairy hygiene, others concerned themselves to replace the old rule-of-thumb methods of feeding by a system that should be based upon the scientific principles that had now been established. The pioneers in this field were mainly County organizers, especially G. H. Garrad in Kent, J. R. Bond in Derbyshire, and Robert Boutflour in Wiltshire, but they included also James Mackintosh, who was a colleague of Stenhouse Williams at Reading.

In 1924 Noel Buxton, then Minister of Agriculture, appointed a Departmental Committee on the Rationing of Dairy Cows, with the object of correlating the field experience of these men with the principles that had been established by Kellner, Armsby, and other scientific nutritionists. The Committee took the advice of T. B. Wood and Charles Crowther on the nutritive values of the common feeding-stuffs and on the maintenance and production requirements of milch cows; and from the farm advisors on the means by which these principles could be applied in the cowshed. The committee's report put the whole business on a sound basis, and the system that it recommended has wonderfully stood the test of time. Some farmers, as might have been expected, have tended to stick too slavishly to 'the book', while others clung too long to their old ways; but most took the middle way.

The country-wide propaganda fell largely to Mackintosh at Reading and to Boutflour, who went from Wiltshire to Harper Adams College, where he had the benefit of Crowther's scientific guidance and where he ran a demonstration herd. To hear first one and then another preaching the gospel was to realize that converts can be made by widely different methods. Mackintosh was mild, quietly humorous, persuasive, always ready with the soft answer. Boutflour, by contrast, emitted a stream of paradoxes, brilliant witticisms and calculated overstatements; and he was somehow able, at question time, to make grossly offensive remarks that were received with universal enjoyment. Even those who refused to go all the way with him—who persisted in growing roots, declined to throw their chaff-cutters into the nearest river, or felt that they could not forget all they had ever learnt about 'dairy type'—even such went back to their cowsheds prepared to modify the old routine.

Wherever the credit belongs, the new and better ideas about cow-feeding and management did spread abroad, and the revolution was probably faster than any other, of comparable importance, in the history of our farming.

This is perhaps a convenient point in our story to speak of Edward Strutt. It is true that he was notable in many other ways than as a breeder of dairy cattle and a pioneer of modern milk production—indeed he was thought of by many of his contemporaries as the greatest agriculturist in England, and there seems no good reason to dispute this judgement. But nowadays he is most often recalled to our minds, if we profess to any interest in stock breeding, by the frequent recurrence of the prefix 'Terling' in the pedigrees of so many fine Friesian cattle. Terling was Strutt's village, and it was to Terling churchyard that he made his last journey—on a farm wagon—in March 1930.

The Hon. Edward Gerald Strutt was born in 1854, the fifth son of the second Lord Rayleigh. He was educated at Winchester and at Cambridge, where he took his degree in 1875. He studied farming and land agency in various parts of the country and under several masters, and in 1882 he assumed the management of the Essex estate of his brother, the third Lord Rayleigh, who was as eminent in chemistry as Edward was in rural affairs.

The time, of course, was the beginning of the longest spell of hard times that British farming has ever known: moreover, Essex, with its high proportion of heavy ploughland and its great dependence on wheat, was as hard hit as any part of the country.

Some land was already 'in hand' when Strutt's agency began, and as prices went from bad to worse, as more farmers broke and as competent tenants with adequate capital became fewer, one holding after another—often in poor condition—was added to the chain of home farms. In the end the concern—known as Lord Rayleigh's Farms—comprised some seventeen thousand acres.

That this great enterprise should have succeeded during the depths of the depression is to say that Edward Strutt was a man of remarkable qualities. It is not surprising to read that he was no easy, indulgent master. His own efficiency, remarkable knowledge of farming detail, and tireless energy, made him impatient of slackness or ineptitude. But all who worked under his leadership knew him for a fair and just man, who asked nothing more than he himself would have given. Moreover, it was recognized that he was leading a fight for the livelihood of the whole community.

In his survey of the gloomy situation Strutt saw one great business opportunity. London was near, was growing, and was wanting greatly increased supplies of milk. Moreover, the quality of the existing supplies left very much to be desired. It might be true that the great majority of consumers were quite apathetic about the quality of the fluid that was provided; but no doubt they could be taught to distinguish good from bad. So the sign 'Lord Rayleigh's Dairies' appeared over a number of clean and well-equipped shops. At the farm end, milk recording started in the 'nineties, a very high standard of cowshed hygiene was set and maintained, the tuberculin test was applied as soon as it became available, and the foundations were laid of what was to become a group of famous Friesian herds. The same kind of efficient business organization was applied throughout all branches of the concern.

Even if the Rayleigh Farms had been Strutt's sole concern, he must have delegated a great deal to his farm managers and bailiffs; but, in fact, he became increasingly involved in outside affairs; in particular he was in great demand as an advisor on all manner of farming and estate-management problems. But his general command of the enterprise, based as it was upon his shrewd judgement of men, the remarkable range of his knowledge and the sound (though not over-elaborate) system of accounting and financial control that he devised, was never lost.

When war came in 1914 Strutt was summoned to the Board of Agriculture as Chief Agricultural Advisor, and became the confidant and counsellor of Lord Ernle, who had long been his friend. His greatest assets were his profound understanding of the English farmer and his prestige as a master of his craft.

Strutt not only fought back against the economic storm as it beset the Rayleigh Estate. He set an example in the application of business principles to farm organization and management; and his hardly-won victory inspired many others—landowners and farmers alike—to continue the struggle.

7

SHEEP AND SHEPHERDING

Through all the brute creation none as sheep
To lordly man such ample tribute pay,
For him their downy vestures they resign,
For him they spread the feast.

DYER

The fact that the Lord Chancellor takes his seat on the Woolsack is a reminder that the sheep was already an important animal in the old manorial farming of medieval England. The keeping of sheep for wool was the earliest form of large-scale commercialized farming, and wool was the main basis of the country's early export trade. All through the sixteenth century there was loud outcry about the enclosure of farms to form sheep walks, and the sheep came to be regarded as the greatest enemy of the small farmer and of the labourer in husbandry.

The townes go down, the land decayes
Off cornefeyldes playne layes,
Gret men makithe nowadays
A shepecott in the church.

Again in the later eighteenth century it was sheep that brought about economic revolution in the Scottish Highlands and drove the people into the cities or over the seas. But there is, too, a credit side to the account. The 'golden hoof' has turned many a stretch of barren heath or downland into arable fields which have grown vast quantities of corn, and have paid wages to many poor men.

The story of sheep breeding in the past hundred years makes a complicated one. Sheep must live under a wide diversity of conditions—on the rich wet pastures of Romney Marsh, on the bare Cumberland fells or between hurdles on muddy turnip fields.

174

If we are to have a breed adapted to each even of the main types of environment it is clear that many breeds must be required. Moreover, each must not only live and thrive, as well as may be, on a given soil and in a given climate, but must produce a readily marketable quality of both wool and mutton. Then, again, the consumer's taste in mutton has changed; in Bakewell's day it was only gentlefolk who cared to have their meat tender and lean; the working man was glad to have it old and coarse of grain, and preferred plenty of fat. Again, the farmer's outlook on the wool question has changed. Before Australia and the other new countries were stocked with Merino sheep the finer sorts of wool were scarce and valuable, and even the long, strong, lustre wools of the Lincoln and Leicester brought useful money. Now the prices of fine Southdown, strong and bright Lincoln and coarse hairy Blackface or Herdwick are much nearer together. The whole importance of wool, in relation to early maturity and fleshing properties, suffered a long decline—except indeed in those breeds, like the Romney Marsh, for which there has been an export trade to the wool-growing countries. The sudden revival of the wool trade in 1950–51 was astonishing, but none ventured to predict what the future might hold in store. Finally, although both sheep and shepherd are placid and peace-loving, the 'battle of the breeds' has been nowhere more keenly fought than in the sheep world.

Any sheep breeder bent upon a pilgrimage of the historic places connected with his craft must put Dishley Grange, in Leicestershire, at the top of his list. This was the home of Robert Bakewell, who may be said to have invented the modern sheep; for out of the coarse-boned, slow-feeding old breed he made the fleshy, symmetrical, and fine-boned New Leicester, whose blood was to be used in the improvement of so many other breeds. Moreover, Bakewell's methods of breeding—careful selection, a greater or less degree of consanguinity in mating, and the application of the progeny test to the sire—and the demonstration of the results that these methods could achieve, were even more important than the actual type of animal which he created. Bakewell died in 1795, but before this date there were New Leicesters to be found in most of the counties of Great Britain as well as in several Continental countries.

Let us first follow the fortunes of the northern branch of Bakewell's breed. When the two brothers Matthew and George Culley, who had been pupils at Dishley (and the latter of whom was the author of *Observations on Live Stock*), went to farm in Northumberland, they took with them some of the Dishley sheep to found a flock. They followed Bakewell's practice of hiring out rams and of watching the progeny, so that, if a particular animal happened to prove a particularly successful sire, he could later be used in the home flock. At this time most wethers intended for mutton were kept until they were three or four years old. The Leicester could be made fat enough at two. Indeed, says George Culley in his book: 'There are two reasons for killing the wethers at two years old: First, they leave the most profit; and secondly, if kept longer they tend to get too fat for genteel tables. To people who are strangers to these sheep this may appear rather problematical; the following facts may remove their doubts: A three-years-old wether, belonging to the author, was killed at Alnwick by James Bolton, the 2nd of October 1787, which measured seven inches and one-eighth of solid fat, on the ribs, cut straight through without any slope.' What a chop!

Many local farmers on both sides of the Tweed followed the Culleys' example and, with them, continued to go back to Dishley when they wanted fresh blood. Prominent among those who bought or hired Dishley sheep were the Collings of Shorthorn fame, Robertson of Ladykirk, and Thompson of Bogend in Berwickshire. The flock of the last named was established not later than 1795, was removed by another generation to Mungoswells, near Duns, and was finally dispersed in 1903. Gradually the local breeds of sheep were crossed out of recognition with Leicester rams, so that the low ground farms in the Border country came to be stocked with practically pure Leicesters. Even the hill-men, in the Cheviots and the Lammermoors, tried what a mild infusion of Leicester blood into their breeds would do; but the experiment was a hopeless failure, the sheep losing their active habits and their ability to thrive on mountain grasses and heather.

It was long before the true use of the Leicester in the hill flocks was discovered. This was to produce cross-bred lambs to be removed from the hills in autumn, the ewe stock itself being kept pure.

Meanwhile, the practice of bringing sheep from the old home of the breed gradually fell into disuse, and the Border type began to diverge from that of the English Leicester. Some have suggested that there was an admixture of Cheviot blood, but the best authorities on the history of the Border Leicester do not accept this view.

In the past half-century pure-bred Border Leicesters have ceased to be bred for the butcher, for the joints are too large and the mutton too fat for the table—genteel or otherwise. The breed is now kept for the production of rams which are mated to Cheviot or Blackface mountain ewes. The latter breeds being small and lean, the large fat Border Leicester is just what is required to produce a popular sort of mutton.

Among the flocks of the Border district that of Lord Polwarth at Mertoun occupied for an exceptionally long period a position of eminence that can rarely have been equalled in any breed. Unlike his ancestor Scott of Harden (who was condemned, for sheep stealing, either to be hanged or to marry the rather unprepossessing daughter of his captor, who went by the name of Muckle-mouthed Meg) Hugh Scott (afterwards Lord Polwarth) acquired his flock by legitimate means. Already in 1778, when Andrew Wight visited Mertoun, he had, after other experiments, bought sheep from the Culleys and also from Bakewell, and the Mertoun sheep were 'not inferior to those of Bakewell' himself. The scrupulous care that was exercised in the selection of the foundation stock was applied to its subsequent management. A few females were bought, up till 1856, from other flocks of known purity, but afterwards the flock was entirely self-supporting. It acquired a remarkable uniformity of type—so much so indeed that, when the fashion changed, as it did in the present century, the Mertoun type could not well be changed. Like all great flocks, that of Mertoun owed much to its shepherds. Mr. Usher of Todrig, himself a flock-master, says: 'Tom Small whom I knew as far back as 1875, was its presiding genius, spurning the idea of using blood not strictly Bakewell.' When Tom felt the infirmities of age creeping on, he suggested his own successor in Andrew Paterson. During the heyday of the flock no ewes were sold except for export, but the regular lots of rams, sold annually at Kelso Ram Fair, commanded high prices and often topped the market.

Some say that in-and-in breeding was pushed too far at Mertoun —that half a century without a change of blood was too long. The other opinion is that the Mertoun type merely went out of fashion. Certain it is that they lacked the high carriage of head and the strong aquiline noses that are necessary features of the aristocratic Border Leicester of to-day. In any case, when, in 1912, the flock came under the hammer of James Swan, he had 'an uphill job' to sell it. The demand for Border Leicesters has been wonderfully maintained through boom and depression. It was thought a fabulous thing when, in 1898, a Mertoun ram topped Kelso sale at £275, but £1,100 was reached in the 'daft days' after the first world war and a Renmure shearling made £550 in 1935. Even these prices have been dwarfed by those of the late 'forties and 1950.

So long as the half-bred ewe (the Bamshire as she is called in Yorkshire, or the Border Leicester as she is commonly but wrongly called in the South) retains her popularity for lowland pastures, the parent breeds—Cheviot and the Border Leicester—must remain very important in the sheep farming of the North country.

The Leicester proper, or English Leicester as it is sometimes called, has rather declined in importance in recent years. It is true that flocks have been established in many of the Dominions, particularly in New South Wales. Also, the breed is used to some extent for producing crossbred lambs in the North of England. But as a farmer's sheep it is now largely restricted to the Wolds of the East Riding of Yorkshire. The great square fields of the Wolds, with their straight-drilled crops of swedes alternating with wheat and barley, were carved out of poor open down only three or four generations ago; and it was the Leicester sheep, folded on roots in winter and pasturing on the clover leys in summer, that made the change possible. The Leicester sheep is still the best of all dung-carts for this bleak and exposed countryside, no other breed being so happily adapted to the way of life. But the butchers' customer prefers the smaller and leaner mutton of the Down breeds, and more and more cross-breeding is being done. The indirect influence of Bakewell's sheep is still very great, for many of our modern breeds owe a great deal to Dishley blood. It was a belated honour to Bakewell's memory when, a century and a half after his death, his grave in the little ruined chapel at Dishley Grange was restored, and a tablet was erected to his memory.

Among the breeds in which Leicester blood flows most freely is the Wensleydale, kept, like the Border Leicester, for crossing with Mountain breeds such as the Swaledale of Yorkshire and the Herdwick of the Lake country. This breed, with its blue face and its remarkable fleece of long, silky, lustrous wool, has been kept in the fashion by eliminating the old Leicester's propensity to 'make exceeding fat' and is tending to increase in numbers. It has even carried the war into Scotland, and is preferred to the Border Leicester, in some parts of the south-west of Scotland, for crossing with Blackface Mountain ewes.

It has already been indicated that the whole sheep industry of Scotland and of the North of England is based upon the two mountain breeds, the Cheviot and the Scotch Blackface, with various crosses superimposed upon them. These two breeds have distinct types of habitat, the Blackface being the sheep of the 'black' or heather land and the Cheviot of the more grassy hills of generally lower elevation. The Cheviot's earliest known home was the border hills, but all the evidence goes to indicate that the Blackface came to Scotland from the Pennine region, where its relatives, the Swaledale and the Lonk, still live. We may readily suppose that some of the early stock was acquired by other than ordinary commercial transactions; but however that may be, the breed was well established in the southern uplands of Scotland as far back as the fifteenth century. Its introduction to the Highlands is a much more recent affair.

There are many contrasts between the two breeds. Cheviot wool, naturally soft and fine, proved very susceptible of improve ment and became the raw material of the famous Tweed industry of the Socttish Borders. On the other hand all attempts to improve the shaggy coat of the Blackface have resulted in a fleece that has been found inadequate to protect the sheep (and more particularly the lamb) against the cold winds and the rains of its mountain country.

There was plenty of exchange of blood under the conditions that prevailed along the border up till the time of the Union, and the breeds must have been freely mixed. Sometimes indeed the reivers got more than they came for; thus the Robsons of North Tyne raided Liddlesdale, and took from the Grahams a flock of sheep which turned out to be infected with the scab. The disease spreading, the angry Robsons returned to hang seven Grahams with the warning that when next 'Gentlemen cam to tak sheep, they were no to be scabbit.'

In later and less exciting times Robson, of Belford and Bowmont Water, who was the first great improver of Cheviots, undoubtedly brought some sheep from the South. He is said to have used a ram from Bakewell, but according to his grandson 'he travelled over the greater part of England for the purpose of seeing various breeds, and eventually deciding upon a breed then existing in Lincolnshire, he bought several rams. The cross answered admirably, improving the flock without lessening the hard characteristics suited to his high and stormy land.' Robson's work gave the Cheviot a new symmetry of form and increased the wool clip by 20 per cent. Having thus stolen a march on its rival, the Cheviot advanced up the hillsides and drove the Blackfaces in retreat to the highest and poorest land. The war, however, has never been lost or won, for the hardiness of the Blackface and its will to live have stood it in good stead.

Indeed one of the classical examples of attempting the impossible in breeding occurred in the history of the Cheviot. About the middle of last century the 'Improved Cheviot' created by James Brydon of Moodlaw, in Eskdalemuir, came into fashion. Brydon bred a sheep of altogether shorter and more blocky build, with a greater thickness of flesh and a rather open coat. For many years he carried off the bulk of the Cheviot prizes at 'Highland'

SHEEP AND SHEPHERDING

Shows, and his biennial sales were attended by buyers from all over the Border country. But Brydon had lost constitution, and when a series of wild winters came along (as they do, according to hill men, every half century) his improved Cheviot was found wanting. The winter of 1859-60 was one of those whose story has become a tradition. There was a fearful mortality among sheep and many shepherds perished in the snow. There was a reaction not only towards the old, active type of Cheviot but also in favour of the Blackface.

Other lessons had to be relearnt from this disaster. Thus William Aitcheson, who owned twelve thousand sheep in three counties, is found urging the necessity for drainage to improve the hill grazings, and of making enclosures of improved land to grow hay—'Hay is the sheet anchor. Go in for hay and the storms of winter may drift up the valleys, and the tempests whistle over the hills in vain.'

The high tableland that makes upper Lanarkshire and the inland part of Ayrshire was the main scene of the improvement of the Blackface breed. Here farmed Gillespie of Douglas Mill, from whom the Ushers of Lammermuir drew the stock for their high grazings. Here too is Glenbuck, which Charles Howatson made so famous in the annals of sheep. Howatson was a man of business in coal and iron, but before he bought Glenbuck he set himself to the improvement of another farm, Crossflat, and to the breeding of better sheep. Later on, at Glenbuck, he carried on the work and produced a short-legged, easily fattened sheep with a rather open coat of strong wool that swept the ground. But some said that these sheep would not do—that they could not get about in snow, and that the ewes were none too generous milkers. The leaders of the other camp were the Archibalds of Overshiels, in the Muirfoot Hills, which they leased in 1847. The grazings of Overshiels run up to the two thousand feet level, and had already carried a Blackface stock for over eighty years. Here James the farmer John the student and Adam the shepherd went quietly to work, following their own beliefs and completely indifferent to the fashion, which ignored the merits of their hardy, close-wooled sheep. All three lived to see some recognition of their work, but

181

it was after the death of two of the brothers that the flock and its master became famous. Adam Archibald was a little like another mountain flockmaster of whom it was said, 'He was a man among sheep but a sheep among men'; he was so shy and unassuming that he had always been regarded as of little account. But when he was left to carry on alone it became obvious that his had been the master mind of the three. At the 'Highland' Shows of the 'seventies and 'eighties Overshiels sheep won a great share of the honours, and at the Lanark and Perth Ram Sales they often brought the top figures.

Another great name among a bygone generation of Border flockmasters was that of Thomas Elliot of Hindhope in Jedwater. He bred many kinds of stock—Cheviot, Border Leicester, and Blackface sheep, Shorthorns and West Highlanders, Clydesdales, hunters, Hackneys, Foxhounds, Greyhounds and Collie dogs. It was the Hindhope Cheviot flock that won his reputation as a breeder, but it was the fame of his Collies that reached the ears of Queen Victoria—Her Majesty would be glad to see Mr. Elliot when next he happened to be in the neighbourhood of Windsor. So Thomas, after a Smithfield Show, went to see the Queen. The Queen wanted one of Mr. Elliot's famous Collie dogs; would Mr. Elliot consider selling her one? Mr. Elliot would take it as a great honour if Her Majesty would accept a couple of his dogs as a gift. But that was far too generous of Mr. Elliot!—And then Thomas's Court manners broke down and he said: 'Noo, what's a pair o' collie dogs atween you an' me!'

The Mountain flockmaster, if he is operating on a large scale, depends greatly on his shepherds. The hill shepherd, leading a lonely life and rarely having anybody to share his responsibilities or to consult in his decisions, develops a great measure of self-reliance and is often a man of great personality and character. He leads a strenuous life at certain seasons such as the lambing time; at other times he has leisure to think his thoughts. Winter storms always bring him acute anxiety, and sometimes place him in danger of his life. Every once in a while, as in 1860, men die in their efforts to save their sheep. The worst storm on record is one described by Hogg, the Ettrick Shepherd, which happened in

1794, and when, on almost every farm in Ettrick Water, a shepherd perished in the snow. In Moffat churchyard stands a record of twelve shepherds buried on one Sunday.

As in the Cotswolds in the sixteenth century, so in the Highlands between 1770 and 1840, the making of the big sheep farms was carried out with a great lack of what we would now regard as ordinary human consideration and social justice, and was the occasion of a vast amount of human misery. Perhaps at no other time in our history was economic power so ruthlessly used, or poor folk treated with so little humanity. It is easy to blame the Highland Lairds; they were blameworthy by modern standards; but they were less inhuman than the owners of the new factories in the North of England, and scarcely more so than the squires and parsons who administered the Poor Law in the South.

It was the Blackfaced breed that began the march from the Southern Uplands to the Southern and Central Highlands. The big flocks displaced not only the few little old soft-wooled sheep of the Highland farms, but also the cattle and the goats. The invaders were welcomed more or less heartily in Dumbartonshire and Perthshire about 1760, but in the North the strange animals with their alien shepherds and owners were everywhere recognized and hated as the enemies of the old inhabitants and the old Highland way of life. By the end of the eighteenth century the Blackfaces had reached the confines of Caithness. In 1806–7 there was a disastrous outbreak of the rot among the goats and the little Kerry sheep of the northernmost county, and so many died that the country was left almost empty for the new-comers.

The rival breed was following fast behind. In 1792 Sir John Sinclair had already brought three hundred Cheviot ewes, as a trial, to his estate at Langwell in Caithness, and ten years later the flock had increased to three thousand. Sinclair was a whole-hearted Cheviot man, and urged with all his 'intolerable energy' that, whatever the nature of the grazing, the Blackfaces must be put away and the Whitefaces substituted. His campaign was greatly helped, after 1800, by rising prices for the finer qualities of wool. If Cheviot wool was worth 28s. a stone and Blackface only 7s. to 10s., how could one argue about relative merits?

Capitalist farmers, chiefly from Northumberland, now began to move with their thousands of sheep, their shepherds and their sheep dogs to the great new sheep runs of Sutherland. The crofters were moved to new villages by the sea, or driven to America. At one time a single one of the immigrants, Reed, held a stretch of country in the Strath of Helmsdale which was eighteen miles long and eight miles across at its widest, and which grazed over eighteen thousand sheep. Even as a commercial system, and quite apart from its social consequences, the new specialized sheep farming has gradually shown its defects. With the absence of cattle the grazings have deteriorated in quality, bracken and coarse grasses tending to spread. Moreover, the drain of fertility from the land was greatly increased by the much higher output of sheep and wool, so that the sheep-carrying capacity of the land has slowly diminished.

The Cheviot breed, in its northern colony, has gradually changed in character and is now bigger, with a less dense fleece of softer wool. Some part of the change may have been caused by an early infusion of Merino blood, for Sinclair and his friends, in their efforts to produce finer wool, took a good many Spanish sheep to Caithness. The pure breed failed to thrive, but a good many crosses were made. But the comparatively low-lying grazings of the North, with their deeper and sometimes more lime-rich soils, make possible a breed with greater growth. Towards the latter part of the nineteenth century the sheep that had driven out the people were themselves ousted from some of the poorer grazings to make room for deer. Between 1883 and 1908 deer paid a higher rent, on the wilder stretches of country, than sheep, and the area of deer forest in the five northern counties increased by one and a quarter million acres.

A good many attempts have been made, in more recent times, to make up to the present generation of Highlanders for all that their ancestors suffered. The remnants of the crofters have been given security of tenure in their crofts; roads have been made and piers built; attempts have been made to foster the old industries like the hand weaving of tweeds, and even to establish new ones. A good many of the big farms have been split up again into small

holdings. But many who know the Highlands well have little hope
that the lost race of sturdy independent peasants can be remade.
The remnants of the old economy, and of the old races of men
and of sheep, still survive in the islands and in the townships along
the west coast. You may still buy Shetland shawls and Harris
tweeds. But the Highlands are for the most part an empty land
where most of the few permanent inhabitants live by the sportsman and the summer visitor.

After the end of the eighteenth century sheep husbandry grew
in importance not only in the mountains but also in the low
country of Scotland. The general use of sown grasses and of turnips made possible the maintenance of breeding flocks, as well as
the winter fattening of large numbers of lambs from the hills.
Gradually the new system of alternate husbandry—corn, roots,
and corn with a two or three year ley—replaced the old sequence
of oats and barley; the land was enclosed and drained. Fat cattle
and sheep, instead of lean cattle and corn, became the leading
products of the lowland farms, except in the west where it was
milk and cheese, and in Lothian where stock remained subsidiary
to grain and potatoes.

We have seen that the first improved sheep of lowland Berwickshire was Bakewell's Leicester, but that, as time went on, this
breed failed to satisfy the public taste in joints of mutton. Moreover, it is always a waste of good land to use it for the rearing of
breeding sheep. On rich pasture sheep make no better growth
than on poor, and they are liable to get unnecessarily and even
unhealthily fat. Moreover, if such land be continuously stocked
with the number of sheep that it will feed it becomes 'sheep sick';
it is an old saying that the sheep's worst enemy is another sheep.
The solution was found in a system whereby the low country
farms drew both their breeding stock, and their lambs for winter
fattening, from the hills.

It was early found that the mating of a Cheviot or of a Blackface
ewe with a Border Leicester ram produced progeny of a size that
was very suitable to the butcher, with a proper blend of fat and
lean meat. It was a later discovery that the half-bred (Border
Leicester-Cheviot) ewe was a most conscientious mother, pro-

ducing twins often, and giving enough milk to nourish them well. Up till about 1860 most half-bred ewe lambs were still sold for slaughter but from that time on increasing numbers were kept for breeding on the partly arable farms of the valleys and lowlands, where some roots were available for winter food.

The next problem was to find a mate for the half-bred ewe. At first the Border Leicester seemed the obvious choice, producing what came to be known as 'three-parts bred' lambs for which Gala water was specially famous. Some farmers indeed preferred a half-bred ram, but the breeding from cross-bred parents on both sides produced a rather uneven and probably less vigorous strain. Moreover, the blend of three-parts fat to one-part lean produced mutton that fell out of fashion and something else had to be thought of. One or other of the dark-faced Down breeds of the South of England seemed to be indicated. After a few trials the almost unanimous choice fell upon the Oxford Down; the following figures from the books of John Swan & Sons for their sales held at St. Boswells in 1893 and 1912 respectively clearly fix the date of the change:

	Number of Lots of Lambs	
	Three-parts bred	Oxford cross
1893	119	16
1912	5	197

In more recent years the Suffolk, which yields a leaner carcass than the Oxford, has increasingly competed with the latter until now breeders are almost equally divided in their preference for the one or the other.

With the decline, since the First World War, in the old system of sheep-folding on arable land, and with the laying down of old arable fields to grass, the Scottish breeds and the Scottish system of breeding have spread far to the south. Half-bred ewes, with lambs by Oxford or Suffolk, are a common sight from Yorkshire to Hampshire.

Bakewell was not the only great sheep breeder of his day. Another man, starting with different raw material and working under different conditions, produced another and a very different new breed. The man was John Ellman of Glynde, in Sussex, and his sheep was the Southdown. His foundation stock seems to have been unpromising, for the local sheep which roamed the Downs are described as small and ill-shaped, with a very short and light fleece of only moderate quality. Ellman's object was different from Bakewell's; he wanted a sheep that would thrive on the poor dry Downlands and that would yield, not a heavy carcass, but a choice quality of meat—fine-grained and flavoury with no super-abundance of fat. His methods seem also to have been different, for, so far as we know, he avoided close in-and-in breeding. His sheep soon acquired a reputation for the quality of their mutton, and Glynde became a place of pilgrimage for flockmasters from many parts of the world.

In 1790 Ellman persuaded Coke of Holkham to try the new breed in place of his old Norfolk Horned sheep. About the same time Francis, Duke of Bedford, gave the breed a trial at Woburn, and later his successor established a pure-bred flock. The Holkham and Woburn Sheep-shearings became great annual gatherings of farmers and landlords from all over the country and from overseas. At Holkham in 1818 there was open house for a whole week; the mornings were spent out of doors inspecting stock and crops and improvements, and at three o'clock in the afternoon the six hundred guests sat down to dine, finishing the day with toasts and speeches and discussions. In those early years of the century there was of course no Royal Show (the first was held at Oxford in 1839) and the annual Sheep-shearings, of which there were many of lesser note than Holkham and Woburn, were the main farmers' gatherings.

Among other early Southdown flocks was one started in 1814 by Hugh Watson of Keillor, famous in connection with Angus cattle. But the mantle of Ellman fell upon Jonas Webb of Babraham in Cambridgeshire. Jonas was born in 1796 and came of a race of yeomen who had farmed for many generations on the borders of Suffolk and Cambridgeshire. His grandfather came from Thurlow to Streetly, West Wickham, with his wife riding pillion behind him and accompanied by a cavalcade of his flocks and herds. His father Samuel, the Patriarch of Cambridgeshire, had already begun to improve the old Norfolk sheep, whose razor back Jonas had found, as a small boy, so uncomfortable a seat.

Jonas Webb started life as manager for Mr. Adeane of Babraham, and it was at Babraham that he came in contact with Ellman, who was still farming at Glynde and at the height of his fame. In 1822 he leased a thousand-acre farm at Babraham and immediately began to build up a flock, buying from the chief breeders in Sussex. He won a rapid success, and after Ellman's retirement in 1829 the Babraham sheep took the lead. Webb stuck to constitution and wool. 'If you have the wool you have the flesh,' he used to say, but anything approaching a 'muffly-faced' sheep aroused his ire. In spite of all the different strains which he blended he never kept a flock-book, and his 'nicks and notches and notes' in old pocket books were the despair of his sons, who eventually persuaded him to write down the pedigrees. At the early Royal Shows, from 1841 till 1856 he carried off most of the prizes in the ram classes, but declined on principle to show ewes, considering that the heavy feeding was harmful to their breeding powers. At Paris in 1856 his sheep were the admiration of all who saw them, from the Emperor downwards. Indeed one ram excited such admiration on the part of the Emperor that Webb felt obliged to offer the sheep as a present, and Napoleon accepted. Webb had already refused an offer of five hundred guineas for the ram, so that it was in fact a fairly princely gift. But generosity brought its reward, and French customers, with choice examples of Southdowns before them, came back to Babraham for more and more of the stock. When the flock came under the hammer in 1861, the year before Webb's death, a thousand people sat down to lunch and the 1,404 sheep realized a total of £16,646. It is not often that statues are erected to the memory of farmers. Indeed, so far as we know, the statue in Cambridge, to Jonas Webb, is the only one of its kind in this country. Its inscription is simply, 'From farmers and friends in many lands.'

The influence of the Southdown has been very wide. Not only is the breed itself well known in America and Australasia but its blood flows in all the other Down breeds, and has imparted to them something of the peculiar and highly esteemed quality of its mutton.

By contrast with the Southdown's history of brilliant success that of the old Cotswold breed seems destined to end in failure. The Cotswold country was famous for wool from very early times. In Domesday book 'sheeps' wool of Cirincester' is mentioned as a 'Queens Due'. You may still see, in the little Cotswold towns like Burford and Chipping Campden, the beautiful stone houses, built in the fifteenth and sixteenth centuries, where lived wealthy wool staplers and merchants like the Celys, the Tames, and the Grevilles. It is an old saying that the richly adorned churches, like Fairford, were 'built on wool'. 'The multitude of sheep yield such fine wool, and so white, that it is coveted not only in other parts of this nation, but in foreign countries; but the inhabitants are so wise that they make such improvements in their wool that the sheep may be said to bear Golden Fleeces. . . .'

But times changed and there were more mouths to feed. The sheep walks were enclosed and turned into cornfields. The old breed was crossed with Bakewell's Leicester in order to make it more apt for slaughter, and the new sheep were made fat upon the new turnips and clovers. The breed again acquired fame overseas, but this time in America and Australia. About 1850–60, when the trade in Cotswold sheep was at its height, as many as five thousand rams would be let at Gloucester Ram Fair alone. There were great flocks and eminent breeders—the Garnes and Slatters, the Larges and Lanes, Hewers, Handys and many more. These families strove hard (and successfully) for two generations to make their sheep big, and their fleeces heavy with long, strong, combing wool. The mutton indeed was on the coarse side, with 'too much for the grease pot and too little for the table', yet it was cheap to produce and seemed to find a ready enough sale. But the change in taste and the competition of cheap imported frozen mutton put an end to the Cotswold's popularity. Most of the flocks were crossed with Southdowns and Hampshires so that in time a new breed, the Oxford Down, emerged. Now (1949) there is but a single flock of Cotswolds remaining. This is still at

its old home at Aldsworth, where its masters have kept it for a
century.

Towards the end of the eighteenth century Mr. John Twynam
retired from his legal practice and settled down on the Manor
Farm at Whitchurch in Hampshire. He gradually added field to
field and, at his death in 1825, was farming ten thousand acres.
He was succeeded by his son, John Talmadge Twynam, then only
twenty-four years old. John could remember the times, during the
Napoleonic wars, when wheat was five or six pounds a quarter
and when, to quote himself, 'every available acre was devoted to
corn. Land already in tillage was forced beyond the limit of its
production. . . . A general enclosure of all sheep-walks considered
capable of bearing corn was effected. Little attention was paid to
sheep. Enough that it was a sheep with the capacity to live on
half a supply of food. It scrambled over the widely extended farm
and devoured the weeds which frequent corn crops had engen-
dered. . . . But soon after the close of the Great War, in 1815, a
new era seemed to arise. Gradually the prices of corn became less
remunerative . . . manufactures began to extend . . . the demand
for wool exceeded the supply.' A new system of green cropping
was necessary to restore the exhausted fertility of the land. With
more keep available and a demand for meat and wool, it was time
to turn serious attention to the flock.

At this time Twynam had a flock of Hampshire ewes. In the
spring of 1829 he happened to visit a friend at Hungerford and
walked over some neighbouring farms. On one of these he came
across a flock of Hampshires like his own, with lambs six weeks
old; but half the lambs were by Cotswold sires, the others being
pure bred. The sheep 'were all living together and well fed on cut
swedes, good hay and cracked peas, oil cake being yet unborn.
So striking was the difference in size and condition in favour of
the crossed lambs that I determined to try the Cotswold tup on a
portion of my own flock in the following autumn.' He did so,
was pleased with the result of his experiment, and repeated the
cross breeding on a greater scale. Such was the beginning of
another new breed, the Oxford Down. A group of farmers centred
round the ancient blanket town of Witney in Oxfordshire—Blake,

Gillett, Druce and others—bought cross-bred rams from Twynam. Others, like Charles Hobbs of Maiseyhampton, started, as Twynam himself had done, by crossing the two breeds, and continued by mating the cross-breds together. Naturally, heavy and long-continued culling was necessary to fix the new type, but there were many breeders working in close co-operation; Treadwells and Hobbs, the Stilgoes of Adderbury and Howard of Biddenham over in Bedford. As early as 1849, long before the new breed had been recognized by the Royal Agricultural Society, we find sheep of Howard's winning a first prize at Smithfield in competition with those of other breeds. It was Howard, too, who eventually persuaded the 'Royal' to provide classes for the breed at the Battersea Show of 1862. Howard was, of course, a leading implement manufacturer but his sheep acquired an international reputation, and his annual sales, continuing for forty years after 1865, drew buyers from ever-increasing distances.

Scotland had already been invaded by the Blackface and the Leicester. A few gentlemen since Ellman's time had kept small flocks of Southdowns, but the tenant farmer had never regarded these as rent payers. The next wave was composed of Oxford Downs. The first trial was with a single ram that Walter Elliot of Hollybush bought, in 1868, from Howard of Biddenham. Next year James Swan sold the first Oxford-Cross lambs at St. Boswells sales. In 1874 Elliott started a pedigree flock. At first the farmers shook their heads over 'these wooly-polled' sheep, while the shepherds despised them as 'house-fed brutes', and it was long before the Scottish breeders would admit that any new breed was required. Indeed at that time the half-bred and three-parts-bred lambs satisfied the butcher well enough. But gradually the butchers began to show a preference for the new Oxford cross, prices converted the doubters, and the change-over, when it once began, was, as we have already seen, very rapid. In 1884 Howard sent the first lot of Oxford Rams to the Great Ram Fair at Kelso. Others followed—old John Treadwell in particular, in a tall white hat, becoming a well-known figure. Numbers greatly increased in the 'nineties, and many pure-bred flocks were established in the North. Sometimes as many as a thousand Oxford Rams have been offered at this one sale alone.

The Oxford has recently had many competitors in the North—Southdowns, Hampshires, Dorset Downs, Kerry Hills, Ryelands and others. But the Suffolk is its only considerable rival.

Buildings of Chilmark stone and wooded Downs make the background for a picture of a flock of three hundred very perfectly matched Hampshire sheep, wide-chested with brown-black faces. They are folded in wattle hurdles, made from hazel grown on Cranbourne Chase. The old shepherd leaning on his crook has not missed their lambing in the fifty years of his pastorate. In the valley below lies a village, built of the same whitish-yellow stone that long ago built Salisbury Cathedral. The Shepherd and his pages are changing fold, the daily task of moving nearly ten score hurdles, of which a man may carry three with ease, four with an effort, or five for a wager. Every day except for a few weeks at lambing (which happens soon after the turning of the year) the flock goes up to the Down to crop the short sweet grass, returning again for a heartier evening meal of kale or vetch or turnips, along with sometimes a separate course of cake and corn. These Hampshires had for ancestors the old scraggy Wiltshire Horns and Berkshire Knots, the sheep that Twynam described as devouring the weeds on the foul stubbles of Napoleon's day.

Some rather haphazard improvement had already been attempted by the use of Southdown Rams, when Mr. Humfrey of Oak Ash and Chaddleworth, near Newbury, started to form a flock by buying the best of the Down sheep that he could find. But he had made but little progress towards the creation of the breed that he saw with his mind's eye—big sheep, with fleshy backs and legs o' mutton, and hardy enough to live in a bleak country of muddy turnip fields. It was in 1839 and the first show of the Royal Agricultural Society was to be held at Oxford . . . doubtless there would be fine sheep on view at Oxford, and perhaps some notions to be picked up. So Humfrey went to Oxford Show. He admired (but did not covet) the big and beautiful Cotswolds. How had this breed been brought to this pitch of perfection?

10. Cotswold rams, with their owner and shepherds. The sheep were the property of Robert Lane, Cottage Farm, North Leach, and were sold on 3rd August 1861, at prices ranging from 80 to 120 guineas each
From a painting by G. R. Whitford of North Leach, now in the possession of Wm. Garne, Esq., of Aldsworth

11. Jonas Webb and his Southdowns, 1841
From a print, in the collection of the late G. H. Parsons, of a painting in the possession of the Royal Agricultural Society

12. Cheviot sheep on their native hills
Photograph by Charles Reid, Wishaw

13. Blackface sheep in Glen Pean, Lochaber
Photograph by A. Brown, Lanark

Why, a cross of Bakewell's Leicester on the biggest and best of the ungainly old breed that had roamed the Cotswold hills for centuries. Humfrey did not want Leicester blood, but it struck him that the Southdown was just what he did want. It was too small indeed, but it had form and flesh and a close, short, fine fleece. So he wrote to Jonas Webb for a shearling ram, and got a son of Webb's great sire 'Babraham'. This sheep was mated to the biggest of the ewes, and left some very good progeny. Two other rams from Webb were less successful, but a fourth, which had won his class at the Liverpool 'Royal', turned out as well as the first. The progeny of these two rams founded the flock, and with it the Hampshire Down breed. Some large ewes had to be introduced later to maintain the desired size, but no new blood was introduced on the male side for twenty years, after which time Humfrey was able to exchange rams with Saunders of Water-combe near Dorchester, who had followed the same plan. But in the end the Saunders' flock became not Hampshires, but Dorset Downs, a distinct though very similar breed.

The Hampshire has suffered with the decline of the old arable system of the southern chalk country, of which system the hurdled flock was an essential part. One view is that the system is, in a sense, irreplaceable, for no other so far discovered will make the poorer chalk soils carry as heavy crops of corn. But, according to many farmers, it cannot go on with the present-day equation of one week's wage = two sacks corn. So there are all kinds of systems—long leys with white-faced Scotch sheep; Hosier outdoor dairying; mechanized corn with bare fallows and chemical fertilizers. Nobody knows what the final outcome may be.

Mr. Edward Lisle of Crux-Easton in Hampshire, who wrote his *Observations in Husbandry* before 1722, records that his tenant, Farmer Stephens, had some ewes that brought him lambs at Christmas and were found again heavy in lamb at the beginning of June. It has since occurred to many people that the habit of bearing lambs twice a year is one to be encouraged, and some effort has been directed to the selection of strains which do so behave. Nobody has yet completely succeeded in the object, but the old Dorset Horn breed represents the nearest approach to success. These have forgotten all their original views about the time to have babies. They will mate in May, to lamb in October, so that the lambs may be fat long before the mint has sprouted. Moreover the ewe will produce families at lesser intervals than a year, though not (like a well conducted sow) at regularly half-yearly periods. The Dorset Horn is an ancient breed and is, so far as is known, nothing but itself, no upstart Leicester or Southdown having been allowed to marry into the family.

The cousin of the Dorset is the Wiltshire Horn, another oddity because it is a sheep without wool. It is no longer to be seen on its native Downs, but has been preserved on the richer pastures of Buckingham and Northamptonshire and has founded a colony in North Wales. The Wilshire seems to have long had the further characteristic of making phenomenal growth. An historic lamb of the breed, its carcass weighing 96 lb., was sold in Smithfield market at Easter 1800. It seems to have been this achievement that induced a member of the Bodelwyddan family to buy some ewes and a ram of the breed to found the first of the North Wales flocks.

Devonshire, as we have seen, possesses two distinct indigenous breeds of cattle. It has also no less than five breeds of sheep. The two lowlanders, the Devon Longwool and the South Devon, were both strongly influenced by Dishley blood. The same process of improvement was applied to the Dartmoor, so that the modern representatives of this breed can hardly be regarded as moorland sheep. The Exmoor Horn, however, is a true native of the uplands, small, neat, hardy, and almost too active. Scotch sheep have penetrated even into Devon, there being Blackfaces on Dartmoor and an interesting old flock of Cheviots in the middle of Exmoor. The Exmoor Horn, however, is not losing ground. The Devon Closewool, produced by crossing the Exmoor with its lowland neighbour the Devon Longwool, is the latest addition to the list of our breeds of sheep.

Another interesting case of the reshaping of a breed is the story of the transformation of the Old Norfolk Horned into the modern Suffolk. It is another example of the influence of Ellman's Southdown. In 1784 the distinguished Mr. Arthur Young was experimenting with a Southdown Ram, lent him by his friend Lord Sheffield. This ram, as it happened, broke bounds and got into a small flock of Norfolk ewes, belonging to one of Young's tenants, and begat seven or eight lambs. When the time came for the farmer to show his lambs to the butcher the latter chose all the strangers before he put a hand on the pure Norfolks. The farmer was impressed, and applied to his landlord for another Southdown. Arthur Young himself then proceeded to experiment with the cross.

The old Norfolks, although, in Ellman's opinion, 'more remarkable for their activity than for anything else', had certain qualities. They were hardy, and their meat was fine-grained and well flavoured. The Suffolk has indeed inherited something of the activity of its local ancestor, combined, however, with the smoother shape and earlier-maturing qualities of the Southdown. By the middle of the nineteenth century pure Norfolks were rarely to be seen; most of the sheep were blends of varying proportions and, largely owing to the continued careful selection of Mr. George Dobito of Cropley Grove, the new type was being fixed as the Suffolk breed. Within the past forty years the Suffolk has spread widely. It is to be found as far west as Devon and as far north as Caithness, kept mainly for the purpose of producing cross-bred lambs from half-breed and other grassland flocks. Like the Oxford, the breed owes something to the support of a wealthy agricultural engineer, Garrett of Leiston: 'There's Howard of Biddenham with his ploughs and his Oxfords, and Garrett with his scarifiers and his Suffolks.' In later days the notable men have been the late Herbert Smith, Sam Sherwood and John Keeble.

The last but one of the pure Norfolk flocks met a curious fate. A few remnants of the breed had been preserved by Lord Coke at Holkham and by two or three others, well into the present century, but they dropped off one by one until only two small flocks remained. One was caught in a flood on one of its native marshes, and every sheep was drowned and its carcass swept out to sea. Only one little family, hardly to be called a flock, now (1950) remains.

No breed has had so chequered a career as the Lincoln. It had an ancient reputation for the length and strength of its lustrous wool and was an early rival of Bakewell's Leicester. It has been bred, by six or seven generations of great sheep experts, for size and frame, weight of meat and weight of fleece. It has been made the biggest sheep in the world; it is not unusual for shearling wedders, in show condition, to scale three hundredweight apiece, and mature rams often exceed 400 lb. in weight. Shearling rams frequently clip 28 lb. of wool and fleeces of 40 lb. are not unknown. The breed, from lowly beginnings, became world famous by the end of last century and in the *annus mirabilis* of 1906, 6,928 stud sheep were exported overseas. In that year the whole Nocton flock was sold for £30,000, and Henry Dudding's 'Royal' Show Champion was sold at auction for 1,450 guineas. Dudding's whole sale in that year created another record which has never since been approached, for his fifty-six rams brought an average of £151.

Dudding was only the greatest of the number of giants in sheep breeding who brought the Lincoln to what was generally regarded as a great pitch of perfection. He began farming in a large way in 1861, and, fifteen years later, moved to Riby Grove, which he made a famous name both for Lincoln sheep and for Shorthorn cattle. He and his contemporaries started breeding at a time when sheep breeding and wool growing, in the Dominions and in South America, were beginning to boom. The overseas men found in the Lincoln just the sheep to cross with the Merino—to increase its size, to make it more meaty, and to tone down the rather too 'gamey' flavour of its mutton. Moreover, although the Lincoln wool was relatively coarse, the want of quality was made up for in the weight, and 'cross-bred' wool had a large market. In 1897 began the series of sales at Riby Grove which became notable annual events. Prospective buyers were entertained at the Yarborough Hotel, in Grimsby, the evening before. John Thornton was there to see them early to bed, so that they might be quick in their bidding on the morn. All North Lincolnshire took a holiday, and sometimes as many as five hundred guests sat down to lunch, while another two or three hundred shepherds and herdsmen were more humbly (but quite as amply) regaled in the big barn, under the presidency of Dick Aves, the head shepherd.

There would be young Jonas Webb, the son of old Jonas, the Southdown breeder, and himself the owner of a fine herd of Shorthorns. There would be other Lincoln and Shorthorn breeders—the Wrights and the Deans, Hicking and Hobbs; and there would be exporters like Miller, Maclennan, Hughes and Casares with long purses and the will to dip deep into them. How dull, by comparison, is a modern sale, where you arrive in a car with a packet of sandwiches and a thermos, buy your lots and rush away!

But the breed and its breeders have since seen other days—days when a tenner would have bought almost the best sheep at Lincoln Ram Fair. It has taken five generations of hard study and careful breeding to make the Lincoln big and fat and to clothe him in his marvellous fleece. But during the present century consumers, whenever they have been in a position to be 'choosy', have decreed that mutton shall be small and lean. It is hard to say, as these lines are written, whether or when they will have any say in the matter. Nor, in these days of synthetics, can one predict the future demand for the long and strong lustre wools. One of its old uses in fact is to make the specially strong bags in which oil-seeds are placed before being subjected to hydraulic pressure. Nothing else can stand the strain as well as Lincoln wool.

The Lincoln's main rival in the overseas trade, and the one that has often had rather the better of the battle, is the Kent or Romney Marsh.

When, in the spring, the full flocks of sheep go down to the Marshes, the south-west corner of Kent, stretching from Dymchurch to the Sussex Border, presents an unforgettable sight. It seems inconceivable that any grassland should feed so many sheep. The deep green sward, close and smooth as a well-kept lawn, is crowded with sheep; all the ewes are Kents, for no other breed would live so thick on the ground. Great numbers of the lambs, however, have the Southdown for their father, for the pure-bred Kent mutton is a little 'ungenteel', and not quite pleasing to the palate of the modern Londoner.

Romney Marsh is curiously unlike other sheep-farming districts. The sheep that nature made is a hill dweller, it loves to lie high and dry at nights, and is able to pick up a living off sparse and arid grazings. Most of its troubles, like foot-rot, liver fluke and stomach worms, are associated with wet soil and with over-heavy stocking. The Kent sheep, then, is an exception to all the rules, and has been made so by its being obliged to crowd on to rich marsh grazing for many centuries. You can see that Romney Marsh has been long a sheep country, for the common inn signs are 'The Fleece', 'The Woolpack', 'The Ewe and Lamb', and 'The Shepherd and Crook'. Indeed the breed can be traced back, in the local records, to the fifteenth century.

The writer of the Agricultural Survey of Kent (1795) says that Kent sheep were 'sold in Smithfield Market every week and are remarkable for arriving at an extraordinary degree of maturity at an early age, and for producing a large fleece of very fine wool. These circumstances combined render this sheep perhaps the most valuable breed in the world.' The words were prophetic, for the little corner of one English county has played a great part in stocking the sheep pastures of the world. The breed early found a second home in the North Island of New Zealand, where the favourable conditions and the skill of the flockmasters have com-bined to make the Dominion a strong competitor with Kent, not only in Smithfield market but in the world market for pedigree sheep. In more recent years the twin sources have supplied a stream of valuable blood to Canada and the United States, to Argentina and Patagonia and even to the bleak and wet pastures of the Falklands.

The example of Bakewell seems to have stirred the breeders of Kent to improve their sheep, but they did not borrow Dishley blood nor, so far as is known, did they follow Bakewell far in his system of in-and-in breeding. Perhaps the greatest of the early improvers was Richard Goord of Milton near Sittingbourne, who devoted his long life to his flock of Improved Kents. The work has since gone on continuously. Even in the last forty years, according to the late Mr. Quested of Cheriton, himself a very noted breeder, the breed has been improved almost out of re-cognition. The modern sheep has a fleece that is not only heavy and valuable but provides, even to the new-born lamb, a safe protection against the keen east winds that so often blow over the open marsh country in the lambing season. If we take the combination that has been achieved, of weight and quality of wool with flesh and the ability to thrive under conditions unnatural to its wild ancestor, the Romney Marsh sheep must rank as one of the most remarkable creations of the stock breeder.

It has been remarked more than once in this chapter that the modern fashion in lamb and mutton is for smallness, for fine-grained lean meat and for the absence of the tallow that the farmer's wife of other days found so valuable for her winter supply of candles. Thus it has come about that the little Mountain sheep of Wales, for long thought hardly worthy of the serious efforts of improvers, have found themselves in steadily growing demand. The Welsh Mountain is the smallest of the British breeds —so small that an eminent Scottish judge of sheep, on starting his day's work at a Cardiff Show, pretended that he could not see the exhibits with his naked eye. Activity is an essential quality in a Mountain sheep, but it is something of a drawback to the lowland flockmaster, and a Welsh ewe is inclined to take the same view about fences as a good hunting horse.

There is perhaps no answer to the question which breed of sheep produces the finest quality of meat. Your Londoner will maintain that there is nothing like Southdown lamb. Your patriotic Scot will not admit that Cheviot or Blackface Mountain can be improved upon; in Manchester Welsh Mountain is in the highest repute. A connoisseur who had tried many varieties once said that the finest he had ever eaten was a saddle of mutton from a teg whose father was a Southdown ram and whose mother was a Welsh Mountain ewe; and the awards of the experts, in the Smithfield Carcass contests, show that his judgement did not err.

It is only in recent times that systematic efforts have been made to apply science to the improvement of the Welsh breed. It is a more than usually difficult task. To fine down the wool and to get rid of the scattered coarse kemp fibres is one object, but it is necessary, too, to have the sort of coat which will keep the new-born lamb warm and dry. To get more thickness of flesh is another aim, but the ewe must be able to live through the bleak and hungry winter and to produce milk in due time, on a diet of bent, heather and cotton-grass. It seems, at any rate, that the improvement of the grazings must go hand in hand with the efforts to improve the sheep, and Wales has been singularly fortunate in having great leaders in both these enterprises.

When Kerry Hill breeders meet after the great sales at Knighton, to dine and discuss prices and prospects, recollections of early days and glowing prophecies of the future of their speckle-faced rent-payer are rife. The descendants of the early breeders, the Hughs, the Davies, and the Pughs tell how, nearly eighty years ago, their grandfathers took hundreds of the tan-faced Radnor sheep from Beguildy to Cwmberlan and on these used two Shropshire rams (not the muffle-headed Shrops of the 'twenties, but the old bare-faced, lean-fleshed, hardy, close-wooled sheep) and so produced a new speckle-faced breed; and how they marked their lambs soon after birth, selecting only those which bore the hard rough over-coat (skith) of the Welsh lamb. They also declare that they can put their heads through a railway carriage almost anywhere in Great Britain and see a Kerry Hill sheep, and that the breed has gone out to Africa, Canada, and Australia. But their enthusiasm stops short of New Zealand, where their breed helps to produce the Canterbury lamb which supplants their home-grown produce.

From the grassy undulating hills round 'Clunton and Clunbury, Clungunford, and Clun' there emerged from obscurity another fine breed. Shropshire men were wont to say that Cluns are just 'Shrops gone wrong'. But in the past quarter century the Cluns have risen in popularity, have multiplied amazingly and have spread widely over the pastures of the Midlands and the South.

It was once said that if there had been a Jonas Webb in Herefordshire the Ryeland would have been a formidable rival to the Southdown. The small white-faced hornless breed which lived in the forests and heaths between the Severn and the mountains was already famous in Drayton's day. In his *Polyolbion* he sings the praises of its

> ... *Lemster ore*
> *That with the silkworm's web for smallness doth compare.*

The breed was the favourite of George the Third who 'wanted no better sort of foreign sheep than the true Hereford Ryland'. For a time his interest in the Spanish Merino led to a good deal of crossing with the Ryeland but, apart from some slight cross with the Leicester, the modern Ryeland is much the same as the ancient breed which Bankes said should earn a 'niche in the Temple of famine' for its capacity of living on such scanty fare. The Ryeland has had its ups and downs of fortune. The rage for Shropshires and other Down breeds threatened it even in its native county until, in 1903, there were only thirty flocks left. Determined efforts by a few faithful farmers, however, raised the Ryeland again into prominence. Flocks increased and the breed joined in the national competition for early fat lamb production.

Neither Professor Wilson of Edinburgh, who praised the Morfe Common sheep for their superior wool, nor the Archdeacon who liked those of the Longmynd as nimble and hardy, and those of Cannock Chase for their fine wool, could have foreseen that in less than a hundred years their joint descendants would become a cosmopolitan breed. However varied the colour of their faces—black, brown, grey, or spotted—it is agreed by all the chroniclers that 'the wool of the sheep in these neighbourhoods is the choicest and the dearest in England, capable of being improved to the thickest felt or drawn to the finest crape.' From the blending of these parent stocks, with a cross of Southdown brought in by Samuel Meire of Harley in 1810, the Shropshire was evolved. Adney was another pioneer, and accounts of his sales in the middle of last century speak of keen competition and high prices, of buyers from Ireland, France, and Australia, of the eight hundred gentlemen who partook of luncheon, well supplied with wine and other beverages. The modern Shropshire is a very different animal from those exhibited by Meire and Adney at Royal Shows from 1853 to 1856. The breeders of the following half century changed the speckled face to a nice soft black, straightened out the crooked spine, shortened the sickle-hocked legs, and covered the naked poll with wool. They changed the open wool into a dense fine staple, and created a demand for their breed in countries such as the United States and Australia for crossing with the Merino and half-bred ewes.

The man to whom, more than any other, the modern Shropshire owes its widespread fame was Alfred Mansell, breeder and auctioneer. His flock, though small, was often represented at the great displays at both Scottish and English shows. His extensive journeys in Europe and America afforded an opportunity of giving first-hand information of the adaptability of the breed to all soils and climates. The export of Shropshires, often running in the years before the war to 2,000 head per annum, was mainly due to the confidence which buyers reposed in his integrity. Mansell started the Shropshire Flock Book in 1882, the first pedigree record for sheep in the world. He also organized the great display of eight hundred and seventy-five exhibits which astonished visitors to the Royal Show at Shrewsbury in 1884. During the inter-War years the battle of the breeds went rather badly for the Shropshire. The showmen, according to their customers, went astray, breeding sheep that were too 'soft' and clothing the sheep with wool from nose to feet. In any case the Clun conquered a good deal of the Shropshire's old territory in the West Midlands, and in far America it lost ground to the Suffolk and the Hampshire. The customer is always right.

The halo of a romantic origin hangs round the hardy little Herdwick sheep, the sheep of Helvellyn, of Skiddaw, of the moors from Kirkby to Ulverston. One is reluctant to give up the belief in the legend of forty little sheep struggling ashore from a Spanish Armada wreck on the coast of Drigg, but from their general appearance and their kind of wool, the later tale of some Scottish sheep being taken off a wreck on the Cumberland coast in the early eighteenth century, and brought by the farmers to Wastdalehead, seems more probable. The little flock is said to have shown such natural sagacity in foreseeing the approach of storms, and in protecting themselves from their violence, and such persistent activity in scratching away the snow to get their food, that the owners, regarding them with almost superstitious awe, determined to keep them amongst themselves.

They formed an association and agreed never to sell a ram, and not more than five ewe lambs in one season, and named their sheep the Herdwick, the place or run of a herd, 'herdwycks and sheep cotes' as it stands in the old charters. But the zealous antiquarian has brought forward yet another theory of Norse origin, which, however, is opposed on the ground that the shepherds, like those in Strathclyde, use the Cymric numerals in scoring their sheep. These are the sheep of the Cumberland and Westmorland 'Statesmen' with greyish face, whitening with age, and smooth, creamy white horns.

Incredibly hardy, they graze on the poorest pastures, picking up a living on the tender shoots of young fern and heather in spring, and in winter, when all else fails, tackling the sharp spines of the juniper.

The communal customs of early days still dictate a good deal of their management. The flocks, often the property of the landlord, go with the farm, and viewers, or, as they were called in Scotland, arbitrars, are appointed to report on the value.

The right of common fell grazing necessitates special marks, which are registered in the Shepherd's Guide; but the sheep themselves, possessing a strong natural instinct for their own flock and their home fell, will often return long distances, with their lambs at foot, to the 'Heaf' on which they were yeaned.

Theirs is the country of John Peel, the hunting hero of Cumberland, where, as in the Cheviots, incessant war has to be waged on the fell foxes, 'as fierce as a tiger and long as a hair-band.'

Clipping days in July, as described by *The Druid* in 1865, were the Dalesman's festival, when neighbours gathered round to help, to argue over the best sheep; to extol Nelson of Gates-garth's famous tup, Thousand-a-Year, the monarch of the Lakes, whose: g.g.g.g.-dam won at Ennerdale in 1845, and whose g.g.g.-dam lived till she was eighteen years old and then died by an accident; to drink a glass of ale and toast: 'Confusion to the Scab!' and 'Pack Sheets and Ready Money'.

An old verse of T. L. Peacock goes:

SHEEP AND SHEPHERDING

The Mountain sheep were sweeter,
But the Lowland sheep were fatter,
And so we deemed it meeter
To carry off the latter.

Perhaps perfection is reached in the sheep which is mountain bred and valley fed. In any case, the rhyme recalls the days when, as children, we used to buy a dozen 'pally' (cull) lambs from our father's Blackface flock and turn them out on a not too lush pasture for perhaps a year and a half. At the expiry of that time the sheep were sold, as fat as butter, to the kitchen, and there never was such mutton.

The Heath breed of sheep, so-called by Low, has been described by Dyer as

. . . goat-horned sheep, of fleece
Hairy and coarse, of long and nimble shank,
Who rove o'er bog or heath and graze or browse
Alternate to collect, with due despatch,
O'er the bleak wild the thinly scattered meal.

Modified by local conditions the type exists to-day in many forms varying from one valley or one stretch of moorland to another. The Lonk flourishes round Clitheroe and Skipton on the coarse, tufty grass (lonk) that is the chief type of herbage. The Rough Fell, or Kendal Rough, is found on the Westmorland Fells from Borrowdale up to Shap and its territory is divided from that of the Swaledale breed by the saddle of Ravenstonedale. Farther south, in the Peak district, is the Dale-o'-Goyt, now known as the Derbyshire Gritstone, and round the town (the highest in England) from which it takes its name, dwells the Penistone.

All Mountain sheep have a very strongly developed homing instinct and this has been the theme of many shepherds' tales. The first prize must be awarded to that of a number of Penistone sheep which were taken, in the earliest years of last century, to Kent. Three of these disappeared from the farm of their new owner, and two of them eventually got back to their old home. In remembrance of their feat their horns were hung in Hope Church.

The best known and numerically the most important of the

English branches of the Blackface family is the Swaledale. Its main territory is in Yorkshire, some of the best flocks being reared on the high-lying farms round Muker, Keld, Askengarthdale, Bassingham, and Bowes; but the breed is extensively reared in Durham and parts of Cumberland. It is an exceptionally bold and hardy breed and will thrive upon what seems the barest subsistence.

8

THE HUMBLE PIG

'Pig, let me speak his praise: The strong man may batten on him and the weakling refuseth not his mild juices.'

CHARLES LAMB

The human race may be divided into pig-eaters and non-pig-eaters. The British people (excepting only the inhabitants of a few parts of the Scottish Highlands, where an old prejudice still lingers) belong to the former division. In England the pig has been called the cottager's friend; in Ireland he is the gintleman that pays the rint.

As an old farmer once said: 'Ther's a lot o' confused feeding about a pig.' He supplies many of the needs of man. The boar's head that is decked with bays and rosemary for the Christmas feast at Queen's College has been called 'the rarest dish in all the land.' Lamb has waxed lyrical about the delights of consuming the 'young and tender suckling, under a moon old.' Lard and jellied pies; fat chaps eaten with a raw onion by the ploughman under the hedge at noon; the huntsman's trotters; home-cured hams pickled in strong beer and spices; an infinite variety of sausage—these are but a few of the gifts to civilization of the humble beast. Moreover, his skin makes saddles and leggings, purses and sometimes fashionable gloves. As a sporting animal it is true that he has suffered from neglect: yet it has been maintained that 'a bit of good pig racing is worth all your horse racing business. It's twice the fun, surely, and nobut one-hundredth part of the expense. It takes up the yale afternoon, and t'Leger don't take four minutes.'

Ever since the days when Gurth's swine fed on the beech mast and acorns in the Yorkshire forests (and long before) the pig has been a 'picker-up of unconsidered trifles', and under the greatest

206

effort in rural planning, by the Tennessee Valley Authority, he is finding place in the scheme of things, feeding upon the mulberries, plums, and cherries that fall from the trees that have been planted to stop the erosion that was wasting the land.

The ancient Chinese were, as is well known, the earliest connoisseurs of pig, and the first to study the animal's characteristics and improve its usefulness. It seems, indeed, that the old Chinese pig would have graded somewhere near the latter end of the alphabet if it had been sold under the Pigs Marketing Scheme; but then the ancient Chinese shared the taste of Mrs. Spratt, while the British consumer in normal times has been a follower of her spouse. But the Chinese pig, reaching England by various routes in the eighteenth century, was an important influence in imparting early maturity, delicacy of flesh and docility to the coarse and scraggy native breeds.

There are now a round dozen of different breeds in Great Britain each claiming ancient origin and, of course, supreme merit; but the fact is that until about the middle of the nineteenth century the animal had had very little attention from breeders, and it was not until 1884 that there was a pig breeders' society, or a printed register of pedigrees. Serious efforts at improvement thus began nearly a century after careful systematic methods had been applied to other classes of farm stock.

The earliest improvers were not farmers, but a group of weavers in Yorkshire, who took to pig-keeping as a useful hobby, and applied to it all the enthusiasm of the fancier. It was Joseph Tuley, a weaver of Keighley, who exhibited a pig of the improved type at the Royal Show at Windsor in 1851 and attracted general attention to the improved Yorkshire breed. Joseph Tuley and his wife stinted themselves, out of their eighteen shillings a week, that the pig might live in luxury. It was watched and scratched for half an hour each dinner-time, if wet, and walked out if fine; it was 'washed after t'maister with Saturday night's soapsuds, and shaved by t'mistress when the judges preferred them without hair.' Keighley Show, in 'The Druid's' time, was a glorious event, when thousands of onlookers thronged the stands to watch the pig classes, and Yorkshire pigs and York Ham have been famous ever since. It was Tuley who first brought the Yorkshire Pig to fame, and provided the chief means to supply the modern breakfast-table with the one half of its traditional standard dish. John Fisher, who was Manager for Wainman of Carhead, a famous early breeder, named his cottage after one of Tuley's sows—because her litter had paid for the building of it.

The greatest breeder of more recent times, the Bakewell of pigs, was Sanders Spencer, of Holywell, in Huntingdonshire. He produced a strain of the Large White Yorkshire that possessed both remarkable merit and exceptional prepotency. It is hardly too much to say that he laid the foundation of the whole Danish Bacon industry, for the leaders of Danish agriculture came to him again and again for consignments of twenty or more pigs at a time. As has happened more than once, a British creation was turned to the fullest account not by the British farmer but by his overseas competitors. He was, moreover, mainly responsible for the creation of the Middle White which for long was one of the main sources of the plump little porkers which London once demanded, and may again want.

One of the difficulties in livestock breeding is that of keeping pace with the fickle taste of the consumer. If the housewife makes up her mind that King Edward and Majestic are the best sorts of potato, stocks can be quickly multiplied, while those of the kinds that are disliked can be given to the farmer's swine. But if people suddenly decide that Cox is the only late dessert apple that is really worth eating, it must either take time, or prove fairly expensive, for the apple grower to carry out his orders. It is rather the same with pigs. Between the wars city consumers, and especially the degenerate breed that inhabits London, decided that pigs, whether for pork or bacon, must be very lean, and the pig-breeder dutifully set about the task of breeding his pigs longer, leaner and lanker, and saw to it that they received only suitably slimming diets. Meantime, the robust and hearty folk in the rural north continued their old preference for fat rashers and chops; others took views intermediate between these extremes.

During the war, when supplies of butter and other fats were short, all consumers changed, by many degrees, their specifications

of the optimum fat:lean ratio. What will happen in the future?
Will the old trend of taste be resumed, and if so how fast will it
go? Will the old local differences in demand be re-established, or
shall we have standardized consumers requiring standardized pig?
And if so—most difficult of all—which particular breeds shall be
condemned to extinction?

Whether, as a Scot, he had a predilection for red hair, or a
liking for a creature with something of the wild still left in its
make-up, a noble friend always declared that the only thing that
sustained him during unwillingly made processions round the
pens of super-fatted pigs at the Royal Show, was the sight of the
Tamworth. Perhaps it reminded him of pig-sticking in India, a
sport to which he had been, in his younger days, addicted. The
Tamworth escaped the Chinese cross and the consequent excess
of fat which the later breeders have had to remove from other
breeds. Long ago Mr. Harris, who saw very clearly the trend of
demand in the direction of leaner bacon, recommended the general
use of the Tamworth for bacon production. The Canadians indeed
took up the breed, in a measure, for this purpose, as the Danes
had adopted the Large Yorkshire. But the British farmer was not
to take up bacon production in earnest, upon a large scale, for
another generation.

In the old days when the White Horse of Uffington was still
'scoured' every year with feasting, with 'backswyrd' play and
rolling cheese down the 'Manger', the native Berkshire pig also
played his part in the fun. With 'greasy ears and tail', he was
chased 'by men and bwoys drough White Horse Vale.' The old
Berkshire pig was sandy white or reddish with black spots, but
apparently the feeling was that half the fun of stock-breeding
would be lost if things were left as they had been. It is much more
interesting to change the colour of your animal—to take spots off
or to put them on. So the early Berkshire breeders decided that
their pig must have white markings on the feet and face and tail,
but nowhere else. But 'fancy' apart, the breed made rapid progress,
and came to be regarded, along with the Middle White, as the
chief source of the best and most succulent joints of young pork
—just as the Large Yorkshire was the source of the best lean

rashers of bacon. The rapid progress of the breed was largely due to the friendly rivalry and co-operation of a group of near neighbours around Wantage on the Berkshire Downs—Throckmorton, Humfrey, Swanwick, and Hewer are the familiar names of the middle of last century. The name of Henry Humfrey in particular should be remembered, for it was chiefly through his initiative that the Breed Society was formed in 1884, and almost entirely by his industry that the first twenty volumes of the *Herd Book*, containing ten thousand pedigrees, were compiled.

Most English pigs still bear the names of the counties of their origin, and although the old Glamorgan is now merged with the Welsh, the Old Spot still preserves its Gloucestershire title. Here it lived for long years in peaceful obscurity, grazing the pastures of the Gloucester Vale country and drinking heavily of the whey from the many cheese vats. After the first world war the breed achieved a sudden popularity and prices up to six hundred guineas were paid at auction sales; but those were foolish times. It was in 1920 that Colonel Brassey exhibited the remarkable 'Winterbourne Blanco', which scaled over 12 cwt., probably the heaviest pig that has ever been seen.

The Saddle Back pigs—black with a white shoulder belt—of Essex and of Wessex are others which, like the Tamworth, escaped the Chinese influence and have therefore preserved comparatively slim figures.

There are still more breeds—the Large Black with its lop ears that grazing farmers like for its docility—due perhaps largely to the fact that the ears obscure the vision and the pigs thus live perpetually in blinkers; but the Large Black sow has other merits, notably that of being a careful and otherwise a model parent. The White Lop Ear of the West Country is of the same type, apart from its colour.

Although the English are much addicted to the eating of bacon it was only in the present century that the British farmer realized the commercial possibilities of the pig. An unkind wit has put it that the average British farmer was too pig-headed to become pig-minded. The farmyard pig of the past was too often like the old barnyard fowl—an unconsidered mongrel. Men who devoted

THE HUMBLE PIG

themselves seriously to pig-breeding were regarded as being not only a little odd, but a little vulgar. All this is now changed. Cabinet Ministers and ex-Cabinet Ministers delight, in their leisure moments, to contemplate pigs; scientists argue about pig feeding; architects devote laborious days to the design of pig houses. In fact, the British pig had risen before the Second World War to a position of considerable eminence in Agricultural Society and, after returning to comparative obscurity for 'the duration' is now by way of recovering its prestige.

9

THE HORSE ON THE LAND

'Some men have a breed of great horses meete for warre and to serve in the field. Others have ambling horses of meane stature for to journey and travel by the waie. Some again have a race of swift runners to run for wagers and to gallop the bucke; but plane countrymen have a breed only for drafts or burden.'

SIR THOMAS BLUNEVILLE

The great horse of England has a long history, but the earlier part of it is concerned with war and chivalry rather than with the dung-cart and the plough. It is well known to all good Shire breeders that Queen Boadicea owed her victory over the Romans to the ancestors of the Shire, and that '1066 and all that' came to pass because the Conqueror's shock troops were well mounted upon chargers which also come into the family tree of the breed. We can trace the development of the Great Horse throughout its history from various contemporary portraits—in the picture of Sir Walter Hungerford, in complete mail, on the Great Seal of England; on the Common Seal, with Charles I riding at full gallop; in Vandyke's picture of the Duke of Aremberg with his English mounted contingent going off to the Palatine Wars; in the pictures of Morland, Stubbs, Zutter, and many more.

It has been reckoned that a sizable mediæval knight, clad in plate armour and carrying his normal accoutrements, had difficulty in making a riding weight of less than twenty-eight stone; so that the army requirements of those days were for horses of a definitely weight-carrying type. But Cromwell's Ironsides, with their buff coats instead of armour, put an end to the use of the Great Horse in battle, and he entered upon a career of peace.

The horse had indeed still another battle to fight, this time for full possession of the farm stable; for oxen, up till nearly the end

212

of the eighteenth century, were preferred for the plough. Indeed, the eminent Mr. Arthur Young, writing in the 1780's, was a stout supporter of the ox against the horse. The ox might indeed be slower, but he could live on straw and hay, and leave corn to feed hungry people. Moreover, a horse was a continually depreciating asset, whereas plough oxen, at an age of say seven or eight, made excellent beef and were worth substantially more than when, as youngsters of three or four, they had first bent their necks to the yoke. But the horse displaced the ox for much the same reasons that the tractor is now in turn displacing the horse—because he was a speedier worker, and enabled his driver to accomplish a bigger day's task.

For a century and a half the Fenlands of Eastern England were the nursery of the Shire breed, and the task of the early improvers was to blend the great weight of the native Lincolnshire strains with the activity and mettle of those of the Midland counties. The docks of London and Liverpool and the rising industrial towns of the North were demanding horses that could move great loads, and this demand largely decided the type of the Shire.

In 1878, following a paper read by Frederick Street at the London Farmers' Club, the English Cart-Horse Society was formed, and the task of collecting and registering pedigrees was begun. Supported by men like the Hon. Edward Coke, Sir Walter Gilbey, James Howard of Bedford and Clare Sewell Read, and with his name changed to the Shire, the Great Horse set out upon yet another stage of his history.

As the Shorthorn is the national breed of cattle of England, so the Shire may be said to be the national heavy horse. In both cases the efforts of farmer breeders have been supported by those of wealthy landowners vying with each other in the honourable task of improvement. Ever since the days of King John the sovereigns of England have fostered the breed, and their late Majesties King Edward VII and King George V were the successive owners of a famous stud at Sandringham. Shires of fame have been bred by Dukes of Devonshire, Westminster, Bedford, and Sutherland. Lord Middleton, in addition to the thoroughbred stallions which he made available to his Yorkshire tenants for hunter breeding, travelled Shire stallions from his extensive stud at Birdsall for the use of his tenants. Perhaps the most famous was Birdsall Menestrel, which later became one of the best sires in Lord Rothschild's Tring stud. Even in the far north of England the Duke of Northumberland bred Shires on his Alnwick Castle Estate and at Underley too Lord Henry Bentinck travelled Shire stallions for crossing with the light-legged Clydesdale mares of the tenants. Pages of history might be written round the Dunsmore, Buscot, Marden, and Tring studs kept by Sir Philip Muntz, Lord Faringdon, Sir Walpole Greenwell and Lord Rothschild, aided by their great horse-masters Jackson, Michael Higgins, and Thomas Fowler. The Carlton stud was made famous by the Forshaws, father and son. The veteran Fenland farmers, Edward Griffin and Alfred Clarke, worked to combine the weight, action, and quality for which the strain of their district became noteworthy. Shire Horse breeding spread to all parts of England except the extreme north, where the Clydesdale had established itself, and the Eastern Counties where the Suffolk has remained firmly entrenched. Notable work was done in the Welshpool district by keen breeders like Edward Green and John Lewis, in the Fylde of Lancashire, and in the Soke of Peterborough, where many good Shires were bred by the Horrell family. Nearby is Bury, noted as the home of John Rowell of 'Bury Victor Chief' fame. This London Champion was one of the most famous Shires of his time. Some will still recall the big black, bald-faced horse with white legs and under markings, a horse of tremendous wealth and weight, and yet so full of bounce and activity—a real 'waggon shaker'. John Rowell served on the Council of the 'Royal' and was for many years a familiar figure in the Large Horse Ring at the Shows, where, mounted on his weight-carrying cob, he would marshal the 'Heavies' for the Grand Parade. But the greatest success achieved by plain tenant farmers was in the Ashbourne district of Derbyshire, where the sound limestone land seems to give the fullest expression to the inborn qualities that go to the making of a good Shire. It was here at Ashbourne that the great Harold, the most famous of sires, saw the light.

Even the shortest history of Shires would be incomplete without mention of Lord Wantage's celebrated Lockinge Stud in Berkshire, which flourished for long in the ownership of the late Mr. A. T. Lloyd and under the skilled management of Mr. E. Lousley. The farms in hand extended over 10,000 acres, and in the old days one hundred working Shire mares and geldings went out daily to cultivate the good chalk loams at the foot of the Berkshire Downs. Fifteen hundred guineas was a big sum in the early 'eighties. The two-year-old son of William the Conqueror was a bargain at this price, for Prince William did service at Lockinge for over twenty years. Another leading sire of his day was Lockinge Forest King. So impressive was he that it was not rare to see five or six of his daughters heading a single class at the Shire Horse Show.

The record Shire sale was held in 1913 when the late Lord Rothschild's Tring Stud was dispersed. The highest price paid was 4,100 guineas for the dark brown two-year-old stallion Champion's Goalkeeper. A lucky purchase for Sir Walpole Greenwell!

The cause of horse breeding owes much to Sir Walter Gilbey of Elsenham. From his father, a coaching proprietor at Bishop's Stortford, who often drove his own coach-and-four to London, he inherited his passion for horses. When, later, he had achieved wealth he turned all his energies to his boyhood's ambition, to breed good horses of many kinds. The Shire, the Hackney, the hunter, and numerous breeds of pony all benefited by his enthusiasm and knowledge, for he not only bred horses, but studied and wrote their histories.

To see Shires in the perfection of show condition one had to go to the spring show of the Shire Horse Society in London. Forty years ago the Agricultural Hall at Islington would be more densely packed with interested breeders and exhibitors than it would be at the London Dairy Show or even at Smithfield Fat Stock Show. Their late Majesties King Edward VII and King George V, then Prince of Wales, seldom missed attending to give away the champion cups. The stands were packed and the rails of the large judging ring crowded ten deep with enthusiastic breeders, many of them tenant farmers. Generally a large proportion of the class winners were bred by small farmers, owning one or two good brood mares which worked in the teams when not suckling their foals. Stud managers searched the country for foals sired by their own stallions and many a three-figure cheque went into the pockets of the small breeder for a foal likely to make a future winner or a successful breeding animal. The Shire Horse Society showed their appreciation of the breeders' skill by awarding subtantial cash prizes (in addition to the exhibitors' prizes) to the breeders of every prize winner. After the day's judging, if you wished to hear marvellous tales of Shire history and horse lore, you had only to wander into the smoke-room at 'The Great Northern' and listen to old Mr. 'Jimmy' Forshaw, entertaining an appreciative company with his Shire memories. Shires may still be seen, in working clothes, by the dockyards and in the streets of great industrial cities, or having a holiday at the Cart-Horse Parade in Hyde Park on Whit-Monday—'Great gallant lion-hearted workers and yet as friendly as kittens. They'll pull till they break their hearts.' But in none of these places, nor even on the clay fields which are their true home, will you see Shires in their wonted numbers. It will be a sad day when the tractor and the motor lorry succeed in doing the Shire out of his job. One can only hope that Gilbey's words will yet again prove true— 'Real worth in horse-flesh is never put out of demand by the changes of man's habits; when it ceases to be of service in one respect it is sure to come into use for another.'

King Robert the Bruce not only struck a blow for Scottish freedom at Bannockburn, but also helped the cause of heavy-horse breeding in Scotland. Large numbers of the great English horses, floundering helplessly in the morasses under their heavily mailed riders, were captured by the Scots, and we cannot doubt that their new owners turned them to good account.

The little mounts of the ancient Caledonians, who harried the army of Agricola on his march to the North, must have been not unlike the hardy ponies that still survive on the Outer Isles. But the almost continuous warfare with England demanded a horse of greater size and strength. Consequently, we find successive

Scottish kings, from William the Lion onwards, importing breeding horses from Hungary, Poland, and England, stopping exports, and enacting under severe penalties that 'to raise the size everyone must plenish their studs with mares and great stallions.' Only the gallant and unfortunate James IV thought more of speed than of weight, and sent two Royal stud grooms to Spain and France to bring back 'the best Jennets and African Barbs'.

The typical horse for pack saddle and riding still remained a smaller animal, bred of the cob brought over by the invading Norsemen, crossed with the indigenous pony. Of this sort was the nag of which Doll said to Pistol: 'Know ye not Galloway nags?'

After the Reformation the old uncontrolled system of breeding, still practised to-day on Exmoor and in the New Forest, began to give place to improvement by selection. By the early eighteenth century the heavy horses of Upper Clydesdale, already marked by characteristic features such as a broad head, a full, vigorous eye, and a large ear, and distinguished by great activity and hardiness of constitution, were much sought after at English fairs. The Lothian farmers, with increasingly intensive cultivation and the need for a horse 'Tae gang wi' the coals i' the mornin'' over tracks hardly to be dignified by the name of roads, were demanding still greater size and weight.

The stallion which John Patterson of Lochyoch brought from England about 1715 was but one of many. In 1721 the enterprising Johnstones, Lairds of Alva, advertised 'four well-sized English Mares with foals at foot, one black stallion as well as other colts and fillies.' The Duke of Buccleuch had 'a remarkable strong black horse' from Dishley, and Bakewell himself sent up Black stallions for sale at Edinburgh and Linlithgow. Whether these were a mixture of the English Great Horse and Bakewell's imported Flemish mares we do not know but, although Linlithgow and Stirling men took to the English Blacks, which certainly increased size and strength of bone, the breeders in Clydesdale itself never really liked them. They declared they were too soft and sluggish, needed more food than the native breed, and competed with themselves for their staple food, the oat.

In the later eighteenth century a great impetus was given to Clydesdale breeding by the Stallion Shows of the old Edinburgh Society, the forerunner of the 'Highland' and, soon after the National Society was founded, it began to hold the ploughing matches which stimulated cart-horse breeding and led to the disappearance of plough oxen.

About the middle of last century a young man was learning the art of stock breeding with his father, an acknowledged master of all kinds of stock, though more particularly of Ayrshire cattle. Like most Lanarkshire farmers, however, he kept a few Clydesdales in the ordinary farming way on his farm at Carmyle Mill. Young Lawrence Drew had his chance when the Duke of Hamilton commissioned him to buy a horse and some mares to win at Battersea International Show in 1862. He selected the stallion Sir Walter Scott and the prize-winning mare Maggie, which, after winning in London, was henceforth known as London Maggie. He continued to manage for the Duke until the latter's death, and in 1866 took over the farm of Merryton. Here he started to build up the stud that made him the acknowledged pioneer of modern draught horse breeding in Scotland and hither, by the 'sixties and the 'seventies, his annual sales were drawing breeders from many parts of the world. One market day in 'His Lordship's Larder' in Glasgow a bargain was nearly struck between an Australian and a Scotsman for a four-year-old horse. As nearly happened with Cruickshank's Shorthorns, the great Clydesdale stallion, Prince of Wales, was almost lost to his native country, when Drew's brother, newly home from Australia with money to burn, joined the bidding at £1,500, and the famous horse was saved for Merryton stud.

From 1870 until his death in 1884 Drew pursued the definite policy of mating carefully selected English Shire mares with 'The Prince', a practice which aroused the fiercest controversy in the ranks of Clydesdale breeders of the time, and hastened the formation of the Stud Book for pure-bred stock. But the Merryton stables, with 'The Prince' and his descendants, continued to draw admiring visitors; on one occasion King Edward, then Prince of Wales, brought over a large company which included the Prince

Imperial. Drew, believing in the feminine touch for washing and preparing refractory youngsters for show, had his imposing array of colts and fillies paraded by 'lassie grooms', who had their charges completely under control.

When his owner died in 1884, the great horse, now eighteen years old, was bought for £900 by Riddell of Blackhall, who had owned him as a colt. He lived for four years more. Through his descendants in nearly every Scottish parish and in every corner of the Colonies the influence of Prince of Wales continued to spread, so that he left his mark on all pure Clydesdale stock.

Andrew Riddell, who bought Prince of Wales at the Merryton sale, also owned 'The Prince's' great rival as a breeding sire. This was Darnley, bred at the Keir stud of Sir John Stirling Maxwell and bought as a three-year-old by Riddell in 1875. Though he won all that there was to win in the showyard, Darnley was a less 'flashy' horse than Prince of Wales, and it was as a breeding sire that he won his greatest renown. His progeny were more uniformly good than those of 'The Prince', and the good qualities were passed on to subsequent generations. Perhaps the Darnley blood was responsible for some loss of size in the breed, but his progeny were of the short-legged type, and had good weight for their inches. The subsequent loss of weight and substance, which MacNeilage, Secretary of the Society, tried in vain to prevent, was due to one of those unfortunate fashions that take possession of the showyard, and not to any inherent fault in the foundation strain.

If Drew and Riddell did the great pioneer work it was the Montgomery brothers, Andrew and William, who had the largest hand in fixing the modern type of Clydesdale and in raising the breed to a position of prominence in the world at large. In the years about 1900 their overseas shipments, often by trainloads, were of immense importance to the horse breeding industry of Canada, the United States, Australia, and New Zealand. Meanwhile, and indeed long before, breeders of Clydesdales arose in other districts, for instance in the Lothians, and especially in Aberdeenshire and the north-east. But in the old home of the breed, on farms round Tinto Hill in Lanarkshire, a group of men held on to the old-fashioned stamp of horse which had earned a great reputation before even the days of the English importations.

Along with the Somervilles of Lampit, the Muirs of Bowhouse, the Weirs belonged by descent as well as by inclination to this group. James Weir of Sandilands still possessed descendants of the famous horse Blaze which bore neither English nor Flemish blood and which had belonged to his grandfather Scott of Broomhill.

What James Greenshields did for Blackfaced sheep, by his balanced decisions in the show ring, James Weir did for Clydesdales. He was one of the progressive farmers of his time, but it was as a consummate judge of his favourite breed, especially of young stock, that he became so widely known at home and abroad. There was nothing that gave him more pleasure than to be faced with a large and difficult class of yearlings, and none who watched him at his task could doubt that here was a master eye that could read the future of each raw colt. 'Hoo dis he ken?' sighed a novice at one such display. Like all great farmers he was reared in a severely practical school. An expert ploughman and swinger of the scythe, he could always say to his men: 'Come along, this is how to do it.' Even in his latter years he might often be found away in the harvest field cutting the laid corn, and he loved to talk of his young days when 'with a good working pair of Clydesdales before me in the plough, I would not have called the King my cousin.' The recollection of listening to James Weir with his father and Muir, another veteran, discussing Clydesdale history, makes one regret an opportunity lost, for many of his memories and much of his wisdom are lost for all time. Like his friend, Andrew Montgomery, Weir was a close friend of Lawrence Drew; yet he was from the beginning a firm supporter of the Stud Book movement, and did perhaps more than any other to win members to the Society and to guide it through its difficult early days.

In 1773, in a local newspaper of the High Suffolk district, there appeared an advertisement of a 'light chestnut horse, full 15½ hands, five years old, to set good stock for coach or road, which said horse is the property of Thomas Crisp of Ufford.' This was the famous 'Crisp's Horse', to which nearly every Suffolk Punch goes back in direct male line.

When this horse was foaled, George II had been dead only eight years. The eastern part of Suffolk was little more than a sea of heath, with sheep tracks where now are good flint roads. For common folks the means of transport from Saxmundham to London was by a hooded wagon with six horses. Swedes and mangolds were then unknown as agricultural produce, and the old Norfolk Horn sheep was the only kind in the district, while no beast was made fat for the butcher under four or five years old. But the Suffolk man already had his Suffolk horse, and throughout the years since the time of Crisp's horse he has been true to the native stock which his forefathers left him, and upon which he has progressively stamped one improvement after another.

The evidence of the fourteenth century illuminated manuscripts shows that there were horses of the Punch type before the Ufford horse, and by Arthur Young's time the 'Sorrel horse of Suffolk' had already improved and become an established breed. The descendants of the Ufford horse, in the first record numbering between seven and eight hundred, were all great drawers of the sandbag, a test of merit peculiarly applied to the county breed. The drawing matches were popular gatherings, where silver cups were offered to be drawn for 'by a team of horses, mares, or geldings, without collars, the seals on their naked shoulders' which had to make '20 of the best and fairest pulls and carry the weight over the block with the fewest tifters.'

In the early nineteenth century there were three great men—Catlin, Crisp, and Barthropp. No names appeared so often in prize-lists as Catlin and Crisp, who spread the fame of the Butley Abbey stock far and wide, and Barthropp, who did so much to keep up the character of the breed.

The breeder of the 'Horse of Ufford' was the grandfather of Thomas Crisp of Butley, whose father's stock of horses at Rendlesham, going back as far as the end of the eighteenth century, had great repute in the neighbourhood. Only nineteen years old when his father died, Crisp took over the farm of 800 acres at

Gedgrave Hall, and soon showed his marked ability both as a breeder and in the management of a large concern. After a time he moved to Butley Abbey, with which his name is forever associated. At the time of his death (from an accident in the hunting field) he was farming altogether over 4,000 acres.

In those days Crisp's remarkable farming feats—in cultivations, as a breeder, prizewinner, and exporter—supplied a constant topic of market talk: even now, whenever great winners and sales are discussed, someone is sure to say, 'Ah, but what about the Butley Abbey days.' Crisp was one of those universal breeders. He beat Jonas Webb with Southdowns at the first Royal Show at Oxford; he kept Shorthorns, although he never went in for fancies, and really preferred the native Suffolk cattle. But it was with his Punches and with the improved Butley type of Black Suffolk Pig, the Small White and the Berkshire, that he gained his greatest renown. From 1837, for just over thirty years, there was probably no single individual who won so many prizes in the same space of time. The stories of his winnings at Hamburg, Stettin, and Paris, and of his trainloads of stock for shipment abroad, have become almost legendary. 'One day every horse-box within call would be telegraphed for to Wickham, for a consignment of Suffolk horses to one of the Colonies. The next week a whole menagerie of animals would be sent off to Prussia; and then the pleasant rumour would go forth to the county breeders that Mr. Crisp was buying up all the decent two-year-old colts because some German Baron wanted six of a certain hue.'

In 1864, when his great horse Cupbearer, whose sire went to Hamburg and was sold to the Prussians for cavalry horse breeding, was only two years old, Crisp said: 'Whoever lives to see him, that will make the best horse I ever had.' At Crisp's death Cupbearer was bought by Garrett of Leiston, another distinguished name in English agriculture, both as an implement maker and breeder of stock.

The Punch has been fortunate in its historian, Hermann Biddell of Playford, himself a successful breeder, who, as he writes: 'In no blind ignorance of the magnitude of the undertaking' devoted his entire time, for two and a half years, to the compilation for the Suffolk Stud Book Association of the history and the first register of breed.

In these modern days, when every breed has its special society and its running system of pedigree recording, it is difficult to realize the amount of work that was entailed in hunting up the records of foundation stock. Biddell's pages are full of the trials of a collector. His journeyings to catch some octogenarian before he died and his tragic disappointments from loss of old memories, remind one of the story of Cecil Sharp in his search for folk songs.

Apart from a few odd advertisements and old horse cards, Biddell had to depend entirely on memories. At the start, parties of the oldest and the best informed breeders agreed to meet at intervals to recall facts and pedigrees. 'Torrents of facts were poured forth.' But much of the information came from men like John Moyse, who, born in 1789, was first apprenticed to a barber, then took to colt-breaking, became a dealer in horses, failed, set up his pole once more and finally ended his days in Sir Richard Hitcham's Almshouse. Knowing almost every horse in East Suffolk, he was almost a walking stud book.

Another source was 'Old Battle', who had been at Mr. Coke's sheep-shearings and had travelled a horse in Yorkshire, but Biddell only discovered him when, at the age of eighty-five, he had moved to his son's house. His evening's amusement of spreading out a thousand horse-cards on the table 'to read over of a night' having been discouraged, he had burned them all. But Biddell found Charles Row and Robert H. Richardson, both Butley men in the Catlin days; the brothers Lewis—John, who had such skill in handling a horse before the judges, and James, who was at Butley in Crisp's day at its prime, and followed Cupbearer to his new home at Leiston; and Bennett, who walked Mr. Freemason's Briton to Oxford in 1839 and won with him at the first Royal Show.

The distinguishing mark of the Suffolk is its chestnut colour, lively and never dull, a star on the forehead with often a thin blaze down the face, arched crest, fine silky mane and the short neck which is said to mean a strong constitution. It was, and still is, a farmer's horse, and since 'a horse must have good bottoms' modern breeders have devoted special attention to the feet. But to meet the custom of the country, which means turning out at 6.30 in the morning and getting back to the stable at 3.30 p.m. without baiting between, the most important point is a big middle. This necessity was realized by a driver during the war who wrote home, 'Before I went to France I was always told to think of nothing else about a horse but legs and feet; but now that I have to look after horses, what I want is an easy doer that has a hardy constitution and a roomy cupboard.'

The Suffolk men made a special effort when the Royal Show was held in their home town in 1934, and the parade of their three hundred Chestnuts in the ring at Ipswich presented an unforgettable sight.

What of the future of the horse on British farms? Will they still survive in face of ever-increasing mechanization? Many large farms are now worked without a single horse, others only keep a few for odd-jobbing and root hoeing. The records of the breed Societies show a marked decline in the numbers of licensed stallions, and the statistics of the Ministry of Agriculture present an even more gloomy picture. Even so at Shows one still sees fairly large classes of all breeds including the more recently imported Percheron breed, and horse teams are still used in brewers' drays and on the docksides to move heavy loads; and on smaller lowland and hill farms they are still an essential part of farm equipment.

GREAT POULTRY FARMERS

While the cock, with lively din
Shatters the rear of darkness thin
And to the stack or the barn door
Stoutly struts his claws before.

Poultry keeping has been accepted as an important branch of farming only in comparatively recent times. This is not to say that the fowl is a new-comer to domestication; the development of poultry from the wild species is still a matter of conjecture, but early interest in poultry keeping was confined largely to cockfighting and utility aspects far removed from egg or meat production. The Tartar hordes carried cockerels as alarm clocks—the birds travelling strapped to the riders' saddle gear—and on many occasions poultry have acted as watchmen.

It is in the field of sport that poultry can look back upon a royal if barbaric history, but the annals of cockfighting seem properly more concerned with the bird than with the breeder. The game fowl appears to be the only animal willing to fight on any and every occasion, and to fight with a dogged courage that raised the meaning of the word 'game' to imply courage of a high order. It is perhaps therefore not surprising that the exploits of individual cocks are recalled long after the names of their owners have passed into oblivion for, in the words of Lewis Wright (1872), the game-cock 'fought for his owners with the courage of his race; until at last the higher meaning of the word (i.e. game) came not from them who had bestowed it, but from the bird who fought so undauntedly for a meaner master's stakes.'

Britain seems to have had the curious reputation of breeding the best fighting game and of making energetic but spasmodic efforts to suppress cockfighting. Both Edward III and Henry VIII passed laws against the sport, but the number of place names associated with it such as Cockspur Street and Cockpit Steps bear witness to its widespread popularity.

The names and something of the history of a few cockers have come down to us. Whether these people can be regarded as farmers seems debatable but, since a few interested themselves closely in the breeding of the birds and in their management, they might be classified as such. Their views on both these subjects are sometimes quaint. Gervase Markham writing in 1614 on the selection of good game cocks says, 'in your general election[*sic!*] chuse him which is of strong shape, good colour, true valour, and a most sharpe and ready heele.' To many of our modern breeders this reliance on breed type would appear sound; it appears also good advice to citizens of a country subject to party politics.

Gervase Markham is important because, in addition to his interest in cockfighting, he concerns himself with the management of poultry for egg production. In his book, *Cheap and Good Husbandry*, he includes an article on domestic poultry, and from his time onwards it is possible to distinguish between poultry kept for utility purposes and birds kept for sport—an interest to be succeeded later by exhibition stock.

That the management of poultry had not greatly advanced in Markham's time can be gathered from his recommended treatment —'If your poultry have sore eyes, you shall take a leaf or two of ground-ivy and chawing it well in your mouth, suck out the juice and spit in into the sore eye, and it will most assuredly heal it, as it hath often been tried.' It may be that the treatment was effective, or perhaps was merely often tried, but it is of interest to learn of Markham's interest in the condition of the eyes of his birds; in this he would find many supporters to-day.

Although by the early seventeenth century poultry keeping for utility purposes had become sufficiently important to receive attention from agricultural writers, it evinced those qualities that have frequently led its followers to describe themselves as belonging to the 'Cinderella of Agriculture'—and usually with obvious masochism. This peculiar attitude seems to have persisted for a considerable time and is worth some inquiry. There is no doubt that there have been few great poultry farmers, and those few have not been of the stature of farmers in other branches of agriculture. It is reasonable to ask whether this arises from the fact that there have been relatively few great poultry farmers and their profession has in consequence failed to attain the lustre relating to say cattle keeping, or is it that poultry *farming*, being a relative new-comer, has from that fact failed to attract great farmers and so remained with its oft emphasized handicap?

In support of the continuance of this attitude of mind, we have the example of Bonington Moubray writing in 1815—two centuries after Markham—on Domestic Poultry. The unfortunate author apparently felt that some stigma attached to poultry for this name is a *nom de plume*, his real one being John Lawrence. Lawrence, or Moubray, includes in his treatise some of the breeds of fowl then common. This list includes Game, Dorking, Polish and others—the latter containing such descriptive names as 'Shackbags, Barndoor or Dung-hill Fowl'. These last names fully indicate the common form of poultry management at the time. Yet the breeding of poultry requires skill, patience, and ability, and the large number of breeds existing to-day bear witness that numbers of poultry keepers possessed these qualities. Many of these men were not perhaps farmers in the accepted sense. For their task big acreages were unnecessary; their animal was small. It is not surprising therefore that many of the breeders whose names are now history were often engaged in other activities and followed their poultry breeding in large gardens or small holdings.

In the realm of cattle breeding and arable farming, the great farmers of the past struggled with painful endeavour towards their goal—many of their empirical methods gaining some support from the scientists' work of later days. In poultry keeping we have a reversal of this position and, if the scientist can be included amongst great farmers, the Poultry Industry can look to an impressive list.

The paradox arose in the following way. The suppression and decline of cockfighting in the early nineteenth century were succeeded by a rapidly increasing interest in exhibition stock—

an activity which no doubt appealed to the stock-minded man without means to develop his interest with larger animals. This development coincided with the rise in scientific interest in inheritance. The scientist working on this problem naturally requires an animal which quickly reproduces itself and, in the fowl, this requirement was satisfied. In addition, plumage, colour, and furnishings were so varied throughout the many breeds that they were well adapted to the geneticists' needs.

Darwin was amongst those early scientists to take an interest in the fowl and its characteristics and, following Darwin, comes Bateson of Cambridge. It was William Bateson who provided the final evidence that Mendel's laws applied to animals. In 1902 Bateson reported to the Evolution Committee of the Royal Society the results of his studies of comb type in the progeny of Indian Game (Pea Comb), Dorking (Rose Comb), Wyandotte (Rose Comb) with Single Comb White Leghorns. His work showed clearly that Pea Comb and Rose Comb were dominant to Single Comb and depended for their expression upon single genes. This provided the first proof that Mendel's laws applied to the animal kingdom as well as to plants.

R. C. Punnett joined Bateson in 1904 and began breeding hens to investigate on Mendelian lines the inheritance of such characters as comb, down, plumage colour and pattern, shank colour and skin colour. It was perhaps fortunate for the Poultry Industry that poultry were used for this work, for rats or some other animal might easily have been selected for purposes of this work on inheritance. As it was, Punnett's choice of animal and his ultimate interest in his experimental material itself led to the elucidation of many matters of interest to the practical poultry-man. These included the breeding out of unwanted recessive characters. Punnett developed Bateson's work on sex-linkage and later, with Michael Pease, produced the auto-sexing breeds of fowl—work which is still progressing.

Punnett records that, at the International Poultry Congress in London in 1919, he tried to rouse an interest in the assembled breeders in his investigations, but few had faith or vision to appreciate how greatly his work was to affect the welfare of their business. However, a few followers of the Fancy had been interested in the work of Darwin and Bateson and, as far as it lay within their power, applied the results of their research to their own breeding problems. The fancier therefore found himself working in a tenuous association with the great.

The importance of this development is manifest by the way in which the more or less scientific systems of breeding for plumage and breed type, carried on by the exhibition men, were followed by those taking an interest in the utility aspect of the fowl. Amongst the latter must be classed William Cook of Saint Mary Cray, Kent (1849–1904), who, with justification, claimed to be the originator of the Buff Orpington.

Cook's efforts to improve poultry as producers of table eggs were paralleled by many. Taking to themselves the breeding methods of the fancier, they also took his breeds, many of which had been 'manufactured' during the middle decades of the nineteenth century. These many breeds were mixed in building up breeds whose outstanding qualities were utilitarian and, from thenceforward, the Poultry Industry as a section of farming began to expand.

This progress was given some impetus by the invention of the self-regulating incubator by Hearson in 1881. To appreciate the importance of this invention, it is necessary to go back some years to the earlier attempts to hatch eggs by artificial means. The Frenchman Réaumur, in the first part of the eighteenth century, took a great interest in artificial incubation and poultry keeping generally, producing a book entitled *The Art of Hatching and Bringing up Domestic Fowls of all kinds at any time of the Year*. According to Punnett this was the first book of any real note dealing with the improvement of utility poultry. Réaumur's book was mainly concerned with artificial incubation as a means of rapidly increasing the poultry population. But Réaumur also outlined methods of determining the most productive fowl and advised on egg size as well as number. His treatise also recognizes the value of the winter layer and suggests ways of throwing hens into an early moult in order to stimulate earlier laying. The preservation of eggs is another aspect of poultry farming described by him and, reinforcing the present-day atmosphere of his work, he suggests oil sealing in the spring flush.

Réaumur's essay into artificial incubation was quickly succeeded by others, and in 1782 Moubray gives an account of his method:

'A number of eggs wrapped in wool, and covered with flannel, in a common wicker bottom sieve or riddle were suspended over a chafing dish of charcoal in a chimney where there was no other fire. We had no thermometer but measured the degree of heat by our own feeling. Constant attendance at least every three hours must obviously be necessary both day and night.'

His comment on this laborious method is not surprising—'no person will attempt artificial hatching but from the motive of mere curiosity and that motive must indeed be powerful.'

The pioneers had blazed the trail and, with Hearson's self-regulating incubator in 1881, a great step forward had been taken. At the same time another development of equal importance was in process, namely, the introduction of the trap nest. This important but simple piece of mechanism allows the breeder to relate each egg to a particular bird. Curiously the invention cannot be ascribed with certainly to anyone and appears to have been designed in the U.S.A. in the middle of the nineteenth century.

The introduction and perfection of the incubator and the trap nest raised poultry keeping from either a hobby or an insignificant activity on the farm to the status of an industry. Since these developments the industry has grown rapidly and, with it, those who can with justification be included in the category of great farmers.

It is perhaps inevitable that, at a time of rapid expansion, the farmers who merit the adjective great were those whose vision enabled them to sense the dangers inherent in the speedy growth of their industry. With that spirit which characterizes greatness, they interested themselves in helping their fellows.

One of the great ones amongst this number was John N. Leigh, and his name will always be remembered for his work in establishing laying trials on a sound basis. At the close of the First World War a demand for tested high quality stock became apparent.

Under the direction of Leigh, a laying trial was established near Ipswich in 1917 with 115 pens of five birds. The test had great success and soon attracted worldwide interest. The trial—known as the National Laying Test—was later removed to Milford in Surrey, and Leigh continued as its Managing Director until his death in 1937 at the age of eighty.

Probably the most outstanding personality at the time was Sir Edward Brown. Born in 1851 in 'humble circumstances'—as he himself says—he became through hard work, courage and vision an admittedly famous man of the poultry industry. Living in the industrial area of Newcastle during the early part of his life, his conversion to an interest in poultry farming was unusual. It came about through seeing a drawing of a fowl by that well-known illustrator, Harrison Weir, on the front page of *The British Workman*. This picture gripped Brown's imagination and he began to take a keen interest in poultry breeding in the locality. He himself began to breed Brahmas; later in 1880 he moved to London and began what was to be his chief and most influential work, writing for the Press.

In 1882 he undertook interviews and visits to most of the leading poultry breeders of the day on behalf of the proprietors of the *Livestock Journal*, and eventually succeeded Lewis Wright as Poultry Editor of that journal. This proved to be the opening phase of a career which was devoted very largely to the interest of the industry. He had at various times many opportunities to study poultry keeping, not only in this country but on the Continent and in the United States. He made several surveys and drew up a number of reports for various authorities. He lectured on poultry keeping in many countries and established a poultry instructional plant at the University of Reading.

His greatest achievement, perhaps, was the setting up of a 'World's Poultry Science Association', of which he became the first President, 1912–27. He was also Joint President of the World's Poultry Congress, 1921–4, and sole President, 1927. In 1920 he was responsible for the establishment of the National Poultry Council and became its first Secretary, remaining in that office until his retirement in 1930.

In America and Canada, Brown was held in high esteem and was accepted on all sides as the 'Grand Old Man' of the World's Poultry Industry. In this connection, it should be recorded that an honorary degree of Doctor of Laws and Literature was conferred on him in 1927 by McGill University, Montreal, at Macdonald College. Finally, at the very height of his power and fame, in 1930 his services to the industry were recognized in the Birthday Honours List of that year, when H.M. King George V conferred on him the honour of knighthood.

It is not surprising that Lancashire, which has been regarded as a poultry area for a considerable time, should have possessed a number of outstanding poultry farmers. Probably one of the best known is Tom Barron. His history parallels that of many who have achieved fame in the world of poultry keeping. Starting as a cobbler, he took an interest in poultry and, like many others, soon left his original employment to make a name for himself as a poultry breeder. This he did with phenomenal success, gaining a high reputation for his stock in this country and abroad. Indeed, only a few years ago it was possible to read poultry breeders' advertisements in North America advertising 'Tom Barron's Strain', although the stock was some twenty or more generations removed from that originally purchased. Such was the esteem in which Barron's breeding was held.

Barron shared with many other Lancashire men high fame as a breeder. Like the late Richard Rodwell—another well-known Lancashire man—his success could not be attributed to any particularly scientific method, but he seemed to have extraordinary abilities—stock sense or intuition, call them what you will—which resulted in continued success, apparently in defiance of the geneticists' opinion.

Another successful pioneer of the rapidly growing poultry industry was T. W. Toovey, of King's Langley, Hertford. He was remarkable in being one of the very few people in the early years of this century who succeeded in establishing a large-scale poultry plant. His King's Langley farm carried 10,000 adult birds, and he reared 40,000 chickens each season. What is remarkable is that he reared and hatched every pullet by natural means. He used no incubator, foster mother or brooder, but relied on the hen for his hatching and rearing.

It may be considered that the Poultry Industry has produced few famous farmers. Those who can lay claim to that honour have often been concerned with activities calculated to improve the industry and raise its status. Through their very selflessness these men must be regarded as great, even though their own farming activities were sacrificed to their public actions. Partially as a result of their endeavours, the Poultry Industry can boast of many successful farmers to-day. It seems a matter of conjecture whether these latter can also be regarded as great but, the fact that the successes of the Barleys, Walkers, Hebditchs, and Watanabés of to-day have stimulated many poultry keepers to attempt emulation of their achievements, entitles them to fame which by the next generation may be translated to greatness.

THE GREAT SOCIETIES

There is a bond between the men who go
From youth about the business of the earth.

V. SACKVILLE WEST

Towards the end of the eighteenth century the idea occurred to several of the great landowners of encouraging the improvement of farm live stock by means of agricultural meetings. The famous sheep shearings of the Duke of Bedford at Woburn and of Coke at Holkham were shows in miniature. John Lord Somerville, a West Country nobleman (whose valuable quiet agricultural work has long been rather overshadowed by that of his voluble contemporary, Sir John Sinclair), began holding a little annual show in London, where he offered prizes for sheep and cattle, and had on view some improved implements, including his own inventions in ploughs and carts.

At the dinner held on the occasion of the first 'Highland' show, at Edinburgh in 1822 Sinclair defined the purpose of agricultural shows as follows:

'Such meetings excite a spirit of improvement. Much advantage is derived from the discussions which they occasion and from the opportunities they afford of viewing the various descriptions of live stock which the country possesses and comparing their respective properties and defects.'

Somerville, addressing the old Board of Agriculture as its second President, referred to another aspect of the Show. 'Such an institution,' he said, 'must be closely followed up by men well grounded in science, who have the means of detecting and separating that which is useful from that which is visionary; who have grafted theory on approved practice.'

234

THE GREAT SOCIETIES

The great National Societies were at once the descendants of older pioneer associations and the parents of a multitude of local societies which they made it their business to foster. The Edinburgh Society of Improvers, the Smithfield Club, the York Society, and the Salford Hundred Society were among the pioneers. The Royal Society of Arts, founded in 1754, was also, in its earlier years, concerned mainly with agriculture and did important work.

About the middle of the nineteenth century a different type of society, the farmers' club, became common, generally meeting in the market town on market days. In the leisurely days of the 'Farmers' Ordinary' before the days of County Organizers and Broadcast talks, the monthly club meetings, where members or guests read papers on farming topics, provided an important medium for the diffusion of new ideas. Some of these clubs, like those at Stalham in Norfolk and Faversham in Kent, have survived till the present day. The most important of all, the London Farmers' Club, has been the scene of debates on every important farming topic from 1844 till the present time.

In Scotland the local clubs were used by the Highland Society to help in carrying out experiments, to manage grants for horse breeding, to organize ploughing matches, milk recording societies, cheese making classes and in other ways. They functioned, as John Speir put it, as 'little schools of agriculture'.

At a time when travel was difficult and before town-made amusements were available to country folk the social aspect of these meetings was itself important to people who, for the rest, led very isolated lives.

Whatever may be said by present-day critics of the value of the show system in determining the best types of animals for the commercial farmer, there can be no doubt that our agriculture owes a great deal to the Show Societies. Without them British pedigree live stock could never have come to play the great part which it has played in the world. Moreover, presenting in their records a survey of progress and change, their history is important in any account of the evolution of British Farming.

THE ROYAL AGRICULTURAL SOCIETY OF ENGLAND

According to Sir Harry Thompson, Englishmen are prone to periodically recurring fits of associative activity. One of these came to a head on the typically English occasion of a dinner at the Freemason's Tavern in Great Queen Street, on 11th December 1837, when the members of the Smithfield Club met to celebrate the success of their Society and to congratulate themselves on its good work. Earl Spencer, an ardent stock breeder, who preferred his farm to his office in Whitehall, was in the chair. In proposing success to the Club, he said that 'if a society were established for agricultural purposes exclusively, it would be productive of the most essential benefits to the British farmer.' The Duke of Richmond quoted the excellent example of the Highland and Agricultural Society of Scotland, and after several other noble gentlemen had expressed a desire to co-operate, they parted with the project fairly launched. By January Mr. Handley, a Member of Parliament, had prepared a pamphlet for issue to the press. 'The farmers of the old school,' he wrote, 'are prejudiced against what they call book learning, but it is in the interests of the young farmer that the aid of science must be invoked.' 'Science,' he went on, 'is the pilot that must steer us into those hitherto imperfectly explored regions where, I am convinced, a mine of wealth is still in store for British agriculture.'

When time had been allowed for this letter to soak into the minds of the agricultural community, an advertisement appeared in the *Morning Herald* and elsewhere, in May 1838, setting forth that 'the undermentioned noblemen and gentlemen, thinking that the management of land in England and Wales is capable of great improvement by the exertions of a Society similar to that in Scotland, request those who concur to meet them to-morrow the 9th of May at the Freemason's Tavern. . . .'

The room was crowded to excess with all the most enlightened landowners of the day, Peel, Graham, Shaw-Lefevre, Long, Pusey and many others, of all shades of political opinion. After a certain amount of opposition to the proposed non-political attitude of the new Society, the dissentients walked out, and the resolution was carried unanimously. The new Society nominated its Governors and bankers and appointed a provisional committee which did not let the grass grow under its feet. Within a week they had held four meetings. They appointed Earl Spencer as President, and twelve Trustees; they drew up rules, set out a comprehensive programme, and nominated Mr. William Shaw, Editor of the *Mark Lane Express*, as Secretary at a stipend of £200 a year. They had soon to deal with one of their projects, for hardly had they settled in the saddle, before an enterprising Scot, Mr. Horn of Carrondale, proposed to lay before them the plan of a machine for ploughing by steam. With youthful enthusiasm they drew up a list of subjects for prize essays, arranged for the publication of a Journal, whose editing they entrusted to Mr. Pusey, chose a design for their medal and, in deference to their President, took as their motto his favourite saying: 'Practice with Science'. Noting that they had a handsome balance at the bank they decided to hold the first country meeting at Oxford on 17th July 1839.

Not only in the surrounding neighbourhood, but in all parts of the country the first meeting of the National Society was a topic of absorbing interest. It was before the days of universal railways and strenuous efforts had to be made by those who proposed to attend. Mr. Drewry of Tavistock, journeying with his friend, Mr. Turner, the famous breeder of Devon cattle, spent three nights on the way. The uncertainty of finding lodgings and food added a touch of adventure to travel. Mr. Kersey Fowler, as a boy, travelled on the dickey of a yellow post-chaise with three of his father's friends stowed inside, and the party came home 'nearly starved to death'. The animals too had hazardous journeys. Mr. Thomas Bates's celebrated Duchesses had to walk from Kirklevington to Hull, thence go by boat to London, then by barge along the Grand Junction Canal to Aylesbury, where old Mr. Fowler was called out one evening to find them a field for the night. Next day they were driven ten miles to Thame, and finally another thirteen miles to Oxford, having been three weeks on the road. Mr. Bates himself stayed in Oxford with his friend, Mr. Pinfold, a wealthy butcher, on whose pasture ground in

Holywell, now occupied by Mansfield College, the Show was held.

During the whole of Sunday and Monday caravans and conveyances of all kinds carrying cattle and sheep were seen hastening to the centre of attraction, and by eight o'clock on Tuesday morning the entire space was filled. *Bell's Weekly Messenger* reports the scene in the city: 'The influx of visitors from many miles around Oxford was exceedingly great, the principal streets being completely lined with gigs, coaches, and other conveyances, whilst the town, throughout the whole day, presented such a scene of bustle as was never before witnessed. The crowd waiting for admission to the showyard was so extensive that immediately the gates were thrown open the rush was so tremendous that many gentlemen had their coats torn from their backs. It was calculated that upwards of 15,000 noblemen and gentlemen reached the town.'

The proceedings began with a trial of implements in an adjoining field. In the afternoon there was prize-essay reading in the Town Hall, when Colonel Le Couteur, the Grand Old Man of Jersey, spoke on varieties of wheat, Mr. Handley on the comparative advantages of wheel and swing ploughs, Mr. Childers, M.P., on shed-feeding of sheep, and the President himself on 'Physiological Observations on the Gestation of Cows'. The day ended with an agreeable dinner party of three hundred and sixty gentlemen at the Star Hotel. In the list of exhibitors appear the names of almost all the best-known breeders of the day; Bates with Shorthorns; Jeffries and Hewer with Herefords; Freeman with Suffolk horses and Crisp from Suffolk with a Southdown which beat Jonas Webb's sheep. The local breeds of sheep were well represented; Mr. Large showed his New Oxfordshires and Mr. Slatter and Mr. Hewer their Cotswolds. Ransome, Howard, and Garrett sent implements.

The annual dinner was held in the Quadrangle of Queen's College, roofed over at a cost of £800, where 2,450 guests sat down to dine at ten shillings each, while their ladies looked on from the windows above. It was a distinguished company, as Mr. Chalmers Morton describes the scene: 'I remember the face and voice of many of our great leaders present, the sonorous voice of the Duke of Richmond, Mr. Pusey's pale and anxious, somewhat absent-looking face; Mr. Handley's hearty jollity; Baron Bunsen's staid and placid countenance; the good nature of the Rev. Dr. Buckland; Daniel Webster also, evidently a great power both bodily and mentally.' The last-named was the guest of the day. 'A visitor', as the President said, 'from a country whose people we are obliged to call foreigners, but who are still our brethren in blood.' Mr. Webster justified his reputation as an orator. 'Whatever else,' he declared, 'may tend to enrich and beautify society, that which feeds and clothes comfortably the great mass of mankind should be regarded as the great foundation of national prosperity. The importance of agriculture to a nation is obvious to every man; but it is equally true that the annual produce of English agriculture is a great concern to the whole civilised world.' When he returned home he pointed a moral to the Legislature of Massachusetts. He had observed that 'no man in England is so high as to be independent of the success of this great interest; no man so low as not to be affected by its prosperity or decline. The same is true with us.'

Before the next meeting, the Society was granted a Royal Charter, beginning the long connection with the Royal Family which has always been so much more than merely nominal. Her Majesty's inherited taste for farming showed itself in her active personal interest, and for sixty years her patronage was an inestimable advantage. The Windsor farms, as Mr. Prothero points out, 'set the fashion, afforded a model to hosts of agriculturists and helped to raise the standard of British farming.'

After the Cambridge Annual Stock Fair, at a market ordinary at the Red Lion Hotel, a proposal to hold the 1840 meeting in the City was cordially welcomed by Mr. Jonas Webb and a large company. They formed a local committee with the Mayor as Chairman and planned to outdo Oxford.

The meeting was held on Parker's Piece, whereby young Mr. Albert Pell, then a Trinity undergraduate, was so worried about the destruction of the cricket pitch that he could not bring himself to enjoy the show. The customary mystery attended the work of the judges. The Duke of Richmond announced that although, as a matter of safety, attendants on bulls and stallions must be admitted with their charges, shepherds were to be excluded, for, he explained: 'The shepherd, who might be considered as the father of his flock, did not like to see his sheep pass over to the care of another; he watched with jealous attention and was sure to be known to the judges.'

The list of prize-winners again included the names of pioneer breeders, and the President won with his Southdowns. Parties for the show were made up all over the country. One such, with Clare Sewell Reade's father and five relatives, started from Norwich 'in a roomy post-chay with four good horses and two post-boys. These were no more horses than were needed, for they were such a sample of Norfolk yeomen as one could hardly find in the country now, all but one standing six feet, and he making up for his want of stature by weighing over sixteen stone. This jolly party had their headquarters at Newmarket.'

Country folk of those days believed in an early start; long before the Show opened at 6 a.m. the approaches to Cambridge were blocked, and by ten o'clock it was impossible to find accommodation in the town.

The bill of fare at the dinner (at which 2,650 guests sat down) was gauged to the capacity of the English yeoman of those days, including hundreds of pieces of roast beef and lamb, tongues, pies, veal tarts, etc., all, of course, home produce, in contrast to the present day, when, at many a show held to encourage the British farmer, one may find a meal composed of Argentine beef, New Zealand lamb, Canadian cheese, and American tinned fruit.

Sir Robert Peel, perhaps with his Corn Law Repeal Bill already simmering in his mind, was greeted with deafening acclamations as the speaker of the day.

The year 1840 was an epoch-making one in agricultural science, for it was the year of the publication of Liebig's book. Mr. Pusey, who had been nominated as third President, determined to make this work a reality. He gathered round him his friends, Buckland, Liebig, Sir Richard Owen, Playfair, and others and induced them to bring their science into closer relation with agricultural practice by addressing meetings of farmers in different parts of the country. With a rare union of endowments, a philosopher as well as an acute man of business Pusey, both by his experimental work on his own farms and by his writings in the *Journal* and the *Quarterly Review*, distinguished both for their imaginative quality and their scientific accuracy, did much to win for agriculture a place among the intellectual pursuits.

Next year at Liverpool, with implement entries nearly doubled, the Society realized the opportunity for congregating mechanicians from all parts of the world. Although the new railway from London brought many visitors, travelling, according to Mr. Pell, was still rather uncomfortable. Having had his purse emptied by the ruinous charges of the hotels, he 'returned at once by night train to London, wet through, in a carriage with no glass, but a substitute in the shape of louvre-board and shutters, to improve the draft and increase the gloom.'

The Society now divided the country into nine districts, in which they proposed to hold shows in rotation, settled in at 12 Hanover Square, appointed Mr. Handley as President, and prepared to visit the West Country at Bristol, where there was a fifty per cent increase in implement entries and sixty per cent more stock. But, lest in the flush of so much new discovery and improvement they might neglect the established practice of generations of practical farmers, Mr. Pusey struck a warning note in the *Journal*. 'The most gratifying discoveries have been those of old practices unknown beyond their own districts. I am certain that four years ago no one knew how much good farming there was in the country.'

The Society chose Earl Spencer for a second time as President, and both at Southampton and again at Shrewsbury, the year before his death, he showed, by working a whole day in his shirt-sleeves and bearing an active part in putting stock into the stalls, that he was no mere figurehead. At the Southampton meeting the idea of founding an agricultural college at Cirencester, already discussed at a local Farmers' Club, was first put before the members by Mr. Robert Brown, who had been devoting his time to secure interest for the project. The project soon afterwards materialized in the establishment of the first agricultural college in Great Britain.

On the death of Earl Spencer the Society appointed to the Council his friend John Grey of Dilston, known in his hot political youth as the 'Black Prince of the North'. Grey, brought up in the tradition of high farming and improved stock breeding, belonged to the group of Improvers which included his schoolmates Maynard and the two Booths, as well as his older friend and mentor, George Culley. Bone manure, draining, and subsoil ploughing were his favourite themes in days when to talk of such things was almost enough to stamp a man as a Jacobin and a visionary. He dared to denounce the Corn Laws as 'the parent of scarcity, dearness and uncertainty'. As the ideal land agent envisaged by Caird, he raised the Greenwich Hospital estates to twice their original value. Meanwhile the Show was increasing in size and importance, assuming, as Mr. Pell wrote, 'more of its present character, individuality and quaintness being swallowed up in the crowd; advertising, puffing and paint were freely resorted to and the yard became less of a school and more of an exhibition.'

The Society celebrated the entry on its second decade by appointing a veterinary inspector and a chemist, and Mr. Pusey reported on the progress of agricultural improvement, which, he says, 'might hitherto be looked upon as a hobby for a few country gentlemen, but has now become the unavoidable business of landowners generally.'

In 1851, the year of the Crystal Palace Exhibition, when Victorian hopes were high and all seemed well in the best of worlds, Mr. Pusey had his implements as part of the Exhibition, and a superlative show of live stock was held in the Home Park at Windsor. The staunch Duke of Richmond was once more President, and the Queen and the Prince Consort, with the ten-year-old Prince of Wales, attended the Show, and showed the deepest interest in every department.

About this time the Council was concerning itself with the question of securing more plentiful and cheaper supplies of guano, then the only known concentrated fertilizer. When Lord Palmerston was approached he thought out a new use for the Navy,

THE GREAT SOCIETIES

causing the Admiralty to instruct commanders of every ship to
search for deposits of guano and mineral phosphates in the rainless
regions of the tropics, and the ship surgeons to be prepared to
examine the amount and quality of each deposit.

At Lewes in 1852, 'the remote locality, unusually oppressive
heat and a general election' caused a falling off in attendance
despite the attraction of a contest of reaping machines, including
McCormick's monster. At Gloucester the Show was held in a
quagmire, coated with sawdust and planked footways, and at
Lincoln there arose a good scandal over the unscrupulous tricks
of the pig exhibitors, who persisted in breaking off and filing the
teeth of their animals in order to falsify their age. In spite of many
remonstrances the practice continued, and it was not till ten years
later that threats of expulsion from the ground finally stopped
the offenders.

In soaking weather at Carlisle, Mr. Clare Sewell Reade made
his first appearance as judge of implements, along with a jolly old
fen farmer, 'a capital machinist, one who could tell at a glance if
an implement could stand the rough usage of the farm and make
good work.' 'The trial field was miles away from the Showyard,'
says Mr. Reade, 'and my colleague would not move an inch until
our lunch was placed in the fly. That fly he always kept in the
trial field, and at one o'clock each day we adjourned to it for our
lunch and his pipe.'

In 1857 at Salisbury, with a well balanced budget and one of
the most remarkable collections of live stock and implements ever
seen, the 'Royal' must indeed have sensed the Golden Age. But
during the latter part of the year there began to be heard disquiet-
ing reports that a Steppe Murrain, coming out of the East, the
ancient home of all plagues, was attacking stock here and there in
Europe. The society's anxiety was quieted by the report of their
veterinary officer Professor Simonds, who, on his return from a
tour of investigation, optimistically reported that 'no fear need be
entertained that this destructive pest will ever reach our shores.'
Unfortunately he was a false prophet.

At Chester, appropriately, munificent prizes for cheese brought
out a display far surpassing anything ever seen in England. Mr.

George Willis won the Championship of £100 with four cheeses of 107 lb. each, which were bought by the local committee to be presented respectively to the Queen, the Emperor of the French, Lord Berners the President, and Lord Derby the Prime Minister.

In 1860 the Show was at Canterbury, where Shropshire and Romney Marsh sheep were, for the first time, provided with classes. At this Show the Council first realized the enormous amount of unsoundness amongst agricultural horses despite the spasmodic efforts that had been made to stimulate and improve the breeding of both heavy and light breeds. The most energetic minds had for some time been preoccupied with steam, but it was now realized that the horse was not yet to be displaced and that the demand for many types exceeded the supply. Dissatisfied with the rather haphazard methods of prize-giving which had been followed in the past, the Society entered on the campaign for improved horse breeding which culminated twenty-four years later in the Thoroughbred Stallion Show at Newcastle, the first effort yet made to place good sires within the reach of the ordinary farmer.

As well as being diseased, the feet of many horses were badly shod, the shoeing smiths being badly trained and ignorant of anatomy. 'Burning on' the shoes was still a common custom. By instituting a scheme of training in conjunction with the Worshipful Company of Farriers, the Society succeeded in raising horse shoeing to the status of a skilled craft.

In 1862, the year of the second great International Exhibition in Hyde Park, the Society determined to make the show worthy of the occasion. Having secured a site on Battersea Fields, they drew up a largely extended schedule of classes for every kind of live stock, and invited the Highland and Agricultural Society to bring its show within their enclosure. The result was an unprecedented exhibit of live stock with, in all, 1,986 entries, of which 238 were from Scotland. The Scots acquired great credit by their cordial co-operation in bringing so many fine animals the great distance of 300 miles. With fine weather Londoners flocked to gaze. One of the treats of the ring was the parade of Suffolk Punches, for the first time in a separate class. Special mention was also made of the admirable arrangements made by Mr. Hall Maxwell, Secretary of the Highland Society, for the one hundred and twenty servants in charge of the Scottish stock, who were encamped in the yard in marquees, and supplied with beds and bedding issued from the Tower by Lord de Grey. The men were described as 'well-dressed in Scottish clothing; a more respectable looking and better behaved body of men were never brought together.'

Next year at Worcester judging in public, first started at Battersea, excited great interest, especially round the Shorthorn ring, where the crowd stood for more than six hours. Although Professor Varnell congratulated the exhibitors on the general diminution of hereditary disease amongst the animals, the superfatted pigs and over-wooled sheep called forth the severe criticism of Mr. Dent. 'It was certainly absurd,' he wrote, 'to see a man sitting beside his pig, and holding up its head to enable it to take its supper. And as for the mysteries of the toilette of the sheep, no young lady going to a drawing-room could have had more pains bestowed upon her than some of the rams. Whilst fat overloads and injures our Shorthorns and other horned stock, the sheep has not only fat, but wool of an indefinite age, to disguise his deficiencies.'

In the twenty-fifth year of its life the Society went in for some stocktaking of its position. Mr. Harry Meysey Thompson, who was specially devoted to chemistry, wrote: 'In the past twenty-five years agriculturists have successfully passed the great gulf which separates the rule of thumb from the rule of three. The man who paved the way for their advance, and manfully led the van through year after year of costly, intricate and ill-appreciated labour, was Mr. Lawes of Rothamsted. The farmer is now in possession of resources whether of machinery, manures or means of locomotion far in advance of the wildest dreams of his forefathers.'

But Mr. Dent, steward of stock at Newcastle in 1864, is depressed about the decline of milking qualities in high-bred stock; he quotes Mr. Riley of Cheshire who declared to him that if he wanted milk and cheese he would rather have his stock related to the short roomy-bodied Cheshire cows of 1800, to the Ayrshire, or even to the Welsh cow, than to a bull of Bates or Booth. He notes also that 'amongst the Shorthorn, Hereford, and Devon classes we have perfect models of female symmetry in every point but that which provides sustenance for the offspring. Year by year we are showing mere cylinders of beef.' The bulls he compares to 'gouty specimens of the human race with figures destroyed by overfeeding.'

The Council too were disturbed about the fancy idea of allowing hunters to be saddled and ridden, and even put over a leaping bar, in the ring. They foresaw the day when a serious show might become a mere circus.

However, at Plymouth, where the members revelled in superb weather, and welcomed the Prince and Princess of Wales and the French and Austrian Fleets, there was every evidence of rising fortunes and of confidence in the complete security of the 'sea-girt Isle'; there seems to have been no thought of the deadly foreign invasion even then within the land. Hardly had the members reached their homes before the Lords in Council issued their first order announcing the 'recent appearance of a contagious or infectious disorder of uncertain nature prevailing within the Metropolis', and advising restrictive measures. By the end of the month two thousand cows from the London dairies had perished. The churches held a day of humiliation and a Royal Commission was appointed, but while it was debating the nature of the disease, the plague continued to spread so rapidly that, by the close of February, the losses had risen to nearly twelve thousand animals a week.

The 'Royal' Council, with commendable energy, resolved themselves into a Standing Committee and, in conjunction with other societies, tried to induce the Government to adopt more stringent regulations. Although the attack lasted little over a year Mr. Thompson, the Society's President, estimated the national loss at no less than three millions sterling. As the country meetings of the 'Royal' had either to be abandoned or held without live stock the Council turned to make exhaustive inquiry into the results of steam cultivation on various types of soil, noting incidentally the effect of the use of machinery in 'imparting more

Defendant. Yes.

THE DAY OF HUMILIATION.

Wednesday last was observed throughout the diocese of Gloucester and Bristol, as a day of humiliation. The following Form of Prayer was used by the clergy, for relief from the plague now existing among cattle and for protection against cholera :—

O Lord God Almighty, whose are the Cattle on a thousand hills, and in whose hand is the breath of every living thing, look down, we beseech Thee, in compassion upon us Thy servants whom Thou has visited with a grievous murrain among our herds and flocks. We acknowledge our transgressions, which worthily deserve Thy chastisement, and our Sin is ever before us; and in humble penitence we come to seek Thy aid. In the midst of Judgment, do Thou, O Lord, remember Mercy, for Thy Son Jesus Christ's sake; stay, we pray Thee, this plague, by Thy word of Power, and save that provision which Thou hast, in Thy goodness, granted for our sustenance.

Defend us also, gracious Lord, from the pestilence with which many foreign lands have been smitten, keep it far from our borders, and shield our homes from its ravages; so shall we offer unto Thee the sacrifice of praise and thanksgiving for these Thy acts of Providence over us, through Jesus Christ our Lord. *Amen.*

The following hymn was sung :—

All Creation groans and travails ; Thou, O God, shalt hear its groan :
For of man and all Creation Thou alike art Lord alone.
Pity, then, Thy guiltless creatures, who, not less, man's sufferings share :
For our sins it is they perish: let them profit by our prayer.
Cast Thine eye of love and mercy on the misery of the

more especially at the Corn Hall, which was crowded. The service was choral. The subject of each address was of course the Cattle Plague. The principal points were :—1 The cause of the plague, viz., our sins in their innumerable forms, and our indifference to the comfort of the cattle. 2 The incurability of the disease ;—having baffled all medical skill, a proof of its being sent by God.' All are affected by it, and all must therefore join in asking Him for its removal. 3 God's mercy in sending it, and the lesson therefrom. From several instances in the Bible, it seems clear that God graciously gives man three warnings or calls to. repentance. First, He afflicts our property, and if this fails to save us He further

A Newspaper Cutting from '65.

accuracy, reliability and promptitude to the habits of the labourer.' When they resumed their annual show in 1868 at Leicester, still under the grim shadow of the past, Mr. Edward Bowly, Senior Steward of Stock, expressed what must have been in the thoughts of many. 'The mind,' he writes, 'almost shrinks from contemplating all we have passed through during the three eventful years, and we would gladly bury in oblivion the recollection of the dreadful Rinderpest, how it pursued its fitful course through our country, sometimes carrying off whole herds, taking some and leaving others, paralysing every effort, and as it were mocking our endeavours to check its fatal course.' The great Shorthorn breeder also refers to the improvement in the general level of stock. 'In the early days of the Society it was the exception to find a pure-bred bull in the farmer's hands; now no intelligent man would be without one.'

This year the Society appointed Henry M. Jenkins to the combined post of Secretary and Editor. Jenkins, who came of Dorset farming stock, was educated in natural science. His naturally alert mind, enlarged by travel and the study of foreign languages, was brought to bear on all aspects of farming, especially in the field of dairy practice and technical education. During his seventeen years of office his wide knowledge of European agriculture enabled him to open the eyes of the English farmer to its unexpected superiority in certain branches, notably in dairy management and the culture of some individual crops.

When, after thirty-one years, the Show again visited Oxford, in 1870, stock prices were reaching their peak; Booth Shorthorns soared to figures of £1,000 and even £2,500 for two-year-old heifers; at the Show, buyers from the United States, Canada, and Australia bought liberally and many relatively humble breeders shared in the prosperity. With British agriculture flourishing, the farming community were ready to respond liberally to an appeal for help to their distressed fellow farmers, the peasantry of the areas which had suffered from the Franco-Prussian war. The Society led the way in the formation of a Seed Fund Committee which from first to last relieved upwards of forty thousand farmers by supplying them with seed corn.

An extensive outbreak of foot-and-mouth disease was a serious problem in this year. Realizing the imperfect scientific knowledge existing about both foot-and-mouth and pleuro-pneumonia the Council, with its usual promptitude, made a grant to the Brown Institute for a series of experiments, and suggested to the Government a system of restrictive measures. At this time the shadow of cattle disease hung almost continuously over the country. At Liverpool in 1877 the dread caused by a renewed outbreak of rinderpest disturbed all sales of pedigree stock. Government prohibitions came into force, in fact, within four hours of the diagnosis of the disease; but Mr. Jacob Wilson, realizing that to wait until an outbreak occurred was no policy, started on a campaign for a planned system of prevention. He persuaded the Society to put forward the resolution that nothing short of total prohibition of the importation of live stock from European ports would ever meet the case. This action led to the appointment of a select committee of the House of Commons and to the Duke of Richmond's Contagious Diseases of Animals Bill; but the provisions of the latter did not go far enough, and many years of disastrous depletion of live stock had to pass before stock-breeders were afforded adequate protection from imported disease.

The Agricultural Holdings Act, affording compensation for unexhaused improvements, having recently become law, the Chemical Committee of the Society was asked to consider means of finding trustworthy data for the guidance of valuers. The Society thereupon took one of the most important steps in the development of scientific agriculture. In 1876 they accepted the generous offer of the Duke of Bedford of the use of a farm at Woburn with a grant to cover the cost of experiments on the residual values of manures.

On the occasion of the Universal Exhibition in Paris, to which British breeders sent notable exhibits, the Council summoned all its experts to compile a special memoir on English Agriculture which showed how, since its foundation, the R.A.S.E. had taken the lead in every important advance.

But after Paris came the disaster of Kilburn. The 'Royal' had decided to celebrate its fortieth birthday by holding in London a show of unprecedented magnitude. The co-operation of the Lord Mayor and the City was secured, the Prince of Wales accepted the invitation to the Presidency, a site was secured at Kilburn and a long prize sheet, for all varieties of English live stock and agricultural products, as well as for foreign exhibits, was prepared.

The scene was set, but the Society reckoned without the British weather which, in 1879, far surpassed the records of gloom established in the two previous years. The rainfall for the year was 46 per cent above the average, the sunshine was barely two and a half hours a day. Almost all summer the icy rain fell persistently.

With great expense the Society had drained, levelled and turfed the site and had made roads; but even before the Show opened the approaches were worked by the transport of the heavy machinery into a wide sea of tenacious mud. Many of the courageous visitors never left the sleeper-made main roads. The Queen and the Prince of Wales helped by their presence to lighten the gloom. Her Majesty, undaunted by the weather, arrived from Windsor at ten-thirty on the Saturday, and watched a stock parade during an interval of comparatively light rain. Although her carriage dared not venture off the main road of the Show on to the Kilburn clay, she passed by the members' pavilion where a party of two hundred Irish farmers received her with vigorous and loyal cheers.

Apart from the wonderful stock, those who persevered through the rain and the mud might have seen in the International dairy, the Laval Cream Separator, as well as apparatus from France for hatching, rearing, and feeding poultry, all deserving careful attention. The germ of a new development which eventually hit the British farmer hard was also on view, in the shape of two refrigerator railway wagons.

At the end of the disastrous year many echoed the words of Professor Wrightson. 'I shall not readily forget the feeling of thankfulness with which I regarded twelve o'clock at midnight on December 31st, 1879. At any rate a doleful ruinous year had departed.' But in the years ahead the farming community were to require all their courage and resourcefulness. They entered upon a series of depressions one worse than another, lasting until nearly the end of Victoria's reign. By this time, with but little in the way of Government help, they had managed to adjust their industry to changed conditions, fighting in an unequal contest against formidably increasing foreign imports of practically all the staple products.

The working dairy and the exhibits of new inventions for the production of butter, cheese, and cream, showed that, from now onwards, the importance of dairying as a standby of the farmer was more and more realized by the Society. In co-operation with the British Dairy Farmers' Association, the 'Royal' took the lead in placing before the farmer the best methods for the production of dairy products. Wet seasons turned their attention to various systems of ensilage. Widespread bankruptcy forced them to study account keeping, and the Society worked hard to persuade the farmer to give up the traditional method of chalking up figures on the barn door, or of depending on the banker's warning of an overdraft. In 1882, the country was presented with the report of the Agricultural Commission, described by Lord Cath-cart as 'a full-length portrait from life of the distressed giant, British Agriculture.' The agriculture statistics of the census, too, gave food for serious thought. The decline in the arable area, though not yet proceeding at full speed, had already reduced the numbers of labourers by 10 per cent, and an increase in the number of farm bailiffs reflected the growing number of farms for which tenants were not to be found.

If farming was depressed, industry was certainly flourishing, for whenever the shows were held in the industrial centres of the North the story is of crowds struggling for admission and of stewards filling their pockets with the shillings of eager visitors too numerous to pass through the turnstiles.

In 1889, their jubilee year, the Society once more ventured on a show near London. The Queen accepted the office of President, gave a site in Windsor Great Park for the Show, and invited the Council and chief officers to a banquet at St. James's Palace. She offered £300 in prizes, to take the form of gold medals, and came down from Balmoral to present them in person.

The advancing years of the Society inevitably found its ranks depleted of those who had seen it started. At the fiftieth anniversary meeting, however, they still had with them Sir Harry Verney, the last survivor of those who had met in the Freemason's Tavern in '38, and who moved the adoption of the annual report.

From this time onwards agricultural education was the subject of prolonged discussion. In spite of constant representations on the backwardness of England in both elementary and higher agricultural instruction, neither the Education Department nor the Universities had so far taken active steps. The Council therefore commissioned Dr. Fream to prepare a text-book for use in elementary schools and classes, and they were soon gratified to find *Fream's Elements* being widely adopted in connection with the courses which were started in the counties. Another source of satisfaction to them was the establishment of a new Board of Agriculture, with their colleague Henry Chaplin at its head. They suggested that immediate steps should be taken to stamp out pleuro-pneumonia, by Government control and with compensation paid out of Government funds. Further, concerned by the general lack of scientific knowledge on animal diseases, they made an annual grant for the establishment of a Chair of Comparative Pathology and Bacteriology at the Royal Veterinary College. The indefatigable Sir Jacob Wilson was again on the warpath, urging a resolution to the new Board that the importation of store cattle from America should be prohibited. When the Diseases of Animals Bill was finally passed, the Society impressed upon their ten thousand members the necessity of co-operation with the Government by the immediate notification of any of the scheduled diseases.

Other diseases were at this time causing grave concern. As veterinary surgeons and professors held the view that everything of consequence was known about Contagious Abortion, and felt disinclined to make further investigation, the Society appointed a special committee to study the incidence and possible cause of the scourge, as well as the spread of foot-rot in sheep and the recurring outbreaks of anthrax.

The summer of 1890 saw the Society once more at Plymouth,

where numbers of Devon and Hereford Cider makers entered into keen competition. Unfortunately the judge reported that 'it is to be regretted that so many of the exhibits were in stinking casks, which shows a lack of good management. No sample is thoroughly clean and free from dregs and apple pulp.' Acting on this information the Council at once asked Mr. Grenville to arrange a 'clean cider' demonstration. Cider mills and presses were marshalled outside the Abbot's kitchen of Glastonbury Abbey. All the new cider makers were hard at work, but the old Somerset folks, accustomed to easy-going ways, were heard to say: 'This b'aint zider makin', I tell 'ee, this 'ere be tur'ble haard wurk.'

In 1894 the President, the Duke of Devonshire, was also Chancellor of the University when Cambridge was visited for the first time since 1840. The University celebrated the occasion by somewhat belatedly incorporating agriculture in its curriculum, so that Dr. Webb of Leeds could no longer deplore the fact that his best students had to go to Edinburgh to take their degrees.

We now note that the more far-seeing men were constantly considering the possibility of finding new products to support the industry under an ever-increasing weight of imports of its main staples. Some of the smaller arts of husbandry, 'La Petite Culture' of the French market gardener, the growing of willows, and the cultivation of fruit and flowers under glass, are noted as subjects worthy of study. All, however, required knowledge and experience. Higher standards must be adopted at home, and foreign products should be marked with the country of origin. Mr. Whitebread suggested that it would be useful if the Technical Education Committees of County Councils could send capable teachers of fruit preserving into country districts, but there were no teachers with the necessary qualifications. A quarter of a century and more was to pass before the Women's Institutes started to train country women in what has since become an important industry. The days of National Marks were still far ahead and Mr. Emory G. Smith from California 'shuddered when he saw ripe, juicy cherries poured into half-cieves from the baskets of the pickers, without any selection or assortment.' It was not until 1911, when the commercial fruit growers of Kent started a show, that any serious attempt was made to standardize and improve the packing and marketing of British fruit. Both Mr. Pell and Mr. Brown reminded Council of the neglected hen, and demonstrations of poultry trussing were introduced at shows.

Milk now began to bulk largely in the deliberations of the Society. Mr. Richard Stratton pointed out that the dairy classes, being a mixture of all breeds, sorts, and sizes, failed in their object, just at a time when dairy interests specially required to be developed by every possible means. In 1899, supported by Mr. Sanday, he secured the provision of classes for cows in milk, thus removing the reproach that the 'Society's Shows were too much on the lines of those of the Smithfield Club.'

The report of the Royal Commission on Tuberculosis had recommended, as a counsel of perfection, the free testing of all cattle belonging to owners who would undertake to isolate reacting animals. This led the Council to issue a leaflet dealing with the disease in dairy stock, and to consider, in consultation with the Highland Society, what steps might be taken to eliminate tubercular disease.

In the new agricultural revolution in which, almost unawares, the country found itself involved, grass acquired a new importance and the improvement of grasslands became a frequent subject of discussion. The introduction of ensilage, too, necessitated more leguminous crops, and the Council sent Dr. Voelcker to Germany to investigate Hellriegel's recent experiments on bacterial inoculation, and, on his return, set him to arrange trials at Woburn.

In the midst of the South African War small attendances at Shows placed the Society in financial difficulties. The question of the migratory Show was brought under review and the Council decided—most unfortunately, as the event was to prove—to look out for a permanent show site near London. In 1900, too, they sent Mr. Martin Sutton to represent them at the International Conference on Agricultural Education in Paris, and his paper must have given them as much cause for pride as it gave reason for shame in Government circles. Mr. Sutton related the Society's efforts on behalf of agricultural education; for more than sixty years the

Society had been the 'heart and brain of English agriculture'—
whereas very little had been done by the State for education. Even
now its grants compared very unfavourably with the sums spent
by continental countries and by the United States.

In 1901 the Royal Patron died. Mr. Prothero's (Lord Ernle)
review of agriculture during her reign presents a picture of self-
help under adverse circumstances. 'It is a picture,' he says, 'of
which landlords and tenants may well be proud. It inspires courage rather than despair. It leaves agriculturists better equipped to
profit by prosperity or to combat misfortune than at any previous
period.' But there was still far to go. The lack of training for the
young farmer exercised the mind of Mr. Gilchrist; the education
of the labourer, said Mr. Sutton, was still untouched.

If the year 1849 'rained away the Corn Laws', the deluge at
Carlisle in 1902 rained away all lingering doubts about the wisdom
of a permanent site for the Show. Relying upon the suffrages of
the Londoner, the Society purchased Park Royal. Two new features now make their appearance at the Shows. British woodlands
were in a very unsatisfactory condition. Apart from the importance of forestry as a branch of rural industry, the supply of timber
would, it was felt, be unequal to any emergency. So it was decided
to include a Forestry exhibit, and shortly afterwards to join with
the Royal Arboricultural Society in instituting a plantations competition. The other innovation was the Agricultural Education
Exhibit, which, although at first consisting mainly of a collection
of photographs and pamphlets, became ultimately an important
agency for disseminating knowledge.

In 1905, after the ruinous experience of three shows at Park
Royal, the Society was forced to recognize the truth of Mr. Pell's
dictum: 'The nearer the Metropolis, the further from profit.' The
'Royal' indeed came somewhere near bankruptcy. But it was re-
constituted on a more democratic basis, backed by the loyalty of
its members and supported by a few generous guarantors. The
first show under the new régime, at Derby, proved a great success.
But Park Royal had been too much for the failing health of Jacob
Wilson, who, responding nobly to the request of the Society in
its difficulties, undertook the Directorship which he had already

laid down after eighteen years of service. Wilson, whose life covered practically the whole of the Victorian era, belonged to the great company of Improvers, always ready even in his old age to change his ways and adopt new farming practices. Of Cumberland farming ancestry, he had acquired his love and knowledge of Shorthorn cattle from his father. As a student at Cirencester College and at Edinburgh University he won his diplomas with honours. Quick to perceive the value of the new mechanical farming, he early began to apply mechanics to practical ends, cut his first harvest himself with a self-delivery reaper, and bought the second pair of ten-horse-power engines ever sold for agricultural purposes.

Probably his most important effort for agriculture was his long campaign in connection with animal disease. He was one of the first to recognize that the only security against the invasion of disease was the compulsory slaughter of all foreign cattle at the port of landing, and to attain this end he laboured long and strenuously against powerful opposition. In the early 'seventies he and his friend Booth of Warlaby, who had lost over £30,000 from repeated attacks of foot-and-mouth disease, spared neither time nor trouble in collecting evidence for the Parliamentary Committee of Enquiry. The Act of 1878, with permissive powers, did not go far enough for them, and for long before 1884, when Mr. Chaplin's Bill was introduced, Wilson had been hard at work, often travelling over two thousand miles a month in his efforts to convert the unbelievers. At last, in 1890, with Chaplin as President of the Board of Agriculture, the recommendations of the Committee under Wilson's chairmanship became law, and provided for the slaughter, with compensation, of animals affected with pleuro-pneumonia. The full fruition of his work came six years later still, when the Act was passed requiring that all foreign animals be slaughtered at the port of debarkation. It is largely to him that British farmers of to-day owe the almost complete immunity of their herds and flocks from imported disease.

Always there was a multitude of relatively minor anxieties for the Council. Johne's disease appeared amongst cattle; increasing motor traffic was raising the dust nuisance on rural roads. A

14. Smithfield Show, 11th–14th December 1839, at the Horse Bazaar, Baker Street, London

15. The Bath and West Society's Show at Newton Abbot, 1857
From a painting in the possession of the Society

16. Royal Agricultural Society's Show, Oxford, 1839

17. Royal Agricultural Society's Show, Oxford, 1950

special committee had to be appointed to watch over possible clean milk legislation, and another to assist the Royal Commission on Agricultural Education. The latter reported that 'although the attitude of farmers had undergone an unmistakable change, the desire for knowledge, which made the task of the teacher in Denmark an easy one, was not a marked attitude of the agricultural classes in England.' How was this to be aroused? Mr. Beaven's reply was, 'You have not sufficiently good material to offer the intelligent agriculturist. Further research is needed. We are still far short of the recommendations of twenty years ago.'

Although at Derby in 1906 the Dairy Shorthorns had appeared for the first time separately from their beefy brothers, Mr. K. J. J. Mackenzie of Cambridge, that champion of the dual-purpose cow, was worried about the low standard of home-produced stores, and Mr. George Gibbons, a West Country pioneer, described the generally deplorable condition of the farm orchards where the newly exhibited spraying machines were yet quite unknown.

In 1910 the Council, as well as the whole farming community, became keenly aware of the great possibilities of the Agricultural Development Bill then before Parliament. A special committee considered its provisions, making recommendations for the assistance to stock breeding and research. Three years later these were brought into effect, financial help being given by the Development Commission to schemes for the provision of high-class sires, to milk recording societies and to various Research Institutions and advisory schemes. In 1914, after the completion of three-quarters of a century of shows, the 'Royal' was again at Shrewsbury. With a magnificent collection of exhibits, a visit from His Majesty King George, deputations of South African and Siberian farmers, the show was a pronounced success, seeming to bear out the general feeling that farming was again definitely on the upgrade. A bare month had passed before the nation was at war. The Council of the 'Royal', like many other bodies, had to form itself into an emergency committee to grapple with a situation unparalleled in history. Not even the Napoleonic Wars had raised the problems that now had to be faced.

'During the latter,' said Lord Ernle, 'through an immense

expenditure of money, much of the land of the country was, for the first time, made, and the great improvements of the eighteenth century enabled the nation, a third of which was then engaged on the land, to endure the hardships of twenty years of almost incessant war. When, during the European war, the fullest possible use of the land again became vital to the national existence, with only one-tenth of the population in agriculture, the advancement of science beyond the dreams of our forefathers was to enable the country to stand four years of terrific strain.' But, he goes on, 'although past experience seemed to afford little or no help in the privations which inevitably followed both wars, the same remedy —increased production and economy—had to be sought. To-day, as then, there is no other way out. We must create the new earth before we can inherit the new heaven.'

Towards this end the Royal Agricultural Society of England has continued to strive, following its honourable traditions of pioneering endeavour, carrying on its experimental and education work, helping wherever it can to uphold the standards of English farming and stock breeding in the face of ever-increasing competition.

THE HIGHLAND AND AGRICULTURAL SOCIETY OF SCOTLAND

Semper armis nunc et industria

The Highland and Agricultural Society had two forerunners. On the 8th June 1723, the Honourable the Society of Improvers in the Knowledge of Agriculture in Scotland was founded by 'certain noblemen and gentlemen, who were impressed by the low state of the manufactures in Scotland, and how much the right husbandry and improvement of ground is neglected, partly through the want of skill in those who make a profession thereby and partly through the want of due encouragement for making proper experiments.' The most important of the three instructions delivered by the Committee of twenty-five to the three hundred members was to 'send up the different ways of the management of their farms, and to form Societies of gentlemen in their various counties.' The foundation of local agricultural associations, still an important part of the 'Highland's' work, was thus fore-shadowed.

The chief service of the Society of Improvers was the provision of advice to its members on such subjects as the improvement of their lands by cropping, manuring, deep ploughing, turnip culti-vation, drilling (instead of broadcasting) their corn, and on the fattening of cattle 'not more than seven years old'.

During the twenty years of its existence the Society's Chronicler was Mr. Maxwell of Arkland, a member of a Nithsdale family which was later to give distinguished service to the 'Highland'. Their *Preses* was Thomas Hope of Rankeilor, near Edinburgh, a man widely travelled in England, France, Flanders, and Holland, and one of the first of a long list of pioneers who, in the next hundred years, were to turn thousands of acres of morass, bog, and barren lands into fertile fields. Few, perhaps, who have attended Highland shows held on the Meadows in Edinburgh ever realize that they are on the site of Stratton's Loch, cleared and drained by Hope, where in 1743 he had 'raised beautiful hedges and trees where gentlemen and ladies resort to walk.' The Im-provers often met, in a society way, at the residence of their *Preses*, probably all wearing linen of Scottish manufacture, according to the request of the Society to its members and their families.

Over the joint they probably discussed Mr. Nelson of Corsock's method of stall feeding black cattle, and observed through the windows Mr. Mackintosh's bullocks feeding in the field outside. Over dessert the talk ran on such topics as the mode of grafting codlins on a Dutch or English stock. A new recipe for making cheese might follow, and no doubt the Honourable Improvers finished up with a dram of the true Rosa Solis, a restorative cordial. But, in 1745 came the Deluge. Of those who sat round the hospitable table, at least half were pledged to the restoration of the House of Stuart, and the 'Forty-Five was the end of the Society, as it was the end of much else.

The next effort for the improvement of agriculture grew out of the Select Society, founded in 1754 by Allan Ramsay, the painter and a son of the poet. Those associated in the foundation of the Society, which was concerned partly with philosophic inquiry and partly with the improvement of public speaking, included Robertson the historian; David Hume and Adam Smith, both reported as never opening their mouths to speak; 'Jupiter' Carlyle of Inveresk; Wedderburn, afterwards Lord Chancellor of England; Home, the author of *Douglas, a Tragedy*, which created a sensation on the London stage, but is now almost forgotten; Sir Gilbert Elliot, founder of the house of Minto—truly a remarkable assembly for the little capital of a poor little country.

In 1755 the Select Society founded the Edinburgh Society, which adopted the policy of offering premiums for a wide range of objects—Scotch ale and porter, blankets, carpets, printed cotton, linen, etc. The first premiums offered for agriculture were a gold medal for the best 'Dissertation on Vegetation and the Principles of Agriculture', and a prize for the farmer who should rear the greatest number of young thorn trees. The last was a sign that the age of enclosing and planting the bare lands of Scotland had begun. In 1756 the prize list had still more of an agricultural bias—ten guineas to Robert Mackail, wheelwright, Dunipace, inventor of a machine for cleaning wheat; a silver medal to Mr. John Walker of Borgue Kirk for producing the greatest variety of marls and other natural manures. (Walker was afterwards Professor of Natural History and lecturer on Agriculture at Edinburgh University.) £10 to Willie Gun for the best stud stallion, and £4 to Ann Wade of Yester 'for the greatest number of calves not under eight weeks old and sold to the butcher.' These two prizes, awarded in December 1756, were the first to be given in Scotland for live stock.

In 1759 the Select Society held a show of stallions, 'no fewer than nine being presented.' But in 1764 a financial crisis occurred in the affairs of both societies, and on August 12th, Mr. Secretary Barclay, after intimating a threat of legal proceedings against the members for arrears of subscriptions, 'closed the books and went shooting'.

For the next twenty years, wars and scarcity followed by agricultural depression, distress in the Highlands and failure of crops, occupied the minds of the agricultural community. It was not until after the declaration of peace with America that, on 9th February 1784, a meeting was held at Fortune's Tontine Tavern in Edinburgh, attended by fifty gentlemen connected with the north-west; at this the Highland Society of Scotland was founded, under the Presidency of John fifth Duke of Argyll.

The Society at once appointed a committee, a treasurer, a secretary, two chaplains, one piper, a bard, a professor of Gaelic, and an 'officer'.

The original objects, while fairly ambitious, were by no means purely concerned with agriculture. They were (1) to conduct an inquiry into the present state of the Highlands and Islands, and the condition of their inhabitants; (2) to inquire into the means of the improvement of the Highlands; and (3) to take steps for the preservation of the language, poetry, and music of the Highlands. A Royal Charter was granted in 1787 and, what was probably more important, two years later the Society got a grant of £3,000 out of the moneys received when the estates, forfeited in the 'Forty-Five rebellion, were disannexed and restored to their original owners.

The state of agriculture in Scotland at this period is described in the Old Statistical Account of 1791–6, the official reports of the Board of Agriculture of 1794–5, and the survey made by Wight on behalf of the Commissioners of the Annexed Estates in 1775–82.

As in England, a mania for improvement had seized the gentry. There are constant references to improved turnip husbandry, to the introduction of the Norfolk system, to Bakewell's Leicesters and Longhorns, to the improved Ayrshire breed, to Cheviot sheep and Lanarkshire horses, to better cheese and improved sorts of oats, to marling, and to drilling-machines.

As befitted its title and objects, the Society was at first concerned mainly with the Highlands, but it gradually extended its operations to the whole country. In their zeal for improvement nothing was too small to escape the members' notice; they offered premiums for local ploughing matches, for reclamation of land, for the cleanest-kept cottage, for the best sheep drains, for plans of new villages in the Highlands, for the growing of osiers, and for the best-manured farm. They gave prizes for essays on the cultivation of native grasses, on the natural history of the herring, the stapling of wool, the use of brushwood, and the dressing of peat land with lime. They reported on carp in fishponds, on bone mills, and on coalfields. They offered premiums for stallions, and for improving the breed of sheep in various districts. Mr. Walter Laidlaw of Menzion in Peeblesshire received a gold medal for the introduction of the white-faced or Cheviot breed of sheep on an extensive scale 'to his own advantage and that of others in his country'. The Society sent young James Johnston to England to 'attend Mr. Elkington and learn his practice of draining', and when Johnston died in 1858 they gratefully engraved on his tombstone, in the West Churchyard of Edinburgh, that 'he was instrumental in improving the estates of a very large proportion of the landed proprietors of Scotland.'

They had their failures, too, for when they imported 'two respectable, intelligent young farmers of Flanders to demonstrate the use of an improved scythe, the Scottish labourer was too lazy to make use of it.' Finally, in the midst of depression that followed the Napoleonic wars, augmented by two bad harvests, they decided to hold a General Show of Stock; this was held on Thursday, 26th December 1822.

To the foresight and spirited direction of Sir John Sinclair, backed by the enthusiasm of the directors, their first show owed its success. They secured from the military an acre of land, the backyard of Queensberry House in the Canongate, and offered prizes for fat bullocks of Shorthorn, Aberdeenshire, West Highland, and other breeds.

The public were admitted at one shilling each and the amount drawn was £52 12s., 'sufficient to cover all extra expenses for advertising, printing, fitting up of the yard, and servants employed'. Shorthorns were the most numerous. Although no premiums were offered for sheep, eight New Leicester two-year-old wethers were exhibited, as well as 'two beautiful pigs'.

Encouraged by success, the Society repeated the experiment in 1823 and 1824. In the latter year a prize was given for 'the two best cows of any breed for the purpose of breeding'—the first for breeding stock offered in Scotland.

In those more leisurely days members often breakfasted together before the show opened, or dined together in the early afternoon, evidently agreeing with Dr. Johnson that 'a dinner with persons whom we esteem expands the heart and kindles the natural mind.' The dinner was often followed by a ball, which was attended by the ladies of the neighbourhood.

Reports of these cheerful gatherings, some of which (judging by the amount of home-grown produce consumed) must have been of practical benefit to the farmer, make amusing reading. The Dukes, Earls, Knights, the many Gentry, and the few tenant farmers who composed the company were full of goodfellowship and patriotic fervour to improve the condition of their native land. At Dumfries in 1857, with 1,200 diners, there were no fewer than thirty-six toasts, ending with 'The Land o' Cakes and Good Roads to Ready Markets.' Ten years later, when the dinner ticket cost 10s., 'including a pint of wine and a bottle of cold punch,' the 'Highland' members drank success to the newly formed sister Society of England. At Kelso they listened to the Duke of Buccleuch's oration, 'distinguished by much feeling,' on his kinsman the late Sir Walter Scott. In Glasgow they entertained a Russian Prince and a French delegation. At Aberdeen the company was so numerous that they had to dine in four separate rooms, and seem to have passed a pleasant evening exchanging members to and fro, 'drinking successful voyages to the deputations' which went to acquaint each gentleman when his health was being drunk in another room.

In 1825 the Society again widened its sphere of activity, this time offering district premiums for dairy products, for draining moss and bog land, curing of beef and pork, plaiting of bonnets from rye straw, for farm book-keeping, and many more.

As one scans the schedules one can picture the progress of stock breeding. In 1829 bulls and cows of Angus breed were shown, and in 1830 an ox of the Shorthorn-Galloway cross, the first of the 'blue-greys'. In 1822 at Kelso, where classes were thrown open to England, the Shorthorn 'that universal intruder', surpassed all other entries, whereas at Inverness in 1831 there was not a single one. We may note the Border Leicester gradually acquiring sufficient distinction to be classed separately and finally superseding the English type; the Cheviot and the Shorthorn creeping northwards; the Clydesdale spreading; the polled Aberdeen Angus supplanting the old horned breed; the improvement in butter and cheese, and the gradually increasing attention to poultry and pigs.

In 1834 the Society took the important step for the future of stock-breeding of deciding on the breeds of cattle and sheep which they would recognize in their future shows; then and for many years afterwards Shorthorn, West Highland, Aberdeen Angus, Galloway and Ayrshire cattle and New Leicester, Blackface and Cheviot sheep were the only breeds appearing in the list.

In the early prize lists appear the names of nearly all the famous breeders of the day—Booth of Warlaby, Bates of Kirklevington, Barclay of Ury, and Amos Cruickshank; M'Combie of Tillyfour, Walker of Portlethen, and Grant of Ballindalloch; Brydon of Moodlaw and Elliot of Hindhope; Polwarth of Mertoun; Riddell and Drew; Archibald of Overshiels; Howatson of Glenbuck, the Biggars of Chapelton and a host more. Nor were members content with displaying their best stock to each other; fervently Nationalist, they were seriously offended at the omission of Scottish breeds from the schedule of the International Show in Paris in 1856. Succeeding in obtaining a supplementary programme for Scotland, they invaded Paris with a deputation of members and a convoy of 155 head of cattle and 182 sheep, their stock outnumbering that of any other nation except France.

The Society presented the Emperor Louis Napoleon with a copy of the *Transactions* of the Society, and a Diploma as Extraordinary Member; they returned home with 80 money premiums and 146 medals—'a profitable expedition', as they recorded in their minutes.

The rise of mechanical inventions is also reflected in the pages of the old reports. Heathcoat's steam plough was brought to Dumfries for the Show of 1837, and was tried on Lochar Moss, and Mr. Heathcoat was given an Honorary Membership of the Society. Bell's reaping machine was shown at Perth in 1846.

Fowler's Steam Cultivator was tried at Stewart Hall, near Stirling, in 1857, and gained the Society's premium of £200.

Another historic occasion was in 1844, when some of the members, gentlemen of Ayrshire, purchased a vessel and sent it out to Peru for a cargo of guano.

Even after its activities were extended to cover the whole country, the Society was not unmindful of the object stated in the original charter—the development of the Highlands. It offered premiums and prizes at shows to encourage the traditional industries—spinning, weaving, and knitting—of the Islands and the North. From these small beginnings arose an increasing demand for Scottish hand-made woollen goods, which now, since the advent of the Women's Institutes, occupy, along with other home industries, an important position at every show.

In some parts of Scotland the live stock was practically wiped out by the ravages of the rinderpest in the 'sixties, and in the long-drawn-out agitation for the stamping out of contagious diseases the 'Highland' naturally co-operated with the 'Royal', making special investigations for Scotland and sending deputations to the Privy Council and to the Board of Agriculture.

Scotland had also special scourges of its own. In a country so largely dependent on the well-being of its sheep stock the incidence of Sheep Scab, of Maggot Fly, Braxy, and Louping Ill was obviously important. The Society was continually on the watch for possible cures, urging the measures of central control that had banished scab from Australia and New Zealand, offering premiums for research in fly preventives and arranging for prolonged investigations by their own veterinary officer.

The researches and writings of Liebig had not passed unnoticed in Scotland. In 1843 a few Midlothian farmers formed an Agricultural Chemistry Association, whose chief promoter was John Finnie of Swanston. Numerous papers by their chemist, Professor Johnston of Durham, appeared in the *Transactions* of the Highland Society and when, in 1848, the Association came to an end, its work was taken over and a consultant chemist, Dr. Thomas Anderson, was appointed. He was followed by Mr. James Dewar, and he again by Dr. A. P. Aitken, notable pioneer in field experiment methods. At the Society's experimental farm at Pumpherston, as well as on the farms of members, he carried out important investigations on the improvement of upland and lowland pastures, on the effects of grazing, the feeding of sheep and bullocks, and the manuring of various arable crops.

Nowadays all south-country growers are familiar with the merits of Scottish seed potatoes, but few perhaps realize that they owe one of the most important discoveries in a great industry to the patient experiments of William Paterson, a Dundee market gardener, who, after the disastrous failure of the crop in 1846, set himself to produce a variety immune from blight.

When more disastrous seasons came in the late 'seventies the production of new varieties and the whole question of potato cultivation became matters of national importance. At this time again the Society played its part by financing experiments and by collecting and publishing information on the methods of the best growers both at home and abroad. In the late 'eighties the Directors were active in connection with the introduction of the new methods of combating plant diseases and pests. They received reports on the methods of fruit spraying adopted in America and in the vineyards of France, where was made the accidental discovery of the fungicidal value of copper compounds that ultimately proved very valuable to the potato grower.

John Speir, who had done so much for the dairy industry in Scotland and had started the milk recording movement in Britain, died in 1910. His labours were carried on, along with a great deal more work in the cause of agriculture, by Charles Douglas of Auchlochan in Lanarkshire. Douglas was a philosopher by training, had been a teacher of his subject in Glasgow University, and he brought to bear on current agricultural problems a calm and dispassionate judgement, a clear head and a capacity for broad views. He filled Spier's place as Chairman of the Scottish Milk Records Association, was Chairman of the 'Highland' Board and served on various Royal Commissions.

He was deeply interested in Horace Plunkett's great work for Ireland, became convinced of the need for organized marketing, especially in the dairy and poultry industries, and was mainly responsible for the formation of the Scottish Agricultural Organization Society. The innate individualism of Scottish farmers made progress very difficult, but by 1907, after two years of work, the Society was established and had forty affiliated co-operative associations.

Another of the services of the 'Highland' was the help that it gave to veterinary education in Scotland. In 1816 the University of Edinburgh refused to consider the Society's suggestion for a Chair of Comparative Anatomy embracing Veterinary Physic and Surgery as 'implying adjuncts scarcely compatible with university life', and the 'Highland' directors determined to find some other means of providing veterinary instruction.

Just at this time a young man, William Dick, son of a blacksmith and farrier, after attending some popular lectures in the Medical and Surgical Schools in Edinburgh, went to London and returned with the Diploma of the Royal Veterinary College and a determination to put his country in a better position in the matter of veterinary training. Animal practitioners at this time used very much the methods of the old Gloucestershire cowdoctor, 'I physics 'em, and I bleeds 'em and I sweats 'em, and if they will die I lets 'em.'

Dick started a series of evening classes in a tiny room in Clyde Street; hearing of his venture the Society came to terms with him; that he should 'for the sum of £30 and furnished with a forge and other appendages for the practical instruction of country farriers accordingly begin his first course of lectures on the diseases of horses, black cattle, sheep and other domestic animals, illustrated by the necessary anatomical demonstrations.' At the first public examination, conducted by six medical practitioners, seven students received a certificate that 'they were qualified to practise the veterinary art.'

Dick's fame grew, students came in increasing numbers, the title of College was conferred on his premises and that of Professor on himself. The London College, however, had been granted a charter with the sole right to confer diplomas and it was not until many years later that the Society's examinations were recognized as admitting to membership of the profession.

Meanwhile Dick, 'the old white lion', continued with all his immense force of character and sturdy determination to press forward to his goal, turning out from his classroom in Clyde Street men like M'Call, Williams, Low, Strangeways, Finlay Dun, and many others who later acquired world-wide reputations.

Aided by the Society, he rescued Veterinary Science in Scotland from obscurity. The final result of his efforts was the establishment of the Royal (Dick) Veterinary College, now equipped to provide a training that is in keeping with the importance of Veterinary Science, and incorporated in the University of Edinburgh.

As Sir John Stirling Maxwell points out, although Scotland possesses wide areas suitable for afforestation, sylviculture had never become traditional in Scotland. There had been a time, indeed, in the latter half of the eighteenth and the early nineteenth centuries, when the face of Scotland became transformed as if by magic by her improving and tree-planting lairds. But the tradition had no time to take root. The old plans were forgotten; commercial land utilization gave place to sport; cheap foreign timber must share with the pheasant the blame for the disastrous change. Still, writing in 1911, Maxwell saw signs of revival, due largely to the work of the Scottish Arboricultural and the Highland and Agricultural Societies. Although the 'Highland' had started in 1870 to conduct examinations in forestry, it was not until 1894 that the two Societies succeeded in raising £5,000 in order to secure, with the help of a Government grant, the establishment of a Lectureship in Forestry at Edinburgh University. Even then there was no State Demonstration Forest, either in Scotland or in England. Students had to get their practical experience in France or Germany or on the estates of a few enterprising landowners like Munro Ferguson who, in 1899, put 800 acres of woods under a regular system of management and made it available for the use of Edinburgh students. In 1790 the Society had recommended its members to attend a course of lectures on agriculture and other agrestic subjects to be delivered by Dr. J. Walker, Professor of Natural History at the University of Edinburgh. Shortly afterwards a Chair of Agriculture was instituted, Sir William Pulteney providing an endowment of £50 a year, and Dr. Coventry was appointed as first Professor. The Society made various efforts to secure more adequate emoluments for the incumbent, and offered their help in the matter, but it was not till 1868 that they succeeded in their object. From then until 1893 they contributed to the support of the Professorship.

In 1831 on Coventry's death, one of their members, Mr. David Low, was an applicant for the Professorship and the Society gave its unqualified testimonial of his 'zeal, intelligence, and practical knowledge, combined with scientific and literary attainments.' Their perspicuity was justified, both by Low's notable contributions to agricultural literature and by the numbers of students whom he attracted from all parts of the world.

In 1858 the 'Highland' instituted examinations for a diploma in agriculture and dairying, and later joined forces with the 'Royal' in conducting the National Diploma examinations in these subjects.

Recalling that from the first they had offered premiums to improve the quality of butter and cheese, the Society formed a special Dairy Committee to assist progress in the dairying industry. They made grants to the Scottish Dairy Association for the establishment of dairy schools and arranged for a demonstration dairy at their shows.

Being told by John Speir that quality is the best safeguard against importations, the Directors invited Mr. Harris, a Canadian, to conduct itinerant classes in cheese making, and later, in 1889, Mr. R. J. Drummond was finally installed with the permanent equipment of a Dairy School at Holmes Farm, Kilmarnock.

Although Edinburgh had had its Chair of Agriculture since 1892, and there were lectures in Glasgow and Aberdeen, there was still no organized system of agricultural education throughout the country. When, in 1876, through the initiative of the Society, the Science and Art Department at South Kensington issued a syllabus of instruction in agriculture for schools, the necessity for special training for teachers at once became apparent. Next year we find Aberdeen providing appropriate instruction, of which full advantage was taken, and later Edinburgh and Glasgow followed suit. The Society meanwhile encouraged the teaching of agriculture in the schools by offering bursaries for subsequent University courses.

Seven years passed, still without any adequate financial help from the Government. Indignant that the interests of Scotland should be so neglected, the Society sent a deputation direct to Mr. Goschen, then Chancellor of the Exchequer; the delegates, with a good deal of plain speaking, pointed out that whereas Ireland was getting an annual grant of £4,000 for agricultural education, Scotland was being starved. In 1885, when Professor Robert Wallace was appointed to the Chair of Agriculture at Edinburgh, there was still no provision for instruction in the cognate sciences like agricultural chemistry and botany. Wallace at once tried to remedy this by getting extra-mural lecturers to provide courses, and in 1892 this body formed the Incorporated School of Agriculture. When, however, the powers of the Scottish Education Department were extended to include Agricultural Instruction the training centres, with the backing of the Society, developed into fully incorporated Agricultural Colleges, with extension services, and affiliated to the respective Universities which by this time had instituted degree courses in Agriculture.

When the Development Commission was set up the 'Highland' was again concerned to see that the claims of Scotland, in the matter of agricultural research, were not overlooked. They saw the fruition of their efforts in the successive foundation of the Rowett Research Institute at Aberdeen, the Scottish Plant Breeding Station, the Animal Diseases Research Association, and the Department of Animal Breeding in Edinburgh.

The story of the 'Highland' would still be incomplete without reference to a few more of the men who, as Presidents, Chairmen or Secretaries, rendered it specially remarkable service.

For the first eighty-five years of the Society's existence there was an unbroken succession of ducal Presidents, all men distinguished by their patriotic desire for the progress of rural Scotland— Argylls and Atholls, Buccleuchs, and Montrose. The first break in the tradition came in 1869 when the Peninsular veteran, the Marquis of Tweeddale, was called to fill the office. He was an enthusiastic improver both of land and stock and his experiments at Yester, in deep cultivation by steam power, are still worthy of study to-day.

Perhaps the greatest of many 'Highland' Secretaries was John Hall Maxwell, who for twenty years devoted his extraordinary powers of organization to the object he had in mind 'to hold Scotland in one great Society's network and never to let a mesh be out of order.' He was something of an autocrat and refused to allow even his President to break the rules by buying a catalogue before the official opening of the Show. It was he, along with the Duke of Hamilton, who organized the exhibit of Scottish live stock at the Paris Show and who led the hundred and twenty Scottish stockmen, with their exhibits, to Battersea fields.

At the shows he insisted that everything should be done with order and dignity. He himself was the field-marshal, living almost the whole week in the saddle, galloping on his bay cob hither and thither and giving peremptory orders to judges and stewards without regard to their ranks and titles.

The twenty years from 1893 when James Macdonald was Secretary was another period of great progress in Scottish farming. With his experience, his complete mastery of detail and his capacity for hard work, Macdonald made the Society, which had been in a somewhat moribund state, a live force, influencing agricultural development not only in Scotland but all over Great Britain. 'His services as a pioneer in the cause of agricultural education were such that his name will ever be associated with the foundation of the system of Agricultural Colleges in Scotland and the institution of the National Diplomas in Agriculture and Dairying.' His journalistic experience enabled him to issue volume after volume of the *Transactions* filled with practical guidance in an attractive form. Not even the prospect of 'the whole show floating into the Solway', on a memorable occasion at Dumfries, could shake his calm urbanity.

Among the many parish ministers of the gospel who, during the past centuries, have played important parts in all spheres of the Scottish life, John Gillespie, an Annandale farmer's son, left the greatest mark on Scottish agriculture. Not for nothing was he called the 'Minister for Agriculture for Scotland'. He came of a long line of tenant farmers who, as he often proudly related, had for over two hundred years held land in his own parish of Mouswald. There he discharged the duties of parish minister for forty-seven years; and from it no offers of preferment could attract him away.

His father had been a pioneer in his day in improved methods of farming. From him he acquired his love of Galloway cattle, which he bred on his Glebe farm with marked success, and for whose progress he did so much; he founded the Galloway Society, editing the Herd Book and doing much to bring the breed into prominence both in Great Britain and America.

To agricultural problems he brought an acute legal type of mind, and an enthusiasm tempered by practical experience. Coming into close contact with the farmers of his parish, he soon appreciated the fact that Acts of Parliament were not easily understandable by them. He wrote a pamphlet on *Farmers and Income Tax*, to make plain their obligations under the Act, and his *Manual of the Agricultural Holdings Act* gained him unrivalled authority as an arbiter. Many a claim was settled, by him and his friend James Biggar, with a minimum of expense and a maximum of satisfaction to the parties.

But it was after his appointment, in 1880, as a Director of the 'Highland', that his powers found their widest scope. For twenty years he filled almost every post on the National Society, as Livestock Steward, as Treasurer and Chairman of Finance, and as Permanent Chairman of the Board. Always an unswerving advocate of popular rights, he had not been many years on the Board before he recognized that the close corporation which it then was should be changed, in so far that some members at least should be elected by a democratic system; and he persuaded his colleagues to adopt the system of nominating Ordinary Directors at district meetings. No other man of his time had anything like the same grasp of the details of the Society's business, and during the first decade of Macdonald's secretaryship, and when he, John Speir, and Gillespie himself were all at the zenith of their powers, the Board of Directors was a force to be reckoned with.

Perhaps it was as Chairman of the Committee on Education

and Publications that he accomplished his most lasting work. His goal had always been to bring the best agricultural education within reach of all, and to this end he especially dedicated himself. He was largely responsible for the founding of the West of Scotland Agricultural College, and became the first Chairman of its Governors.

His work for agriculture, which would have sufficed to occupy the whole time of an ordinary man, was equalled only by his devotion to his profession as Minister of the Church of Scotland, in which he justly attained to the highest dignities. Possessing the 'blessed gift of making friends', he had the confidence and affection of all classes, and especially of the farmers, to further whose interests he laboured unceasingly throughout a long life. In the words of one who served as editor under his Chairmanship for twenty years, 'There was only one Dr. Gillespie, and there will never be another.' He had such natural dignity that he never required to stand upon it. The last recollection of him, for many Highland members, is that of a benevolent old gentleman in a top hat and carrying an umbrella, making 'comic business' in the Highland ring with a wayward Shetland foal.

THE BATH AND WEST SOCIETY

Work and Learn

The City of Bath in the late eighteenth century, the Bath of Dr. Johnson and Horace Walpole, of Sheridan and Garrick, of Fanny D'Arblay and the blue-stockings, might seem an unlikely birthplace for an agricultural society. The rank and fashion were more interested in dress and pleasure than in ploughs and turnips. But it was a pregnant age. The seeds of a new world were being sown. What time Great Britain was losing one Dominion through the folly of her rulers, Warren Hastings was building a new Empire in the East and Captain Cook was setting forth to discover yet another. Gilbert White was observing the workings of nature; Herschel was watching the movements of the heavenly bodies; Priestly was laying the foundations of modern chemistry, and James Watt was harnessing steam to revolutionize industry.

In 1775 there came to Bath, from Norfolk, one Edmund Rack, a man of humble Quaker parentage, with little schooling beyond the three R's. Having retired from a shopkeeping business at the age of forty with a modest competency, he set about repairing his lack of education, and soon blossomed forth as a writer of essays and letters. His volume of poems gave him an entrée to the literary circles of Bath and he became a frequenter of the fortnightly re-unions of Lady Miller, the well-known blue-stocking; he was included, too, in the select circle of the handsome Mrs. Macaulay, the ardent republican, and thus acquired the habits of elegant society and got an opportunity to develop his innate literary gifts. Before he had left Norfolk, he had shown his interest in agriculture by contributions to the *Farmer's Magazine*. He had noted the fine farm that Coke had created out of a rabbit warren, and he was at once struck by the relatively backward state of farming in the West Country. Mr. Crutwell, a publisher in Bath, commissioned Rack to write a series of articles for the *Bath Chronicle* on the need for a combined effort to improve agriculture. In these he developed his plan for a Society which 'should offer pecuniary and honorary rewards to the diligent and ingenious who have excelled in the departments of husbandry, in useful manufactures, and in the most famous specimens of art.'

Rack invited the nobility and gentry of the counties of Somer-set, Wiltshire, Gloucestershire, and Dorset in general and the citizens of Bath and Bristol in particular, to come to a meeting at York House on September 8th, 1777. The first Committee met in October under the presidency of Dr. Falconer, a distinguished physician, a versatile man and a Fellow of the Royal Society. The new Society was formed, drew in some of the leading nobility and gentry as President and Vice-Presidents, and elected Mr. Rack as Secretary at the honorarium of £50 per annum.

By the end of the year Rack announced in a letter full of modest exultation that he had collected a sum of £350 to be spent in premiums. The Society started off to encourage the setting of corn on the Norfolk system. They persuaded a member to try Mr. Blanchard's new plough, and arranged a ploughing match, 'held to be the first of its kind in this or any other country.'

In the same year they circularized the High Sheriffs of every county, appealing to them as 'gentlemen of public character and liberal minds' to provide them with lists of practical farmers in their districts from whom they proposed to collect information about the best farming practices. In response to their questionnaire, they obtained a curious collection of useful practical knowledge mixed up with many superstitious notions, such as a method of destroying weevils by throwing live lobsters on the heaps of stored wheat, 'specially fatal if left till they stink.' The Society extended its area to include all the western counties, and began a campaign to introduce the Norfolk plough. Finding, however, that only one farmer out of five hundred adopted it, they were inclined to lay the blame on the 'prejudice of the ploughman and the indolence of the master'.

The improvement of the local breeds of sheep and cattle next occupied their attention. Crossing with Bakewell's sheep to increase the wool, and the use of his improved bulls on the Somerset and Devon cattle, were recommended. Premiums for live stock were offered and a prize of £10 was awarded to the Rev. William Quartley, for the best bull and dam of the North Devon breed.

In 1779, the Society carried out 'a spirited extension of their original plan' by acquiring an experimental plot of ten acres on the farm of Mr. Bethell of Weston. It was the first of its kind in England, the precursor of Rothamsted. Arthur Young wrote to say that he hoped it would have some effect upon the farming practice in the county as 'nothing sounds so wonderful to East Country farmers as hearing of the conduct of their brethren in the West who do not hoe their turnip crop.'

In spite of ill-health Rack continued his zealous work, comparing costs of ploughing by horse- and ox-drawn ploughs, compiling lists of plants 'eaten or rejected by cattle', and inquiring into the progress of agriculture in the eastern counties; he was well supported by his friend Mr. Billingsley, a farmer famous for having, in the course of a few years, enclosed and improved over 5,000 acres of valueless hill and moorland on the Mendips. But in 1787 he is found writing to a friend, 'I seem to be verging downwards to that valley which terminates in the shadow of death.'

Under Matthews, Rack's successor, the Society honoured the memory of its late President, Francis Duke of Bedford, by instituting the Bedfordian Gold Medal, bestowing it not only for distinction in Agriculture, but also upon Parry for Arctic exploration as well as upon Chantry the sculptor. Receiving by Sir Thomas Beevor of Norfolk a few seeds which had come to him from Germany, the Society planted and harvested the first crop of mangold-wurzel ever grown in the West Country. At first the leaves, fed to pigs or boiled as spinach for the table, were more appreciated than the root. The Society also urged more attention to the field cultivation of turnips, parsnips, carrots, and potatoes, especially the last, since the crop was 'of inestimable value, not only as a constant dish in great and opulent families but, in times of scarcity and dearness, as the whole subsistence of the poor.' They were concerned about the state of the labourers, advising allotments which 'give the labourer a sense of security in the civilised class of society, thus generating a strong tie to the higher classes and a disposition to protect rather than to attack property.' They fathered the formation of Friendly Societies, and submitted plans for improved cottages. As was natural in an area of butter and cheese production they took an interest in the progress of dairying, even suggesting clean milk regulations—'that the cow's udder should be washed with clean water before milking.'

As the wealth of the Cotswolds was founded on wool-growing, so the riches of the West arose from cloth manufacture. The old industry still flourished in the towns and villages from Frome to Stroud, and many great families owed their rise to the profits resulting. Sir Benjamin Hobhouse, a supporter of the Society, was a clothier before he became a banker. It was appropriate that the 'Bath and West' should foster the trade by improving the quality of the local wool, and for nearly a quarter of a century it supported the efforts of 'Farmer George' to popularize the Merino sheep. Prominent members appeared dressed in blue and black broadcloth, and the President wore a uniform of white Kerseymere, manufactured from the wool of Lord Somerville's Ryeland-Merino cross sheep.

The discussions on arable *versus* grassland farming strike a modern note. Mr. Davis of Longleet noted 'a tenant of a grass farm made money, while a corn farm of the same size starved its occupier.' Indeed the scarcity of cheese and butter was laid at the door of arable farming, although an indignant member, who could get no butter with his tea although he saw a hundred tubs ready for the London wagons, was inclined to blame the merchants rather than the farmers.

On the whole, the Society had proved its utility, but about 1820 signs of decay set in and membership declined. Improvement had been so great that there seemed to be no more worlds to conquer; farmers, unjustly blamed for the scarcity and dearness of provisions during the war years, were unpopular and got little sympathy during the years of depression that followed. The Society had to sell out its stock, give up its house, and change the Bedford Gold Medal into silver. By the 'forties it had begun to 'dwindle, peak and pine' and might have faded out of existence if, in 1847, a West Country squire had not made up his mind to retire from Parliament in order to devote himself to the management of his estates.

Born in 1809, Thomas Dyke Acland the Squire of Killerton, belonged to the group of pioneer landowners among whom were his friends, Phillip Pusey, Earl Ducie, and Lord Somerville. When he gave up parliamentary life an old friend said to him, 'Whatever you do, don't go to sleep.' He took the advice, and started to inform himself about agriculture, 'by jogging along the road with some shrewd old farmer, teasing him with questions.' When Garrett, Hornsby, and Crosskill brought their implements to the R.A.S.E. Show at Exeter, he determined to make an effort to bring all the advantages of such an exhibition within reach of the West Country. Convinced that 'there was life in the old dog yet', he laid before the Society a scheme for its reorganization, suggesting that it should hold its meeting in a different place each year, raise sufficient income to give prizes for implements as well as stock, and distribute printed reports of careful experiments, 'in short, to carry into every corner between Dundry Hill and Dunkerry Beacon the results attainable by practice with science.'

The first Show under the new regime was held at Taunton in 1850 with 238 entries of live stock and 400 implements. When the 'Bath and West' visited Taunton again in 1870 the exhibits of stock had risen to 908 and the almost innumerable implements covered 9,200 square feet of ground. The keynote of Acland's policy was to induce selected practical farmers to demonstrate new methods to their neighbours and to undertake experiments whose results should be published in the *Journal*. Having helped Pusey in editing the 'Royal' *Journal*, he had the experience necessary to run the other Society's *Journal*, whose editorship he retained for seven years. He wrote many articles himself, covering almost the whole field of farming practice. In the introduction to each number he displayed a humour and style that placed him in the front rank as a journalist.

Acland once described himself as 'one of those old-fashioned survivors of the pre-scientific period, who was taught at Oxford by Aristotle that the only way to become a shoemaker was to make shoes.' Yet realizing the value that he himself had got from a course in chemistry at King's College he was quite alive to the fact that the farmer had much to learn from science. He drew attention to the work of Lawes, Gilbert, and Voelcker, and was always trying 'to do something to render science more practical and practice more scientific.' His balanced mind saw agriculture not as an isolated business, but as a part of the general life of the nation. He saw that the usefulness of agricultural societies would decline if they concentrated all their efforts on their annual shows of stock and implements. In 1885, therefore, he urged that less money should be devoted to prizes, and more to experiments, research, practical instruction in agricultural operations, dairying, new methods of dealing with produce, new systems of cultivation, rotation of crops and other efforts to maintain cultivation of land under the probable low price of corn. He insisted that all experiments on his own farms should be carried out on lines that would be practicable under ordinary conditions.

Up till the last years of his life, his tall, finely built figure, clad in rough homespun, with a satchel of agricultural literature for distribution slung low down at his side, was a familiar sight in

BARNEYHILL
DUNBAR

the showyard. When he died, in his ninetieth year, his own West Country people felt the loss of a friend and the whole farming community that of a man who had never stinted his service in the cause of their enlightenment.

One of the chief contributions of the 'Bath and West' to better farming was the establishment in 1885 of a working dairy at its shows. A few years later, largely owing to the initiative of Mr. Gibbons, were started the itinerant schools of butter- and cheese-making which spread knowledge of these subjects in the villages.

Meanwhile various members had been concerned about the haphazard way in which cider, an essentially West Country product, was being made. Mr. James Harper of Ebley near Stroud had been making experiments in order to induce farmers to adopt better methods, but the genesis of the movement which eventually resulted in the formation of the Fruit and Cider Institute at Long Ashton, was the research begun at Butleigh Abbey. A talk with Mr. Neville Grenville, the late Squire of Butleigh, who was still, despite his eighty years, full of pioneering spirit, made one realize how short a time had elapsed since scientific research has been applied to the production of many of our valuable home products. About 1900 we were importing nearly half a million gallons of cider annually from the United States, while our home orchards were full of pest-ridden and neglected trees, renewed on the principle of 'A was an Apple Tree'. 'The great and noble art of cider-making was for the most part conducted in the ignorant and careless way common in the country.' Convinced of the necessity of research, Mr. Grenville persuaded Mr. F. J. Lloyd, who had been conducting a cheese school at Butleigh, to keep his laboratory going and to examined the cider problem. In the following year he induced the Society to take the matter up in earnest.

With great difficulty he convinced the Board of Agriculture that research must precede education, and a grant of £100 was extracted from the Government. Hundreds of farmers and others interested in cider making visited the station to learn the science and the art. Vintage cider was still made in the great old tithe barn, by Frank Talbot, a veteran of seventy-one years. Grenville was a pioneer of the steam age, and one of the first six Fowler Cultivators, which he brought into Somerset over fifty years ago, was still in active service.

The directors of the 'Bath and West' have never been mere adorning figureheads, but men ready to turn their hand to anything. On one show-day, finding some of the cattlemen late in clearing the lines, the steward got hold of a cart and started to help. Whereupon an old Somerset cowman called to another, 'Come 'ee 'ere, Bill, come 'ee 'ere. 'Ere's a real lard a-loadin' muck cart.'

Since the formation of a special committee in 1887, the Society has spent large sums in conducting experiments dealing, among other things, with improved methods of cultivation and the improvement of pasture land. It has also financed valuable surveys of agricultural industries and in many other ways has lived up to the original ideas of its founders that it should 'diffuse the knowledge it rewards, and render the successful efforts of individuals the means of general improvement.'

12

THE PRESS AND THE PILGRIMS

'Thus, Sir, have I led you about the country. All sorts of things have I talked of; at the end of a hundred miles or two of travelling, stopping here and there; talking freely with everybody; hearing what gentlemen, farmers, tradesmen, journeymen, labourers, women, girls and boys and all have to say. At the end of a tramp like this you get impressed upon your mind a true picture, not only of the state of the country but of the state of the people's minds throughout the country.'

COBBETT

The agricultural Press played an important part in the reawakening of the farming world which began in the 'forties of last century. In those days there were still few facilities for travel, the literature of the time of Young, Marshall, and Sinclair was nearly half a century old, and the agricultural press became the chief means for the diffusion of information and the exchange of ideas. Old-fashioned farmers might laugh at the notion that a man sitting in a newspaper office could know anything about farming. But most of the men who became prominent journalists had been bred on the land and had a real background of knowledge. Some set themselves to understand and to interpret the still new agricultural science. Some made a special study of machinery, others of pedigree live stock, and so on. Among the greater names are those of Guthrie, Stevenson, and Young of the *North British Agriculturist*, Chalmers Morton of the *Agricultural Gazette*, MacNeilage of *The Scottish Farmer*, Bear of the *Mark Lane Express*, Clarke of *Bell's Weekly Messenger*, Fream of *The Times*, and the remarkable Macdonald family, no fewer than five of whom became eminent agricultural writers.

Another group who, like Arthur Young and Cobbett, wandered widely over the country-side and wrote their 'Tours' includes

James Caird, Henry Dixon ('The Druid'), Rider Haggard, and Sir Daniel Hall.

Among frequent contributors to the journals of the great societies—The 'Royal', the 'Highland', and the 'Bath and West' —are to be found a good many, like Pusey, Coleman, Bear, and Plowman, who combined wide knowledge with considerable literary gifts. In more recent times, with the growth of a wider interest in the country and in rural life, grew up a new school of journalism led by John Robertson Scott. Fortunately, too, English agriculture attracted an historical scholar of eminence in Lord Ernle (R. E. Prothero). Lord Ernle indeed was many things besides an author—among others Minister of Agriculture. But he will probably be longest remembered by his *English Farming Past and Present*.

If we turn over the pages of any early agricultural journal we are struck by the variety of the subjects with which the editor had to deal, for information on many of which we should now turn to scientific journals, Ministry of Agricultural bulletins or Research Station reports. In his reminiscences of the early days of the *North British Agriculturist* M'Connel tells how, in 1846, he and a draper's assistant, the son of an Ayrshire farmer, used to meet three times a week in M'Ilwraith's lodging in Ayr, which served both as living room and editor's office. The two boys had to deal with readers' queries while the editor (who wrote all the articles himself) strode up and down the room playing his fiddle.

In the somewhat later days of Guthrie and Stevenson the *N.B.A.* tried to keep its farmer readers, as well as the merchants with whom they dealt, not only supplied with farming and market news but informed about the fundamental principles of agriculture. We can trace the influence of these men in focusing farming opinion, as yet hardly organized, on political questions. Not seldom the paper exercised quite important influence; for instance, under Stevenson's leadership, it resolutely opposed a return to protection and set the Scottish farmer to think how he could best carry on under free trade. Meanwhile the English agricultural Press was still hankering after a duty on corn, and keeping alive the vain hope that it might one day be reimposed.

The five Macdonalds, as has already been said, were among the most distinguished agricultural journalists of the nineteenth century.

Four of them, William, James, Alexander, and Charles were brothers, all born on a rough Banffshire farm that lies high up in the shadow of Ben Rinnes. They had the double training necessary for their trade, for each in turn had 'whistled at the ploughtail' on their father's farm and had then passed on to the office of their uncle, Provost Black of Elgin, who was owner and editor of the *Elgin Courant*. There they received what a great living journalist has described as the best training in the world—'devilling in the office of a local newspaper'.

William, the eldest, soon showed that he had the gift of the pen and became farming correspondent to the *Scotsman*. In this capacity he had many opportunities of meeting all the leading breeders of pedigree stock and, like Cameron of the *Glasgow Herald* in later days, he combined a remarkable 'eye for a beast' with a remarkable memory both for beasts and pedigrees. It is told of him that, after walking round Smithfield Show he would sit down, without a single note, and write a report, on one breed after another, that showed the wealth of knowledge of an expert and the judgement of a real 'critic of stock'. His accounts of famous sales, like those of the Aylesby or the Dunmore Shorthorns or of Drew's Clydesdales, were no mere catalogues of prices but were full of racy descriptions of men and beasts and events.

James Macdonald had his chance when the *Scotsman*, foreseeing the possibilities of the Western Prairie States of America as a great potential source of meat for the British market, sent him out as special commissioner to collect first-hand information on the resources and prospects of the Far West. After the appearance of his articles on 'Food from the Far West' he found plenty of work. He did a good deal of miscellaneous journalism, edited farming papers successively in Dublin, London, and Edinburgh, helped to compile and edit breed histories, and revised and indeed largely rewrote Stephen's monumental *Book of the Farm*. Later he became Secretary of the Royal Dublin Agricultural Society and ended his strenuous career as Secretary of the 'Highland', which bestirred itself into renewed activity under his influence.

'Sandy', who followed James to his uncle's office, must have been a raw lad—'Lord, Black, far did ye get that een' was the remark of one of the Provost's friends on seeing the youngest recruit. But he too was a 'lad o' pairts', and soon reached London to become Editor of *Bell's Weekly Messenger*, the oldest agricultural paper in the world. Soon, however, he started his own *Farmer and Stock-Breeder*, editing it from a single room over the Coach and Horses Inn in the Strand. To begin with he had an uphill fight, but his genial personality made him many friends, and the tall lanky figure with the fiery red beard became a conspicuous one at all the shows. His venture began to thrive, but he himself was cut off in the prime of life.

Charles, the youngest, after a spell of editing, succeeded Dr. Fream as Agricultural Correspondent of *The Times*. Not only did his wide practical knowledge and his sound common sense win the respect of his farmer readers, but, especially during the years of post-war depression, he did a good deal to win the interest and sympathy of the general public to farming and its troubles. Although his office was in Printing House Square, the roots of his life were in his farm at Chiddingfold in Surrey among the cornfields and animals that he loved. It is probably true that a great stock breeder was lost in Charles Macdonald.

The fifth of the Glenrinnes family to follow the now well-trodden path was James, the nephew of the other four. According to a brother journalist 'Young Jimmy' was the greatest of them all. He had the gift of being pleasantly provocative in conversation, so that none had more success in extracting the words of wisdom and experience from the ordinarily inarticulate farmer. Forced by the early death of his father to leave school while still very young, he began to learn his job on the staff of the *Farming World*. He owed his sound knowledge of farming and stock breeding to holidays spent with David Buttar at Corston, one of the best-managed farms in the fine Strathmore country and, rather surprisingly, the home of a Shropshire flock with an international reputation. After a year or two with MacNeilage on the *Scottish*

Farmer he succeeded to the editorship of the *Farmer and Stock-Breeder*. Here he set himself a high standard of honesty and of service, and showed that he held a profound faith in his mission. In his short life he had the distinction of being the editor of the first agricultural journal to reach a circulation of a hundred thousand copies.

Archibald MacNeilage was bred up on a typical Scottish west-country dairy farm where he worked for three years after leaving school. While still a lad he went as clerk to the office of the Clydesdale Horse Society. Dr. Dykes, the Secretary, was quick to note the boy's remarkable ability and enthusiastic interest in horse breeding, so that, on his retirement, he recommended that he should fill his own shoes. For fifty years thereafter MacNeilage ruled over the Stud Book, working incessantly in the interests of the breed and ever ready to stand forth as a fearless critic of any fad or fashion that seemed to endanger the usefulness of the Clydesdale as a draft breed.

But he was not content with an influence, strong though it was, in this limited sphere. Taking full advantage of the educational opportunities which Glasgow offered he attended lectures in Logic and on Moral Philosophy in the University and—strange combination—evening classes in Greek and in shorthand.

He began his journalistic career as a freelance, with articles for the livestock papers, both of this and of overseas countries, and his reputation as a writer steadily grew. In 1892 a group of landed proprietors and farmers in the West of Scotland decided to found a new farming paper, and MacNeilage was the obvious man to fill the editor's chair. Backed by the enthusiasm of the great Dr. Gillespie he threw all his tireless energy into his new task and from the first number the *Scottish Farmer* bore the stamp of his personality. He was a man of independent mind, of fearless courage, and he could upon occasion, dip his pen in gall. He gave hard knocks and stood up to hard knocks in return, so that many who had come under his lash yet learned to love and esteem him for his uprightness and honesty of purpose. Moreover he could be infinitely kind, especially where he thought he recognized young men of promise. He had the gift of vivid and inspiring speech, and his Glasgow Discussion Society, which he directed for over forty years, was regularly enlivened by his wit. If any one had some genuine contribution to make to the cause of agricultural betterment MacNeilage found him out, gave his ideas the publicity of the platform, and followed up with a verbatim report and a critique in his paper.

The journals of the great Agricultural Societies provide the best of all pictures of the ever-changing British farming of the last hundred years. Lord Ernle has said that the Societies 'commanded the pens of masters in the lost art of agricultural literature, men who wrote with the knowledge of specialists and with the simple ease of practical men of the world.' Men of this type were Clarke, Coleman, and Chalmers Morton, whose activities practically coincided with the first half-century of the 'Royal'.

Clarke was a son of the Fens and his earliest writings were on the all-important subjects, in Fen farming, of levels and drainage. Combining, however, a flair for machinery with a strong imagination, he was specially attracted by the possibilities of mechanization and of steam power, and it was these subjects that he eventually made his speciality. By his articles and surveys for *The Times*, by his admirable reports on farm inspections for the 'Royal', and in the Journal of the Chamber of Agriculture, which he founded and edited, he did a great deal to spread knowledge of the growing developments in Agricultural Science and the new resources in the way of machines. Among his other works are some graphic pictures of Irish country life and farming. During the last five years of his life he reached, as Editor of *Bell's Weekly Messenger*, practically the whole body of agricultural readers.

Like Clarke, Coleman grew up in close touch with farming. He was the nephew of the Founder of the Royal Agricultural College at Cirencester and went there, as its first student, in 1845. He became an estate agent of the enlightened type which Caird wanted to see multiplied all over England. He became Professor of Agriculture at his old College, Agricultural Editor of *The Field*, and was constantly at work for the R.A.S.E. in connection with its implement trials, exhibits and farm inspections. He was Commissioner for the northern counties on the Duke of Richmond's

Commission which sat from 1879 till 1882, inquiring into the extent and causes of the distress which had settled upon the once flourishing industry.

John Chalmers Morton was wont to say that his life was shaped mainly by the circumstances that made him a student in the old Agriculture classroom of Edinburgh University under Professor Low. At the age of nineteen he was summoned from Edinburgh to take charge of the Whitfield model farm on Earl Ducie's estate, where his father was agent. A few years later, in 1844, he was chosen to start and direct the new *Agricultural Gazette*, and for forty-five years he threw the bulk of his energies into his editorial work, supervising the publication of thirteen hundred successive numbers without a break, until his sudden death in 1888. He found time to write a great deal for the 'Royal' Journal and to edit a series of seven handbooks, among which was Warrington's *Chemistry of the Farm*—perhaps the nearest approach to the perfect agricultural text-book that has ever been written.

But perhaps Morton's greatest service was to edit, for the house of Blackie, the *Cyclopaedia of Agriculture*, which ran to more than two thousand large and closely printed pages and appeared in 1855–6. It was, for its time, probably the finest work of its kind ever published. Morton assembled a galaxy of distinguished authors—Lindley and Bentham on botany and plant physiology, Lyon Playfair, Way, and Voelcker on chemistry, Curtis on insects and Spooner on veterinary subjects. On the more practical side of farming, he had J. A. Clarke and James Caird, Philip Pusey, and John Wilson of Berwickshire, the last of whom also wrote, about the same time, the articles on agriculture in the *Britannica*. Added to these was a great army of leading farmers, land agents, and landowners who wrote each on the particular subjects in which he was specially competent. Morton himself covered farm machinery, and the inimitable Wren Hoskyns dealt with the history and general philosophy of agriculture, with education and with land tenure. The work presents the best and most detailed picture that we have of the science and craft of farming, at the time when Britain was about to attain world leadership in both.

A few years earlier, in 1850, when James Caird set out to survey

English farming for *The Times*, the age of science and machinery had well begun. The implement section of the Great Exhibition, arranged by Philip Pusey, had shown the immense possibilities of mechanical invention. Peel's drainage schemes were just beginning to take effect. Lawes had recently laid down his wheat experiments on Broadbalk field at Rothamsted. Progressive farmers were looking to improved live stock products to help them to pay their high rents in face of a rather alarming (though, as it proved, a very temporary) fall in corn prices. But improvements were slow to spread, and Caird's own pamphlet, *High Farming the Best Substitute for Protection*, had made few converts. Caird's task was, in his own words, 'on account of the excited state of the agricultural mind, a delicate and difficult duty which he endeavoured to discharge impartially and without offence.' Before setting out he consulted Sir Robert Peel, at whose door most farmers laid the blame for their present distress and their fears of worse to come. Peel encouraged him in his enterprise, putting before him the benefits that might accrue if different systems of farming were put 'before men who seldom travel beyond the bounds of their own parishes.'

Caird might well have quoted Hamlet's line: 'Look here; upon this picture and on this'—'The contrasts are striking; on one side of a hedge a plough with five horses and two men and on the other side of the same hedge a plough with two horses and one man doing precisely the same amount of work. In adjoining fields may be seen a foul turnip crop, under ten tons an acre, and a luxuriant one above thirty. On neighbouring farms of similar soil the wheat may vary from twenty to forty bushels an acre, and probably the man who grows twenty pays not less than 9s. for threshing by hand, while the other threshes his forty bushels by steam for 3s. 6d.'

One day he sees modern machinery, the next antiquated winnowing appliances 'worthy of the days before the Conquest.' 'Rickety wood and thatch barns, devoid of every known improvement for economizing labour, food, and manure, which every gale threatened to bring down; where the miserable cattle stood with rain pouring in a stream on their necks and shoulders or discontentedly pursuing each other through the wet and miry yard, a state of things incredible in an old and wealthy country', are compared with the sleek well-housed stock on the farms of Fisher Hobbs and Lord Ducie. He contrasts the usual manner of allowing manure to run to waste with Mr. Huxtable's system of tanks and piping to conduct it over the fields. With the same good land and tenants of equal skill two estates in the Vale of Gloucester show a remarkable variation. On one, with an indifferent absentee owner, all nutriment is drawn from the soil by the vast straggling hedgerows which the tenant is allowed to cut only once in every seven years, so that harbour may be provided for the game which feed upon his crops. On the other, with well-cleared timber, the fields are straightened and well-drained, and the tenants are encouraged by precept and example to improve their stock and to clean their fields.

At Mr. Pusey's he sees the results of the new machinery and of the lesson duly learnt by neighbours—confirming the entries in the diaries of a contemporary Gloucestershire farmer: 'Visited Mr. Pusey's farm to inspect his new Garrett's horse hoe': 'Bought a drill as used by Mr. Pusey.' But on the Downs, close by, instead of using Crosskill's roller, farmers were still persisting in walking the sheep to and fro over the cornfields. However, in spite of the usual suspicion of institutional farming, the influence of Cirencester College and other model farms was gradually permeating the district. 'Prejudices were yielding to satisfactory evidences of success.'

Although the larger part of the country, and even of the heavy lands, was still undrained, landlords like the Duke of Portland had been energetic tile-drainers long before the day of Parkes or Smith or Deanston, and many were taking advantage of Peel's loans. A peep into Sir John Conroy's 'Bigot's Hole' at Arborfield, where two main pipes were constantly pouring out the drainage of forty acres, 'improving the stiffest soil which most farmers thought a waste to drain at all' made him hope that 'the style of remunerative farming adopted by a gentleman bred in the camp and the court may be adopted by other country gentlemen now compelled by necessity to look strictly to their own business.' On

Lord Hatherton's estate in Cannock Chase, thirty years earlier a tract of worthless undrained waste, the drainage of a swamp had been used to provide irrigation and power and to turn the land into a rich and fertile domain.

Still, in spite of the high lights of such landlords as the Duke of Wellington, 'whose private duties as a landlord are performed with the same wisdom, attention, and unswerving faithfulness which have rendered his public character so exalted'; as Mr. Chaplin of Blankney, that perfect example of a resident owner; as Earl Talbot, Lord Overstone, Earl Yarborough, and others, whose intelligent management had raised the standard of whole districts, he comes to the conclusion that 'the great body of land-owners have been practically unacquainted with the management of land and have left their estates in the hands of agents, no better qualified; mostly lawyers whose sole interests lay in rent-collecting and whose only remedy for bad times was to advise reduction of rents.' He suggests the remedy of better education, but for that the country had to wait another half-century. 'Of all classes, he [the landlord] is the only one who received no special training. Our great Universities offer him no peculiar instruction to fit him for the important functions of his station.'

In nearly every county where estates were more than usually neglected, the reasons assigned were financial embarrassments and encumbrances on landed property, and the difficulty and expense involved in the transference of land. Caird notes the capricious regulation of rents, formerly calculated upon proximity to the Metropolis, but now depending on the character of the landlord and agent rather than on the value of the soil or the commodity it produced. The traditional corn-and-fallow farming was dying hard, and even in the counties near London little advantage was being taken of the increased railway facilities to fill the great market with vegetables and other perishable produce. By contrast the farmers of the North Midlands and the North, with more highly rented land, were genuinely striving to meet the require-ments of a rapidly increasing population for more meat, more butter, cheese, and milk, and were changing their farming with the changing conditions.

THE PRESS AND THE PILGRIMS

In Leicestershire, Lancashire, and parts of Yorkshire, 'the new capitalists from the towns who have purchased estates, manage them with the same attention to principles and details as gained them success in business.' In the colliery area, on the contrary, 'where the easier harvest is reaped from mineral wealth and sums paid in compensation by railway companies, the skill and enterprise lavished below ground shows a marked contrast to the absence of improving qualities and evident defect of capital everywhere too conspicuous on its surface.'

The strict preservation of game on some large estates is bitterly commented upon by one of the tenants as 'completely eating up the farmer, against which no man can live or farm.'

On one large estate where the tenants had always been considerately treated, he sensed 'that indolent feeling of security in Protection, a great estate standing still for half a century.' The depression was undoubtedly least severe on the light lands, where the extension of green crops and feeding of stock had raised the fertility and enabled them to produce corn at less cost than on the strong clays, formerly looked upon as the true wheat soils. one of the improvements chiefly needed to raise the standard of farming on the clays—tile drainage—was already begun, though there was a long way to go. The other was the application of mechanical power to the heavy task of tillage. There were already hopes of steam, and these were to be partially realized within a few years. But the real answer was the crawler tractor, and that was still in the far distant future.

Another generalization that emerges from Caird's report is that the north was now more progressive than the south. This was especially true in regard to the use of new machines, but it was true also in a more general sense. Partly at least this can be explained by the northward migration of industries which, on the one hand, had provided better markets and, on the other, had raised the wages of the farm worker and forced the farmer to think hard about economy in manpower. By contrast, there was a surplus of labour in the south and wages were very low. The extreme range was from thirteen or fourteen shillings in Lancashire and the West Riding, to seven shillings, or seven-and-six, in Gloucester, Dorset, Wiltshire, Cambridge, and Suffolk.

Caird reckoned that, although in the eighty years since Young had made his survey the average rent of land had doubled, yet the prices of butter, meat, and wool having also practically doubled, the value of the annual produce had kept pace with the increase of rent. Mixed husbandry, always the sheet anchor of the British farmer, was proving the safest course. The best farmers were attaining success, not by a blind adherence to a given rotation, but by a constant adaptation of their plans to the growing wants of the country, by taking advantage of railway and steamboat communications to reach the best markets, and by using the new manures and cattle foods to make good the increasing drain on the fertility of the soil. Apart from what lay within the power of individuals, Caird suggested five measures of a public character which might help the industry on the upward path: (1) The cheapening and facilitating of the transfer of land; (2) The sale of overburdened estates; (3) The encouragement of leases with liberal covenants; (4) An alteration in the law of settlement; and (5) The collection of agricultural statistics. But like Hall, who wrote seventy years later, Caird realized that it was 'to education in its widest sense that we must look as the most powerful aid in the further progress of British agriculture.'

He ends on a note of hope. 'Look in what direction we may, we have good prospects of success for agriculturists; increasing markets without which his produce would be valueless; increasing wealth to enhance its price; resources of manure at home and abroad to maintain and add fertility to his farm. He wants but a reasonable adjustment of his rent, intelligent co-operation on the part of his landlord and the security of a lease to render well-directed enterprise successful.' But there is also a warning. 'In this country the agricultural improver cannot stand still. If he tries to do so, he will soon fall into the list of obsolete men, being passed by eager competitors, willing to seize the current of events, and turn them to their advantage.'

In Caird's survey, dealing as it does with broad problems and general farming conditions, we seek in vain for accounts of the pedigree live stock that was soon to win world-wide fame for British breeders. Fortunately there set out, a decade later, one Henry H. Dixon, much better known as 'The Druid'.

From Border ancestors Dixon inherited a wandering, adventurous temperament, and from them, too, his love of country things and country sports.

' *"He'll never get to Lunnon, maister,"* said Dick, the first whip and kennel huntsman to the Orkney Harriers, *sotto voice,* as I took the mare from his hand in the Orkneys; and I was not quite sure on the point myself. Because we didn't go with him from Kirkwall to Wick, Captain Parrot will have it to this hour that we swam the Pentland Firth, just by way of a relish at starting. The journey, to a man who has a good horse and can send his luggage on to points, must be a remarkably easy and pleasant one; but when you have only a shy half-bred nag, quite out of condition and have, perforce, to spend so many months roughing it, in a country to which you are not acclimatized, it becomes no May game. Still, with fine weather, and a steady practice of getting off to lead for every third or fourth mile, it is a grand independent way of travelling.' Months later, in a blinding snowstorm, he rang feebly at the door of his house in Kensington Square.

Dixon could, like greater authors before him, have earned his bread in the ease and comfort of a Government Office, but he could not then have written *Silk and Scarlet, Saddle and Sirloin, Field and Fern,* for to do so meant that he had to spend months and years upon the road. Speaking of his Scottish journey he says: 'I had to pluck the heart out of three summers, a winter and a spring; to sleep away from home some two hundred and fifty nights . . . before I wrote a line. . . . There was often nothing for it but to steel myself against all bed regrets and to face the moors at night. There are many weary passages in a man's life; but wiping down a·mare, very short of condition, in your shirt-sleeves in a cow-house on a wild moor, by a spluttering dip at midnight with the wind sighing through the broken panes and heavy raindrops pattering on the door sill, and a forty miles' ride before you, has very few to match it.'

If 'The Druid' himself had to live strenuous days in order that he might write and live, the picture that he paints is one of hearty and leisured squires and thriving tenant farmers who rode to hounds two days a week. It was the Golden Age. The clouds of the early 'fifties had rolled away and were forgotten, while the trials of 'seventy-nine and its successors were yet undreamt of.

It is a different picture that we get, a quarter of a century later, from Rider Haggard, who after making a fortune by his 'thrillers' settled down to farming and who, in 1901 and 1902 felt the urge to study the condition of rural England. His two fat volumes are now little read, for the story that they tell is one of almost unrelieved gloom. There is a constant iteration, page after page, chapter after chapter, county after county, of the same stories of distress and decay, of farmers going bankrupt and land going derelict, of cottages and farm buildings crumbling into rubbish heaps; of old labourers carrying on because they have no option, while their sons flock to the towns. . . . 'English agriculture seems to be fighting against the Mills of God.' This was the back of a canvas which bore, upon the other side, a picture of busy shipyards, smoking factory chimneys, steamships plying a flourishing trade, and large dividend warrants. Both sides of the picture were England under Free Trade; most people had been looking only at the bright side. Rider Haggard called upon his country to consider the other.

Of the three classes of agriculturists, Haggard considered, and he was doubtless right, that, taking the country through, the landlord was bearing the brunt of the depression. In some counties the possession of land was becoming, or had already become, a luxury for rich men to whom the soil was a costly toy or a means of indulging a taste for sport. The farmers did no more than make a hard living and were steadily losing capital. The labourers were more prosperous than they had been, employment being plentiful for those who had remained, and wages, by comparison with those of past times, high; while food and other necessaries were cheap. But in many cases the housing of the labourer was so bad that the main ambition of the young man was to escape from the land and try his fortune in the city, whither he was attracted by higher wages, by company, by cheap amusement and by shorter hours. As a wage-earner without outlook or prospects, he had nothing to tie him to the land; he left behind him half-tilled fields and shrinking hamlets.

As to the attitude of the Government towards the industry, Haggard does not mince his words. 'English Governments', he says, 'look upon the land and its interests in a totally different way from that in which it is regarded by those of most other civilized nations. Here they cannot be brought to recognize that the matter is one of any real importance. The President of the Board of Agriculture might be something more than a compiler of labour statistics, an officer for the enforcement of regulations as to diseased cattle, a disseminator of useful information about beetles, and a peripatetic utterer of speeches at Agricultural Shows, which are reported in paragraphs upon the outer sheets of newspapers.' He closes with the following warning: 'I am convinced that one of the first objects of the rulers of Great Britain should be to promote the true welfare and prosperity of British Land in every just and reasonable way, and to multiply the homes thereon. If our country is to decline from its present high position, the principal cause of its fall will be our national neglect to maintain the population on the land. If high civilization necessitates a flight from the villages, then it is of a truth that broad road which leads to the destruction of advanced peoples. One of the worst fates which can befall England is that her land should become either a plaything or a waste, and her greatest safeguard lies in the re-creation of a yeoman class, rooted in the soil and supported by the soil.'

Ten years later, and exactly sixty after Caird's survey, *The Times* again 'felt a concern' about the state of agriculture and commissioned Mr. A. D. Hall (Sir Daniel Hall) to undertake an extensive tour over the whole of the British Isles, which took him the better part of the three summers of 1910–11–12. Caird's journey was made when farming was on the threshold of a great revival. When Hall started, the land and its management had 'somewhat suddenly become a matter of interest to our general population, and the farming community, after a series of depressions one worse than another, was just becoming conscious of a return to prosperity that promised to last for some time, and, encouraged thereby, was beginning to take more interest in the applications of science and education to their industry.' No one could have foretold that in two years' time nearly the whole civilized world would be plunged into a war whose ultimate effect was to bring more and much greater changes.

The sustained interest of Hall's masterly survey of the farming scene of Britain, the vivid landscape vignettes, the apt literary and historical allusions, cannot fail to attract the general reader as well as those practically concerned in farming. Reading it again to-day one is constantly struck by the changes which have come over great parts of the country in the forty years since the book was written. Take the start in Wiltshire . . . 'sheep raising, still the characteristic note of our Agriculture' . . . 'typical corn land farmed on the Wiltshire rotation, in which two years of straw crops follow two years of root crops eaten off by sheep' . . . 'The sheep are the big and rapidly maturing Hampshire Downs . . . though we did hear of one north-country immigrant who has introduced and still swears by Cheviots.' And now the great flocks of Hampshires and the four-course farming are hardly to be found, the typical scene being made up of corn, grass, dairy cows, and alien sheep.

He passes on to the 'sound conservative type of farming in East Dorset', further east to the 'rich productive maritime districts of Sussex', over the South Downs with their sheep, the heirs of Ellman's genius; through the specialized hop-and-fruit farming, 'always running together on the Kentish soil, that grows fruit buds, not wood', and into Essex, but 'no more the derelict Essex, once the type example of ruined English agriculture.'

Here he notes two fields of sugar beet, 'a crop which was rather a novelty on a large scale, which a Dutch firm were preparing to buy for export to Holland.' He then proceeds northward, past South Mimms with its memories of Arthur Young's poor gravelly soil, now built up with 'enormous amounts of London manure' on to the black soils and silts of the Fen country, by Wilberton, the home of that typical English country gentleman, Albert Pell, up to the great breeding ground of the Shire horse, the land of 'sturdy, independent folk of prime value to the State even if they sometimes do vex the souls of clergy and gentry.'

He finds Norfolk still a shire of half wheat-and-bullocks, half sheep-and-barley, and viewing from a distance Coke's most enduring monument, the great area of reclaimed salt-marsh, he wends his way by Spalding, where already there are fields of bulbs as well as of potatoes, to the heath and wolds of Lincolnshire, where land, which a century ago had been open rabbit warren, was now worth £25 to £40 an acre.

He went, too, by 'the patchwork of the Isle of Axholme, a crystallized remnant of the Middle Ages in the midst of the twentieth century', and stood on the classic ground of Cornelius Vermuyden, whose memory is perpetuated in the Dutchman's Drain, but whose great work, destroyed in the rage of civil war, took generations of Adventurers to restore. . . . And so on.

What were Hall's conclusions at the end of his pilgrimage? Like other observers, he is struck with the variety of conditions under which farmers have to work, and with the skill of the men in adapting their methods to special environments. There was still much bad farming alongside of good, and bad business habits were too common. The disintegration of the great estates had already begun, though the characteristic system of English land tenure was still practically intact. But the landowners 'unlike those of the second quarter of the nineteenth century, were deficient in leadership.'

The late Lord Haldane once said that what the tillers of the soil wanted most was more and better education. Both Caird and Hall agreed, and stressed the need not only for technical instruction, but first and foremost education in the widest sense which 'alone gives that flexibility of mind and openness to new ideas, enabling men to take advantage of all that the new world of science has to offer.'

In the harvest time of 1933—a fine-weather harvest of big corn crops—one of the present writers set out upon a rapid farming tour which took him from Inverness to Land's End and Romney

Marsh, and he related his impressions in a dozen wireless talks.[1]

A dozen years had elapsed since the collapse in prices that followed closely on the end of the First World War, and farmers in many parts were now up to their ears in debt. In the hill countries the story was that the previous year's clip of blackface wool had sold for fourpence a pound; that it had taken a good strong lamb to fetch half a sovereign; that bracken was spreading fast over the better parts of the sheep-walks and, while there were plenty of unemployed men who would have been glad to come bracken-cutting, there was no money to pay their wages. . . . In Kintyre, in August, farmers were selling milk for 3½d. a gallon to the local creamery, and the creamery stores were chock-full of cheese which was hard to sell at 4½d. a pound, the lowest price that could pay for the making. . . . By October, oats, in Aberdeenshire, were 13s. 6d. a quarter, and potatoes, in Angus, were £2 a ton. . . . Good bullocks from Midland pastures were selling at a price equivalent to sixpence a pound for the beef so that, for the third or fourth summer in succession, graziers were losing two or three guineas on each beast that they had fattened. . . .

'Passing through a rich farming country like Strathmore or Lothian, the Vale of York or the Lincoln Silts, you find very little visible evidence of agricultural depression. You miss indeed some of the frills and fancy touches. Ricks are not quite so well trimmed; hedge-bottoms not so well weeded; there are a few thistles in the pastures. But the arable ground is still clean and in good heart, the grass well stocked with fine cattle and the buildings in pretty good order. To get at the truth of the matter you must dig below the surface when you find, too often, that the cattle belong to the auctioneer who owes the price of them to his bank; that the seeds and manures which have produced the good crops are still unpaid for; and so on; in fact the whole community —bankers, merchants, auctioneers and farmers—are struggling manfully but desperately to hold each other up.'

One old farmer, from such fertile country, was quoted: 'I am going to farm this place, as it should be farmed, till I bust—and

[1]Published as *Rural Britain Today and Tomorrow* (Oliver & Boyd, 1934).

then somebody else can have a go.' In Norfolk there was a bitter jest which said that soon there would be only five farmers left in the county—the Big Five Banks. The big men, with many hands to pay, were harder put to it, as had often happened in the past, than the smallholders, living on their own produce and spending next to nothing.

The other two partners in the farming business were little better off than the farmers. Farms in Dorset, on the thin chalk, would no longer bring as much in rent as they were supposed to pay in tithe. On the Yorkshire Wolds a good many farms were held for no rent at all, and the story went that one landlord, in the stout-hearted belief that the land would be wanted another day, was paying his tenants to carry on rather than let his farms fall derelict. The landowner who had no other resources than his land could no longer do the right thing by his property—drain the wet field, repair the tumble-down cottage or modernize the stuffy and dark old cowshed.

Wages Boards were already in operation in England and Wales; so that the worker had at least the assurance of enough to live on —if he could find a job. But a very old farmer on the Yorkshire Wolds 'had never dreamt that so many first-class men would ever be out of work.' Scotland had as yet no Wages Board, with the result that her farm hands—for the first time in a century—were more poorly paid than those in Midland and Southern England; and rural Scotland also had unemployment.

Of course, this crisis was by no means peculiar to Britain. America, for instance, was bribing her producers to stop producing, handing out dollars to those farmers who would promise to grow less maize or wheat or cotton or to feed fewer pigs— because, though there was hunger in America as elsewhere, the hungry could not buy.

But there were, in 1933, already some signs of better weather ahead. The Wheat Act was already in operation; ten shillings a hundredweight might be no very princely price, and even this was not firmly guaranteed if production increased; but it should put a stop to disastrous losses in wheat growing. The better quality barleys—and there was much fine grain in 1933—were fetching something like the prices that they had been wont to command. The Marketing Boards—for milk, hops, potatoes, and pigs—were either in operation or were taking shape. Measures for the support of the industry did not indeed make up a very logical scheme—'A mixture of controlled production, import quotas, tariffs, wages boards, subsidies and so on; some elements perhaps socialistic, some individualistic.' But there was a feeling that the measures might work, in practice, as well as any of the plans being tried elsewhere.

Moreover, upon the whole, British agriculture, if one judged by the volume of its output, was not declining. The industry was indeed employing fewer men—it had lost a hundred thousand workers in the previous fifteen years—that was one worker in every ten. But the nine remaining were producing more food than the ten had done. Many things had contributed to this result— better varieties of plants; better cultivation and manuring; better control of crop diseases and pests; better breeds of animals, more knowledge of nutrition and better control of their diseases, and so on.

'Country life is changing as farming is changing—in some ways regrettably but on the whole for the better. The disadvantages of isolation, of long dark winter nights, of gruelling work on the land are gradually being mitigated. We need only give the country-man a fair reward for his toil in order to make his lot happier than it has ever been. And—apart from financial anxieties—the life on the land is still the best life of all.'

13

GREAT SALESMEN

'Auctioneers talk wild, but Trumbull makes money.'

MIDDLEMARCH

In the early years of last century farmers brought their stock to the local town and exposed it for sale on straw laid down along the sides of the streets. The inhabitants often bought their winter supply of meat on the hoof, which transaction, in Scotland, was called 'laying in the mart'. Up till a few years ago the street market was still common in England, and even in later years, in the little Gloucestershire town of Chipping Sodbury, a market of this description was to be seen. In past times, too, some farmers had periodical sales of stock on their own farms, where perhaps 80 or 100 head of fat sheep and 10 or 20 fat cattle would be sold singly to butchers. These sales were pleasant social gatherings, often finishing up with a dinner. Because of the Government duty of 1s. 6d. on each insertion, newspaper advertisement was somewhat expensive, and hence the custom was to announce sales by handbills which were posted in towns, villages and country smithies, or conveyed to possible customers by the pupils of the village school. But a large proportion of the live stock was sold at great fairs or, as they were called in Scotland, trysts; at the larger of these, thousands of sheep and cattle changed hands.

In October 1858, the roads leading to Falkirk Tryst were blocked with stock, the sheep numbering over eighty thousand head and showing by their rather woebegone appearance the severe weather they had encountered on the way; even as late as 1889 it was an unforgettable experience to attend Falkirk Tryst. The continuous lowing of cattle and bleating of sheep—wild West Highlanders from the Islands, Galloways from the south-west, Irish stirks and Angus from the north-east; Blackfaces from Sutherland, Cheviots from the Border; the crowds of men and dogs, and the mingling of tongues and dialects—Gaelic, Erse, Lowland Scots, Yorkshire, and the softer Southern English—have left an indelible impression even at this distance of time. Some of the convoys might have spent weeks on the road and, when sold, might spend weeks more before reaching their destinations. The old drovers were a remarkable set of people, rough but not unkindly to their beasts, full of curious lore and with a marvellous knowledge of the roads, of the 'bieldy bits' to spend the nights, of the best grazing on the way, and of the best ways of avoiding the toll-bars. Tom Turnbull, one of the best known, used to boast that he could drive his beasts from Sutherland to Falkirk with only one toll, the Bridge at Stirling.

At St. Boswell's the Lammas Fair was the annual holiday of the Scottish Hind of the Borders, as well as his hiring place. At Boroughbridge, on the Great North Road, with a constant stream of Scottish cattle halting to be shod, one smith would often make as many as thirty thousand ox-shoes in a season. Here Barnaby Fair, with cattle, sheep, horses, booths, stalls, tinkers, and gypsies all intermingled, was the great event of the year. At York the animals thronged the narrow streets, and at Northallerton one of the four-yearly fairs was frequented by horse dealers from the Continent, and another was specially famed for its cheeses. At Ilsley in Berkshire sheep poured over the Downs, filling up acres of wattle hurdles in and around the village. Even up till forty years ago, at Stow-on-the-Wold in Gloucestershire, one might have heard as much Welsh as English when the drovers with their strings of horses and ponies thronged the streets.

It was not till well towards the middle of last century that an essentially conservative class accepted the change from the leisurely buying and selling, with its thrills of long-drawn-out individual bargaining, to the more impersonal rapidity of the auction mart. Even Inverness Wool Fair, once famous for its all-night sittings in the Square, with bargains struck at daybreak, is not what it was.

In England, with a larger population and shorter distances, the smaller auction markets, many started about the middle of last century, still persist; but motor transport tends to their decay in favour of larger auctions. Even the home sales, once a regular event in most pedigree herds, have decreased.

The two events to which the great development of the auction mart was largely due were the repeal of the tax on auction sales and the general extension of the railway system. At the present day the spread of road-motor transport, which in some districts has completely superseded the railway, tends to still further centralization; and the opinion has been expressed that, in Scotland at least, the smaller markets, of which there are still a few, will have completely disappeared in a few years.

The dealer, although in England he still maintains something of his old position, is in Scotland much less concerned in the live stock trade.

With the great development of both commercial and pedigree live stock, there arose a type of auctioneer who was a skilled judge of stock and of its value, and who, if he specialized in a certain breed, often possessed an exhaustive knowledge of its history and its pedigrees. These men, who maintained a high standard of integrity in their business methods, exercised a profound influence upon British live stock breeding. It is not too much to say that, without the work of such men as James Swan, James Oliver, James Fraser, William Elliot, Alfred Mansell, and John Thornton, our live stock industry would never have gained the position in the world which it holds to-day.

In 1847 the earliest Scottish auction sale was started by James Oliver and his son at Hawick, Roxburghshire, close to the original home of the Cheviot sheep, with whose fortunes the firm's great sales of the present day are linked. After four years of work the sales, as the following bill shows, were still miserably small:

1 Kyloe cow	...	...	£3	17	6
1 Kyloe cow	...	...	£4	0	0
1 grey mare	...	...	£7	15	0
			£15	12	6

In the whole year 1851 only five hundred and thirty-five head were sold, whereas in 1881, at Hawick and Edinburgh, over two hundred thousand sheep and lambs passed through the firm's hands. In 1860, having erected a permanent building, the Olivers started holding special August lamb sales, thus laying the foundation of the great store-sheep sales which are a special feature of the present-day auction system in Scotland. A passenger on the old Midland Scottish express, speeding north for the 'Twelfth', might look down at Hawick on a sea of Cheviot and Blackfaced lambs, often as many as sixty thousand, in the pens far down below the railway. Having the complete confidence of both buyers and sellers all over the country, who trusted them always to sell good stores and reliable tups, the Olivers, both father and son, with their intimate knowledge of the value of hill sheep as well as of the practice of farming, were in constant request for valuations of stock between ingoing and outgoing tenants.

John Swan, the founder of the firm of Swan & Sons, Newtown St. Boswells, was the son of an East Lothian farmer, born (in 1819) at a time when farming was one long struggle to make ends meet. He started out, at the age of eleven, to fend for himself. After trying several occupations without much success he began business as a butcher in the little Border town of Earlston, on Leader Water. He was fortunate in his wife, a farmer's daughter who, till her very last days, put all her energy and resource into the business.

It was she who saw that in Earlston there was no scope; so, getting references from 'eleven gentlemen' to the effect that her husband 'might be depended upon as a good man of business', they moved to Edinburgh, where, in 1843, he started as a live stock commission salesman. The eleven gentlemen were justified. John, in his white hat, was soon a familiar figure not only in Edinburgh and Glasgow but in Darlington and Newcastle, putting thousands of sheep through the markets.

His two sons James and Tom had the same Spartan upbringing. From the time they were ten years old, they never went to school on Wednesdays, the Edinburgh market day; they had to start off at 2 a.m. to get the stock, which had spent the night in grass fields round the city, into the market; this began at five o'clock in summer and six in winter. In the afternoon, while they made out the accounts, their father commented on their valuations of the stock. James Swan often said that he owed his eye for stock, and his sense of value, to that early training. A well-known Border farmer related how, as a boy of fourteen, he felt 'countrified and inferior' when, arriving in Edinburgh with twenty-five of his father's fat cattle, which he had driven, all through the summer night, the forty miles over the hills from Caddon Water, he handed them over to these two boys, so much younger than himself, to value and get ready for market. After a good dinner and kindly words of encouragement from 'the old lady of Lauriston' he went off with his money, determined to beat them at farming. In later life he became one of the largest customers of the firm.

In 1856 John took his sons into partnership, and soon the firm had the largest live-stock business in the country, selling often in one year as many as 65,000 Scotch and English sheep as well as 12,000 foreign, and a total of about 200,000 cattle. But the Swans soon realized the trend towards auction sales, and here again Mrs. Swan took the lead. When they thought of founding a mart at Earlston she insisted on getting written support from 'a deil's dizzen' of prominent farmers in the neighbourhood. John never sold by auction, but both sons started at once. The first day James was seized with nervous shyness and was not getting on very well. One of the Elliots went up to him and whispered: 'Look up, Jimmie, look up, man!'—and from that day he never looked down. They now decided to move to a better centre, and in January 1872, the Southern Central Mart was opened at Newtown St. Boswells, close to the railway, about a mile from the old town where for centuries the Lammas Fairs had been held.

The new Mart began with a show of fat cattle and sheep, at which nearly all the noted Border farms were represented, the stock amounting to 1,773 sheep, 161 cattle, 8 calves, and 13 pigs, which realized in total a sum of £9,800. A dinner and a pleasant evening at Mrs. Rodger's Inn closed the day. One of the most notable of the early sales at this mart was in 1875, the day before Lammas Fair, when James Swan, starting at nine o'clock and going on till half-past six without a break, sold 37,000 sheep and lambs. The lambs made from 38s. to 44s.—extraordinary prices, for they represented a rise of 10s. to 18s. on those of the previous year. This sale is also of interest for the fact that the great bulk of the lambs were 'three-parts-bred', a class now almost never seen. At another sale in 1875 the consignment of fat cattle from a single farmer made an average of £45 5s. 10d., the biggest weighing 29 cwt. and realizing £72. Such bullocks are unknown now.

Both James and Tom soon became well-known figures in the ring, dressed in long white coats, without collar or tie. Tom always sold the cattle from the middle of the ring, and James the sheep from the rostrum. During a long trying sale his only nourishment was a bunch of grapes. James was a born stockman. He made no pretence of interest or skill in horses, but in the matter of valuing or selling cattle, both store and fat, and as a judge of sheep of every breed and class, he was a master. His eye for a sheep was almost uncanny; on one occasion he recognized a flock of sheep which had been stolen from the author's father's farm, and the judge, Lord Young, accepted his word as sufficient evidence of their identity.

James Swan was an extraordinarily rapid seller. It was said of him, 'He never prosed, he never dosed', but his running commentary of pat remarks added immensely to the cheerfulness of the ring. Although he did not inherit his father's stature, he had his bright and humorous eye. 'The strong, clean-shaven, impressive countenance, the sturdy build, the deep-chested strength, the ringing voice for the outer reaches, the pleasant conversational style for the nearby, the rare wit and kindly humour formed an irresistible combination that one can never forget.' One of the secrets of his success was his fairness. The shepherd's little flock or the child's single lamb got the same careful attention as the largest consignment. Probably nothing in his life gave him so much pleasure as the portrait by Martin Hardie which the shepherds of Southern Scotland presented to him in recognition of his kind consideration for their comfort at his sales, and the pains which he took in selling their flocks.

James Swan was at his very best at Kelso Ram Fair. The

auctioneer must be not only a judge of stock, but a judge of men. Swan valued at a glance every ram as it came into the ring, asked the price he thought the sheep was worth, and rarely failed to get it. He never wasted time; often, at Kelso, when he had got down to the last half-dozen sheep, he began to get out his collar. While his men were changing the animal he would button one end, sell another sheep, adjust the back stud, sell another sheep, and finally do up the other button. In the short intervals between selling the remaining sheep he put on his tie, took off his white coat, got into his waistcoat and coat, and when the hammer fell for the last time, he stepped from the rostrum ready for the train and his Edinburgh office. For sixty years he sold at Kelso Ram sales; the last time he had reached his ninetieth year, and immense crowds gathered to see him sell the first three lots in the familiar No. 3 ring.

The books of the firm reflect many changes in prices and in farm practice—from an average of 34s. 10d. for draft half-bred ewes in 1909 to one of £9 4s. 0d. in 1919, and back again to 35s. 4d. in 1932; from Mr. Scott's 29 cwt. bullock to Templeton's baby beef of 9 to 10 cwt.; from the three-year-old Blackfaced wedders to two-months'-old fat lamb, from the days when the Yorkshiremen, Billy Harrison and Whitaker, thought nothing of buying two or three thousand sheep at one sale, and paying for them in gold, to these dull days of bank cheques. Twenty years ago as many as 2,600 English North-country store cattle were often catalogued at the weekly sales; now, largely owing to the increased crossing with dairy bulls for milk production in Northern England, their place has been taken by Irish and home-bred stores. In early days the half-bred ewes were all bought for Scotland and Northern England, whereas now thousands are sold to go as far south as Sussex and Kent.

The part played by inherited qualities in farming may be hard to estimate, but there is no doubt that it counted for much in the career of William Elliot. He came of a long line of Border farmers. Of his grandfather Walter Elliot of Newhall, it was said that, by his own work and the force of his initiative, he made the once bare and barren hillsides in the Vales of Gala and Caddon, 'smile to their tops with the golden grain.' His father and four brothers were all notable experimenters and innovators, both in live-stock breeding and in arable farming. Trained as a boy on his father's farm, he served his apprenticeship in the firm of John Swan & Sons who had then a commission agent's business in Glasgow. During this period he several times crossed the Atlantic in charge of cattle shipments, acquiring that intimate knowledge of live-stock transport, both by sea and rail, which later stood him in such good stead in his various struggles for improved methods on the railways.

From the days of William the Lion, when horse racing for Silver Bells was established there, the ancient Burgh of Lanark had always been associated with the horse-breeding industry. It was the home of the Clydesdale, and from the high moorlands came some of the finest Blackface sheep. Under Elliot's energetic leadership the Lanark Auction Mart became famous for its pedigree live-stock sales and for its up-to-date methods. It was characteristic of the man, from the first determined to be a master of detail, that before he took over the sales he attended them unbeknown. In 1886 and 1887 the mart was closed for 42 weeks on account of pleuro-pneumonia, a disastrous experience which tested even his resourceful powers to the utmost, and made him a convinced opponent of all importation of animals except for immediate slaughter. In later years he was confirmed in his belief, when the 1926 outbreak of foot-and-mouth disease forced him to move the mart from Lanark to Symington, and eventually, when a further outbreak occurred, to arrange for the slaughter and marketing of over 5,000 lambs. Throughout his career he owed much to two men of great standing in the farming world, both supreme in their own spheres—James Weir of Sandilands, breeder and judge of Clydesdales, and James Greenshields of Weston, the Blackface sheep expert. These older men took him into their friendship, and on many occasions when it came to a question of national policy, especially as regards the stamping out of disease, they formed a formidable triumvirate.

Although he made no pretence to expert knowledge of pedigree stock, Elliot was a skilled judge of all classes of commercial animals. Perhaps the secret of his success lay in his power of organization, and in his inexorable integrity, which gained him the complete confidence of his customers. He held the view that a commission agent should never become an owner, and that a live-stock salesman was in fact a commission agent. From the very first, therefore, he determined that all the bidding in his ring should be genuine. If he discovered anything in the nature of 'white-bonneting' he was ruthless, and on one occasion risked the loss of large custom when he ordered a prominent customer 'to take himself and his stock out of the ring and never return.'

Like Swan, he had the essential qualities of an auctioneer, an eagle eye for a bid and unerring judgement in valuing the stock he was selling. The slight still figure, the piercing eye, the humorous, rather one-sided twist of the mouth, the original caustic wit breaking through now and again, the disarming smile to follow, gave him a sale-ring manner that was all his own. He had the power of sustaining attention by apparently simple means. It was said of him that his was the art that concealed art. Innumerable tales are told of his ringside remarks. On one occasion an old farmer was selling a very lean poor bull. Elliot got it started at £3 and after some hard talking worked it up to £4 10s. The farmer, holding up his hand called out, 'Dinna sell him, dinna sell him,' but the hammer fell and, looking down at the owner, Elliot said very seriously, 'Man, it's no you I'm sorry for, it's ye're wee bit beastie, it's awfu' badly in need o' a change.'

He was a convinced advocate of the Ayrshire as the most suitable milch cow for the West-Country farmer. The first time Friesian bulls came into Lanark market, even without tuberculin tests or milk records, they made about £10 to £12 more than the Ayrshires. After the sale an Ayrshire breeder suggested that he was in the wrong breed. Elliot, looking straight at him said, 'Ye're what! They'll pit a wheen o' them oot o' their ferms yet.' A few years later the few Friesian bulls offered were almost unsaleable, whilst Ayrshire prices were soaring; in his laconic way the auctioneer remarked to the same friend, 'Weel they hae din what I telt ye.'

William Elliot followed in the family succession as a Director of the Highland and Agricultural Society, where his services in committee were invaluable. It was at his suggestion that the Society started the award of Long Service Medals for farm servants. Before initiating a reform in the method of gate collection and the sale of catalogues, whereby he effected a saving of hundreds of pounds, he personally supervised the work, a task involving long days of close attention during the whole week of the Show. Turning to catering arrangements and the supply of alcoholic drink at exhibitor's tents, he succeeded in enforcing the hitherto disregarded regulations.

Although ready to co-operate with officials he had no toleration for the official attitude. The last time the author saw him was at a London breakfast-table, after an all-night journey, cheerfully on his way 'to fight those chaps in Whitehall.'

The memories of John Fraser of Invermay, who was still hale and active until his ninetieth year, went back a long way. In 1862, as a boy of sixteen, he left the farm at The Peel, Tibbermore, to enter the land-surveying office of Macdonald in Perth. Two years later, in a very humble way, the weekly stock sales were started; in the early years it was thought a big thing when 7,000 sheep and about 1,600 head of cattle per annum passed through the rings; by contrast, in 1922, 552,000 sheep, 93,000 cattle and 6,600 horses were sold by the firm.

In 1864, when the firm started its Shorthorn sales (with a few Aberdeen Angus) £12 to £20 was thought a useful price for a bull calf. Even in 1901 the sum of 650 guineas for a Shorthorn and 360 guineas for an Aberdeen Angus seemed almost uncanny, but by 1920 Shorthorns were soaring to 5,000 guineas at Aberdeen, and at Perth to 6,600 guineas. Still higher prices have since been recorded.

Fraser was always convinced that the farmer's strength lay in live-stock. His integrity and business ability, combined with his great knowledge of pedigree, soon gained recognition, and he was asked to undertake private sales. When the hand-to-hand selling of the sheep stock from the great runs of the North of Scotland at Inverness Fair was dwindling, he started auctions there and at Lairg, where now hundreds of thousands of Cheviot and Blackfaced sheep change hands every year.

Upon a day in his old age he recalled the changes in agriculture that he had seen, the prosperous times during and after the Crimean War up to 1866, the rinderpest that broke out in that year and swept all the cattle from one farm after another in the course of a few weeks; the remarkably short time that elapsed before farming broke into its stride again; the years of prosperity in the 'seventies, when proprietors were spending freely, fencing and draining, and tenants tumbling over each other to get farms; merchants and others, who had made something out of the Crimean and Franco-Prussian wars, rushing all over the country, taking farms for themselves and their sons; the end of all that with the disastrous harvests of 1877 and 1879; no subsidies or quotas to help the farmer in the distressful 'eighties and 'nineties. Then was shown the grit of the Scottish farmer, and the generosity and good feeling of the proprietors came into play.

Cruel and disastrous as these years were, a gleam of sunshine broke through now and then upon the breeders of pedigree animals, who deserve so much credit for their continued efforts to improve the live-stock of the country through the years of depression. Ballindalloch, Southesk, Spott, and Kinnochtry herds of Aberdeen Angus were kept at high-water mark, and the Shorthorns of Strathallan, Keir, Lawers and other herds were keeping pace. As a result, remarkable sales kept on. In 1887, Mr. William Duthie of Collynie took Fraser by the hand and pushed him along with all his vigour. A foreign buyer, Mr. Donald Maclennan, appeared at the Perth spring sale in 1884, buying four bulls for the Argentine, and a few years later, at a wonderful sale at Towie Barclay in Aberdeenshire, a foreign and an English buyer opposed each other for the first time at a Scottish ring-side. The Englishman, Mr. Deane Willis, prevailed at £100 for the pick of the bunch.

Besides the 'red-white-and-roan' and the 'black-but-comely', there were the Leicester sheep at Dalhousie and Barrelwell, where at record sales young breeders took the opportunity of improving their flocks by laying in a sure and good foundation. Then the Clydesdale world showed up at the Montrave dispersal sale in

1892, when 'Queen of the Roses' trotted out of the ring, breaking all records at 1,000 guineas.

It was the success of these events that strengthened Fraser's determination to make Perth a great world centre for the disposal of pedigree stock, and he lived to see, in February and October of each year, all roads from all parts of the world leading to Perth and Aberdeen.

Straightforwardness and punctuality were his watchwords, and these qualities have made the name of Macdonald and Fraser a household word in every country where good stock is the mainstay of farming.

No one who ever heard John Thornton, once called a 'herdbook in trousers', enlarging on one of his favourite Shorthorn families, like the Pye or the Wildeyes, could fail to recognize his profound grasp of his subject. In later years, when the knowledge of pedigrees was more general, some of the younger generation may have thought him apt to discourse a little too long, but in early times this habit, of giving what almost amounted to a lecture before a sale, was of immense value.

His soft musical voice carried wonderfully well out of doors, where the greater part of his selling was conducted. One can see him now conducting a home sale—the rubicund face with the well-trimmed beard under the half-topper, the twinkling eyes behind glasses, the immaculately clad, short, stocky figure leaning over the improvised rostrum in the open field, with the crowd of customers on farm carts round the ring. Shading his eyes to catch the bids, he deftly waves his sand-glass and looks encouragingly at the hesitating bidder. 'He draws the bids like cockles, that little old chap in spectacles.' At one sale in Ireland his waving sand-glass was regarded as a magic wand by two Irishmen unaccustomed to its use. The audience responded quickly to his eloquence and bidding was brisk. He had knocked down a beast at a high figure, when, in the lull, a voice was heard exclaiming: 'Sure, it's not the man that makes them bid, 'tis the little glass he has!'

Left an orphan child, Thornton began to earn his living at thirteen years old in the Audit office of the Eastern Counties

Railway. By a stroke of luck he found, by advertisement, work congenial to him in the office of Strafford, the chief Shorthorn auctioneer of his day, and proprietor of Coates's herd book. For four years he worked by day in the railway office in Shoreditch and in the evening at Mr. Strafford's in Euston Square, until, finally, he entered the latter as a whole-time clerk, thus winning the opportunity of acquiring that intimate knowledge of Shorthorns which in later life stood him in such good stead. As clerk he assisted Strafford at all the pedigree sales. He helped at the famous Golden Sale at Windsor, of Sheldon's American stock, celebrated by 'The Druid' in *Punch* in the poem beginning:

> *'Twas Strafford raised his sand-glass and Thornton held the pen,*
> *When in a Windsor Coffee House flocked scores of Shorthorn men.*

He was fortunate in his friendships. At an early age he got to know H. H. Dixon, 'The Druid', who, after a short life, shortened by hardships endured in his constant journeys up and down Great Britain, on horseback and on foot, left behind him in books like *Saddle and Sirloin* and *Field and Fern*, some of the finest records of the farming and sporting life of the middle of last century. Intimate friendship in this cultured family must have done much for the lonely young man, and it was largely owing to Thornton's influence that Dixon so carefully recorded the Shorthorns' pedigrees of the period. Another friend was William Torr of Aylesby, the famous Shorthorn breeder, who, after failing to persuade Strafford to take the promising young man into partnership, advised him to set up for himself and offered him a loan of £200 to add to his own savings of £100. 'My dear Boy,' he writes, 'what a fool you are to put up with it. I can get you £500 or £1,000 as a start, and the game is in your hands.'

Opening his office on the ground floor of Langham Chambers, he took out his first auctioneer's licence on 31st October 1868. He sent round a circular with his photograph, stating that he had established an office for the sale of pure-bred Shorthorns, and proposed opening a register for such stock. This was the beginning of the invaluable *Thornton's Quarterly Circular*, which was published periodically by his firm until, in 1928, it was taken over by the Shorthorn Society. Although only twenty-five years of age, Thornton must have had the confidence of cattle-breeders, for his first large commission came from The Hon. W. Cochrane to buy and ship £40,000 worth of pure-bred Shorthorns to Canada. With the conscientious care and attention to detail which characterized him, he personally supervised the shipment of every consignment of these cattle. This transaction led him to pay a visit to the United States and Canada, which did much to enlarge his connection with America. He also gained an insight into the methods of transport then prevailing which, with his love for animals, he determined to get altered. He writes in his diary: 'Few know the sufferings of sea life and the risk and anxiety occasioned by the transport of valuable stock,' and later, 'After several hours on a cattle train it was borne forcibly in upon me that the present railway system is not good.'

The start of his business coincided with the pedigree boom of the 'seventies, and since he specialized in Shorthorns, he got most of the great sales of that breed. He sold his friend Mr. Torr's herd, 84 head, at an average of £519 19s. od., making a total of £42,919 16s. od.

Thornton was a man of immense energy. His constant companion, a big black note-book, was always being filled with memoranda, to be worked up before he slept each night. He had the eager and inquiring mind, and, added to his quick intelligence and wonderful memory, a great power of concentration upon the matter in hand. He was won over to take an interest in the Jersey breed, then just starting to spread in England, by his friend Sir Walter Gilbey, who finally persuaded him to undertake the compilation of the Jersey Herd Book. This was an immense labour, involving the investigation of the antecedents of all the imported cattle. He had to visit the Island, where he and his clerk personally inspected all the herds and spent days in searching records in the Museum and Library at St. Hellier. Within six months he had tabulated the pedigrees of about 275 bulls and 1,000 cows.

Although born a Londoner, Thornton was at heart a country-man and a sportsman. He was never happier than when, each Easter and October for twenty-six years, he stayed with two Irish Shorthorn breeders, first conducting their sales, and then fishing their streams for trout. In the last seven years of his life he realized the excitements of salmon fishing, and never failed on the opening day with an old friend in Perthshire. Latterly, he travelled abroad every winter, after the sale season had closed, still recording everything in his note-book. He was always ready to place at the disposal of the public his wide knowledge of families and herds, and it would be difficult to overestimate the value of his work in the cause of improved cattle-breeding. He was fortunate in his associates during his life-time, and, after his death, in those whom he had trained and who remained to carry on his work in the earnest way he would have appreciated.

In his own words, Alfred Mansell of Shrewsbury spent a life-time among Shropshire sheep. His father was one of the pioneer breeders and from him he gained his intimate knowledge of sheep generally, and especially of the breed which he himself bred to perfection, and which, as an auctioneer, he so skilfully put before the public of every country. Breeding is an art, and an art is a ruminating business. Rotary cultivators rush about tearing up the land, combine harvesters hurry on the gathering of the grain, but the breeder must still stand and gaze, slowly evolving the image of the ideal which he has set himself to create. He must commune with his fellows quietly round the fire, or at gatherings at shows and sales.

In former days the sales which Mansell conducted each August and September in Wales, Scotland, Ireland, and the English Midlands were pleasant affairs. 'A good lunch, some interesting speeches, and good prices secured in the majority of cases. There were no motor-cars in those days and buyers stopped to have a comfortable cup of tea. A great feeling of comradeship prevailed amongst the breeders, who were all imbued with the spirit of making the sale a success.' Mansell's skill was the admiration of his contemporaries and the inspiration of many younger men.

The familiar figure, without which no agricultural meeting in England seemed complete, is described by one of them thus: 'At every Royal Show one would see, strolling down the sheep lines, a typically well-dressed Englishman, tall and spare, with well-trimmed beard. Umbrella on arm and catalogue in hand, he critically scans each pen as he passes, stopping occasionally to prod an exhibit on to its legs or to lift the head of some prize-winner, that he may better examine its features. He probably has orders for a hundred or more sheep, of various breeds, for overseas buyers in the United States, Australia, Canada, France, and elsewhere. A glance of recognition, that look of absorbed concentration vanishes, he greets you with a firm grip of the hand, accompanied by a smile of genial welcome, both from the strong, mobile, humorous mouth, and from those clear blue eyes, so widely set beneath the broad forehead. No Smithfield or Farmer's Club dinner was quite complete without Mansell. His sense of humour, ready repartee and most infectious laugh, threw around a feeling of good-fellowship.

'At a breed Committee or Royal Council meeting he would sit upright with folded arms and chin on chest; when he rose to speak his words were to the point, carrying weight from the sense of conviction behind them.'

Throughout his long life Alfred Mansell gave ungrudgingly of his time and services to the cause of agriculture. In every generation we are fortunate in having such men who, by their capability and honesty of purpose, command the universal confidence of stockbreeders. The reputation of British stock is safe in their hands.

14

NOW AND TOMORROW

If this book had been intended as a serious and comprehensive history of the last century of British agriculture, a great deal more must have been written. Much must have been said about legislation—about Agricultural Holdings, Fertilizers and Feeding-stuffs, Seeds, Marketing, Small Holdings, and other Acts. We should have had to trace the origin and development of Farmers' and Workers' Unions, of the Co-operative Movement, of the growth of Government Departments and the organization of research, education and advisory services. There must have been a chapter on Tithes, and there must have been repeated inquiries into the economic causes of the changing fortunes of our industry as a whole, and of landlords, tenants and workers separately. But all these things are beyond the scope of the book, whose simple purpose has been to convey some notion of the contribution of four generations of British farmers to the progress of their most ancient craft.

It has been a fairly common error to suppose that our towns, in the course of the past two centuries, have constantly depleted our countryside of its best human material, leaving on our farms only the less able, less progressive and less enterprising. But the facts of the matter are that, throughout the century that ended in 1879, British farmers led the world; that, during the sixty years that followed, they displayed high courage, faith and resourcefulness in the face of heavy discouragement and bitter adversity; and that, during these last ten years, they have not been wanting either in enterprise or in public spirit.

Our townsfolk, for their part, have been blamed for the shortsightedness and waywardness of their attitude towards the

317

land; and indeed they have blown, at times, very hot and, at others, exceeding cold. But, in regard to matters of food and farming, it is hard for any mortal to see so clearly or so far as to reach decisions that will prove, in the event, to have been wise. Yet we cannot shirk the attempt to arrive at a long-term plan for our future.

Of course, the trends of the times point to the need for continuing and intensified efforts to extract increasing amounts of food from the world's soils. The human family is increasing at a terrifying rate—a rate which, if it should continue, will double and redouble our numbers at intervals of only two generations. It is only here and there that birth rates are markedly declining, while the progress of medical science and of health services is constantly improving the expectation of life.

Again, despite praiseworthy and successful efforts at soil conservation in several countries, the rate of loss by erosion, over the world as a whole, is probably higher than it has ever been; moreover land is wanted increasingly for purposes other than food production. Then too, our reserves of virgin land—of the sort that, in the light of present knowledge, can be regarded as potentially good material for the farmer—are small and shrinking. Finally, many of the world's people are now inadequately fed, and some hundreds of millions are living in the permanent shadow of famine.

On the other hand, the rate of discovery and invention, in the field of food production, is faster than it has ever been, and is accelerating rapidly; and farm practice is following ever more closely on the heels of science. How then will the balance swing?

Perhaps the best guess is that the world's farmers, given reasonable encouragement and opportunity, will be producing, a generation hence, more adequate rations than those of to-day, even for the increased numbers of consumers. But clearly it is hardly conceivable (as indeed Malthus suggested long ago) that the volume of farm production should for long follow the present trend of population. Possibly, however, this trend may change; or perhaps man will achieve a second revolution in food production, as important as the change from food gathering to farming. Perhaps the greatest of the more immediate dangers is that some accidental, local, temporary or even unreal surplus of some few food commodities will be misinterpreted as a sign that the World of Plenty is at hand.

It has been said that the pace of progress in farming will be, and indeed must be, accelerated. Probably in future an increasing proportion of the forward steps will arise out of the researches of professional scientists and engineers. It is to be expected that more will result from the exchange of ideas between farmers throughout the free world, whose contacts are becoming ever closer and more frequent. But it will continue to be true that the advance of our own British farming will depend in the main on the ingenuity and originality of the few, combined with the progressive spirit of the many.

INDEX

INDEX

Bankes, on Ryelands, 201
Barclay, Captain (of Ury), 144
Bare fallows, disappearance of, 95
Barford, 189
Barham, George, 168
Barham, Titus, 169
Barra cattle (Isles), 162
Barron, Tom, 232
Barthropp (horse-breeder), 221
Basic slag, 134, 136
Bates, Thomas, 142
Bateson, Thomas, 96
Bateson, William, 228
Bath and West Society, The, 78, 273–80;
  Norfolk corn and, 274; Rack's work in,
  274–5; see Great Societies
Bath Chronicle, 274
Battersea International Show (1862), 191,
  218
Baumshire, 178
Bear (editor), 281, 282
Beaven, Dr., 82
Bedford, Duke of, 89, 121
Bedford, Francis, Earl of, 31
Bedford Level Corporation (Fens), 33
Beef, *see* Cattle names; decline of, in Scot-
  land, 159–60
Bell, Patrick, 49 seqq.; Reaper invented by,
  85
Bell's Weekly Messenger, 238, 281, 284, 286
Bennett (horse-breeder), 223
Bentinck, Lord Henry, 149, 214
Benzies, John, 158
Berkshire Knot sheep, 192
Berkshire pigs, 209
Bertram, Hugh, 105, 108
Berwickshire: herbage seeds, 120; sheep,
  185
Biddell, Hermann (horse-historian), 222–3;
  journeys of, 223
Biffen, Sir R., 82
Binders, early, 64, 65; defects of, 65; *and
  see* String-tying, Swaths
'Birdsall Menestrel' (stallion), 214
Birdsall horses, 213, 214
Blackface sheep, 177, 181–2, 183, 194, 308,
  311; mutton from, 204; spread of, in
  Scotland, 183
Black polls, 156, 157
'Black Prince' (sire), 157–8
Blacksmiths' work, 53–4; *and see* R.A.S.E.
  in Great Societies
Black Suffolk pigs, 222
Blair Atholl fold, 162
'Blaze' (stallion), 220
Blue-greys (Shorthorn cross), 160
Board of Agriculture (old), 72
Bog reclamation, 19 seqq.
Bogue, T. A., 157

Bond, J. R., 171
'Bondagers', 106
Bone manure, 91, 125; on grassland, 125;
  see Doncaster Report
Bonheur, Rosa, 162
Book of the Farm (Stephens), 283
Booths (Shorthorn breeders), 142, 143
Bordeaux mixture, 80
Border Leicester sheep, 177, 178; Cheviot
  cross with, 185, 186
Bordlands Farm, 104, 108, 109
Borthwick Hall (Midlothian), 129
Boswell, James, 132
Boulder clay (Cockle Park), 136
Boutflour, Robert, 171
Bracken mowing, 115
Bradley, A. G., 105–6
Brahmas (poultry), 231
Brassey, Col., 210
Braxy, 265
Breadalbane fold, 162
Breaking of subsoil, 16, 17; *see* Subsoil,
  Tillers
Breeds, reshaping, 95, 152, 194, 195; *see*
  breeders' names
Bright, John, 102
Brine Pits Farm, 125
Britain, livestock lead of, 140
Britannia Implement Works, 54
British Dairy Farming Association
  (R.A.S.E.), 251
British Farming, 125
British Workman, The, 231
'Briton' (stallion), 223
Broadbalk Field, 77, 110
Brodie (dealer), 157
Brown, Sir Edward, 231; honours awarded
  to, 232
Brush-draining, 13
Brydon, James (of Moodlaw), 180–1
Buccleuch, Duke of, 217
Buchanan, Archibald, 14, 15, 23
Buchanan, James, 14
Buff Orpington, 229
Bulls, hypothetical milk records of, 167
Burford, 189
Burnet, 133
'Bury Victor Chief' (stallion), 214
Buscot Stud, 214
Butleigh cheese school, 279
Buttar, David, 284
Buxton, Noel, 171

CAIRD, James, 95, 166, 282, 287–8, 290,
  291; pamphlet by, 288 seqq., 295; pro-
  posals of, 292
Cambridge Annual Stock Fair (1839), 229
Cambridge School of Agriculture, 83; *and
  see* Great Societies

INDEX

INDEX

Consanguinity in mating, 175
Consumer's taste in meat, 208, 209; *and see* Mutton
Contagious abortion, R.A.S.E. and, 252
Contagious Diseases of Animals Bill, 249
Continuous swath, abandonment of, 64
Cook, William (poultry), 229
Cormacks (seedsmen), 121
Corn: bullock feeding on, 112; improvement of strains of, 80; sheep folded on, 112
Cornham Farm, 25, 26–8
Corn Law Repeal Bill, 240
Corn Laws, 242, 255
Corn rents, 100
Corn, undersown, 113
Cotswold brash, 110
Cotswold sheep, 189–90; breeders of, 189; crosses, 189–90; in Domesday Book, 189
Couch grass, 133
County Cork cows, 164
Coventry, Andrew, 83, 269
Cow-feeding, changes in, 171–2
Cowgrasses, 117
Cracked peas as fodder, 190
Craibstone mixtures, 138
'Crisp's horse', 221
Crisp, Thomas (of Ufford), 221, 222
Cromwell, and the Fens, 32
Crosskill, 53
Cross-pollination (cereal), 80
Crowbar (Elkington's), 14
Crowmarsh Battle Farm, 111–13
Crowther (nutritionist), 169, 171
Crude oil (U.S.A.), 67
Cruickshank, Amos, 144–8
Cruickshank, Anthony, 144–8; on livestock fashions, 145
Crumb structure, 132
Crystal Palace Exhibition, 242
Culley brothers, 141, 176
'Cultivated Grasses' (pamphlet), 118
Cumberland fell sheep, 174
'Cumberland Willie' (Galloway bull), 160
'Cupbearer' (stallion), 222, 223
Cupressus Lawsoniana, 127
Curtis, W., 120; grasses of, 120–1
Cyclopaedia of Agriculture, 1855–6, authors featured in, 287

DAIRY and corn (Chamberlain system), 112
Dairying, R.A.S.E. on, 251
Dairy Research Institute, 82
Dairy Shorthorns, revival of, 149 seqq.; R.A.S.E. and, 257
Dale o' Goyt sheep, 204
Dalkeith Farmers' Club, 15
Damp grain, combines and, 66

Danish bacon, 208
Darby digger, 63
'Darnley' (stallion), 219
Dartmoor sheep, 194
Darwin, Charles, 228
Dauncey (of Horwood), 163
Davis, Hewitt, 86, 88, 91
Davy family (Devon breeders), 154
Davy, Sir Humphry, 72, 122
Day of humiliation (cattle plague), 146, 147
D.D.T. and other sprays, 80
Deanston plough, 80. *See* Inventions
Deanston, village and works at, 15
Deanston Weir, 15
Deep: drainage, costs of, 19–20; ploughing, in Fens reclamation, 39; rooting plants, in sward, 133
Deer on grazings, 184
Degrees awarded in agriculture, 83, 134
Denton, John B., 22
Department of Agriculture, Edinburgh, 270
Depression of '80's, 251
Depths of field drains, 16, 20
Derbyshire gritstone, *see* Dale o' Goyt
Devon cattle, 154: *Herd Book*, 154
Devon sheep: five breeds of, indigenous, 194; Longwools, 194
Dexter cow, 164
Dick, W., 267–8
Dinners, *see* Great Societies
Dirleton, 98, 104
Diseases of Animals Bill, 252
Diseases, 252, 265; *see* names of diseases
Dishley, 194, 198, 217; sheep, 175, 176 seqq.
Dixon, Henry H. ('The Druid'), 282, 293–4, 313
Dobito, George, 195
Doncaster Report, 124–7
Dongola Arab horses, 25
Dorkings, early, 227
Dorset horn sheep, 193–4
Dorset Down sheep, 193
Double Gloucester cheese, 141
Draft horse, flexibility of, 63
Drainage Act (1840), 21
Drainage: 'Bigot's Hole', 289; costs, 19–20; Deanston, 16–18; Fenland, Improvement companies and, 22; Mechie's, in Essex, 89; principles of, 19; *see* 'Frequent' drainage
Drew, Lawrence, 218, 220
Dried grasses as book illustrations, 121
Drifting of alluvial soil, 40, 41
Drill husbandry, 116
Drills, use of after drainage, 22–3
Drought-resistant plants, 133
'Drowned-out' wheat, 14

INDEX

INDEX

INDEX

INDEX

Hogg (Ettrick shepherd), 182–3
Holkham, see Coke, Woburn
Holmes Farm (Kilmarnock), 269
Holm Fen, 34
Home industries in Higlands, 265
Homing instinct of sheep, 203, 204
Honeycombed peat, 40
Honeymead Farm, 25
Hon. Improvers' meetings, 258–9
Hooke, Sir J., 79
Hop spraying, 80
Hope, George, 97, 98
Hope, Robert, 98 seqq.
Hopetoun wheat, 81
Hornless cattle, 159
Hornsby's traction locomotive, 68
Horrelis (horse-breeders), 214
Horses, 212–24; breeders of, 213, 214, 215; compared with oxen, 213; disappearance of, 23, 69, 93; ducal breeders of, 213, 214; future of, 224; improvement of Shire, 213 seqq.; industry and, 213, 216; in paintings, 212; kings' interest in, 213, 215, 218; labour of on land reclamation, 36, 38, 40; Lanarkshire breeders of, 220; pedigree register of, 213; Percheron, imported, 225; R.A.S.E. and, 244; war (great horses), 212; see also named stallions, and references to: Alnwick Castle, 214; Ashbourne (Derby), 219; Berkshire, 215; Butley Abbey, 221; Clydesdales, 214, 216, 220; English Blacks, 217; Fylde of Lancs, 214; heavy Scottish, 216–20; Lockinge, 215; Soke of Peterborough, 214; studs, 214–15; Tring, 214; Underley, 214; for Punches, see Suffolks, Shires
'Horse of Ufford' (stallion), see Crisp's horse
Hortus Gramineus Woburnensis (George Sinclair, 1824), 119, 121, 127
Hosier outdoor dairying, 194
Hoskyns, Wren, 63, 86
Howard, Frederick, 54
Howard, James, 54, 213; and Charles, 55
Howard, John, 54
Howard (Biddenham), 191; Oxford Devons of, 191
Howatson, Charles, 181
How to Farm Profitably (Mechi), 95
'Humble pig, the', 206–11
Humfrey (of Chaddleworth), 192–3; pigs bred by, 210
Humus theory: and Liebig, 72, 73; and specialized corn production, 113
Hunter, James, 134
Hunter, Engledow and Bell, cereal developments by, 82
Hunters, jumping of, R.A.S.E., on, 246

Husbandry, minor branches of, R.A.S.E. on, 253
Hussey, reaper, 52; trials, 103
Huxtable, the Rev. F., 86, 88, 94
Huxtable liquid manure and sparred floor system, 94, 289
Hygienic milk production, 169–71

IFORD herd, 149
Implements: at Bath and West (1850), 278; see Howard, Ransome, etc.
Imported livestock, R.A.S.E. and, 249
Improved: Cheviots, 180–1; Kents, 198; Shorthorns (Teeswater), 150
Inbred sheep, 178
Inchmichael, 51
Inclosure Commissioners, 21
Indigenous ryegrass, 115
Inn signs, 198
Intercrossings, clover and grass, 117
Internal combustion engine, 66; weight of, 68
International Conference on Agricultural Education (Paris, 1900), 254
International Exhibition (Hyde Park, 1862), 244
International Poultry Congress (1919), 228
Inventions at Deanston, 15–16
Irrigation, 94; see Liquid manure
Isle of Wight, 23
Isles: cattle in, 161; landowners in, 162; shielings in, 161; travels of cattle from, 162
Islington Agricultural Hall, 215
Italian ryegrass, 113, 125, 128–9; introduction of, 128; Lowson's description of, 128–9; undersown, 113
Ivel agricultural motor, 68

JACKSON (horse-breeder), 214
Jefferies (of Lyonshall), 152
Jersey cattle, 163; breeders of, 163; New Zealand, 163; *Herd Book*, 163, 314
Johannsen, 82
Johne's disease, 256
Johnson, Dr., in Hebrides, 161
Johnstone (Clydesdale breeder), 217
Jones, E. T., 82
Journal, of Bath and West, 278
Journal, of R.A.S.E., 237, 241

KEIGHLEY Show, 207–8
Keir Stud, 219
Kellner and Hansson, on milk, 168–9
Kelso, 13; Kelso sale (Ram Fair), 178, 306, 307
Kent sheep, 197, 198
Kerr: on cattle, 157; on natural grass-seed, 120

INDEX

INDEX

INDEX

INDEX

INDEX

INDEX

INDEX

Spooner, Gerald, 28
Spring waters, 13, 14
St. Faith's cattle, 159
St. Leger, Colonel, 124
Stalham Farmers' Club, 235
Stall-feeding, 92
Stallion shows (Edinburgh Society), 218
Stanley (Lord), 1841, 22
Stapledon, Sir R. George, 64, 82, 132, 139
State demonstration forests, 268
'Statesmen' sheep, 203
Stationary oil engines, 67
Statistical Society, 55
Steam, innovation (and tillage), 59, 60; introduction of, 57 seqq.; R.A.S.E. and, 246–7; rural unemployment and, 58; tackle for ploughing, 62
Stephens's *Manual of British Beetles*, 79
Stephenson, G. and R., 62
Steppe murrain, 243
Sterilization of milk, 170
Stevenson (editor), 282; Robert Louis, 159
Stillingfleet, Benjamin, 120
Stomach worms, 198
Stow-on-the-Wold, 302
Strafford (auctioneer), 150
Stratton, Richard, 148–9
Stratton's Loch (drained by Hope), 259
Straw: combine and, 66; coverage, 93; fuel, for engines, 65–6; on reclaimed fen-land, 39
Street, Frederick, 213
'Stretches', 13
String-tying binder devices, 64–5
'Stripper' principle (harvesting), 66
Strutt, Edward, 172–3; Friesians of, 172; Rayleigh Farms and, 173
Stubble: and combine harvesters, 66; as partridge cover, 93
Stud Book (horses), 218
Subsoil, disadvantage of breaking up, 17; plough, described, 17; Mechie and, 90, misapprehension concerning, R. H. Elliot's, 33
Suffolk: drills, 94; horses, 214, 220–4; 'Punches' described, 223–4; R.A.S.E. and, 244; Stud Book Association, 223; sheep, 186, 192, 194–5, 202
Superphosphates, 75, 86, 91; at Cockle Park, 136; with basic slag and lime, 136; Lawes and, 91 seqq.
Superstitions, Bath and West's collection of, 275
Sussex cattle, 155–6; as draft animals, 155; for beef, 155
Svalöf Plant Breeding Station, 82
Swaledale sheep, 179, 204, 205; best flocks named, 205

Swan, James, 303, 305, 306, 307; John, 304–6; Tom, 304
Sword, 175, 176; *see* Grass
Swing, Captain, 89; Swing riots, 85
Sylviculture: 'Highland' and, 268; R.A.S.E. and, 255

TAKE-ALL, 113
Tamworth pigs, 209
Taunton, revived Bath and West at, 278
Taylor, George, 149
Telford, 34
Tennessee Valley project, pigs and, 207
Thomson, Dr. A. T., 74
Thornhill, G., 34
Thornton, John, 103, 196, 303, 312–15; and *English Herd Book*, 103
Thornton's Quarterly Circular, 314
Thoroughbred Stallion Show (Newcastle), 244
'Thousand-a-Year' (tup), 203
Three-parts-bred lambs, 186
Three-year ley, wild white clover in, 138
Threshing, and steam power, 67
Tile drains, 18 seqq.; substitutes for, early, 13
Tillage and manure, 72
Tillyfour Angus, success of at Paris (1878), 158
Times, The, 281, 284, 286, 288, 295
Timothy meadow, 126–7
Tindall, Thomas, 59
Tiptree Hall Visitors' Book, 97
Tiptree Heath, 86 seqq.
'Tom Barron's Strain', 232
Tomkins family (beef breeders), 152
Toovey, T. W., 232
Torr, William, 157
Tours, Young's, *see* Young, Arthur
Terling Fresians, 172
Tractors, early, 67–9; imports of, 69; ploughing by, 68
Transactions ('Highland'), 264, 265, 271
Trap nest, introduction of, 230
Treadwell, John, 191
Tree Field plots, 134, 135–8
Trefoil, 125
Tring: herd of Shorthorns; Stud, dispersal of, 215
Trinity Market (Brechin), 156
'Trojan' (bull), 158
Tuberculosis, milk and, 170
Tuley, Joseph, 207
Tull, Jethro, 72, 111, 116
Tumbledown ley, 115
Turf: as manure, 132; fertilizing value of, 133
Turf-filled drains, 38
Turnbull, Tom, 302

335

INDEX

Turner, George, 57, 154
Turnips: 95, 97, 104; barley with (Bedford-shire), 109; experiment, 74–5; mixed tillage and, 124–5; subsoiled land and, 18; store-to-beef cycle and, 160; test on, with bone manure, 124; test on Liebig's, 74, 75; three-year ley and, 28; West-country practice with, 275
Tweeddale, Marquis of, 61
Twynam, John, 190–1

UNDERSOWING, 113, 125–6
Universal Exhibition (Paris), 249
'Up horn, down corn', 109–10
Ushers: (of Lammermuir), 181; (of Tod-rig), 177–8

VALES, THE, 13
Vegetation, underlying principles of, 71–2
Vermuyden, Cornelius, 31, 32, 297
Veterinary inspection (R.A.S.E.), 242; training, by Dick, 268–9
Victoria, Queen, 158, 182
Vilmorin, 129
Vine mildew, 80
Vintage cider, 279
Voelcker, Dr. J. A., 38, 75, 77, 78, 82, 286

WAGE BOARDS, 299
Wainman (pig-breeder), 208
Wallace, Robert, 135 seqq.
Wantage, Lord, 215; pig breeders of Wan-tage, 210
Warping, 38
Watney, Dr. (of Buckhold), 163
Watson, Hugh (of Keillor), 52, 144, 156; Southdowns of, 187
Webb, Frederick, 149
Webb, Jonas, 187–9, 200–1, 222
Webb, Samuel, 188
Weed control, 110; by bastard fallow, 112; by chemicals, 80
Weir, Harrison, 23
Weir, James, 220, 308
Wellington, Duke of, 290
Wells, William, 35–41; offices held by, 41
Welsh Plant Breeding Station, 82
Welshpool horse-breeders, 214
Welsh sheep, 194, 200
Wensleydale sheep, 179
Wessex pigs, 210
West Highland (Kyloe) cattle, 161
West of England Drainage and Inclosure Co., 38
West of Scotland Agricultural College, 273; foundation of, 167
Wheat Act, 299
Wheat, at Fenton Barns, 100; at Rotham-sted, 76–7

Wheat prices, 84, 111; from 1870–1939, 109
When Squires and Farmers Thrived (Brad-ley), 105
Whey-fed pigs, 210
White clover, 123; *see* Clover, Wild White
White-face, *see* Sheep; Hereford contro-versy, 153
White lop-ear pigs, 210
White Park herd, 153
Whittaker, James, 156
Whittlesea Mere, drainage of, 33–9; Cam-den on earlier, 33; early sluices at, 34; Eau Brink, 34; finds in the course of, 35; preparatory work in, 34; Wells, and, 35 seqq.
Wight, Andrew, 177
Wildmore Fen, 33
Wild white clover, 133, 138
'William the Conqueror' (stallion), 215
Williams, R. Stenhouse, 169–71
Willis, Deane, 147–8, 311
Willowbank Dairy Farm, 168
Willsher and Smith (cattle-breeders), 156
Wilson, James (editor), 83
Wilson, John, 125–6
Wilson, Professor (Edinburgh), 201
Wiltshire horn sheep, 115, 192; pastures of, 194
Windsor farms, 239
Winter corn, 113
'Winterbourne Blanco' (pig), 210
Winter fodder, 126
Wintering of flocks: Exmoor, 28, 30; hill, 181, 182, 183; in yards, 40
Wintershed Farm, 28
Wisbech, buried boat at, 31
Witney sheep district, 190–1
Woburn, 121; seeds mixtures, 122, 123; shearings, 72, 187, 234; tests made at (bacterial inoculation), 254
Wolff and Kellner, 82
Women's Institutes, 253
Wood's Knotter, 64
Wood, T. B., 83, 171
Wool, as staple export, 174; Babraham, 188; Blackface, 180, 183; Cheviot, 179–80, 183, 184; Cotswolds, 189; Galloway, 159; Herdwick, 179; Kent, 198; Lincoln, 196; Merino, *see* Merino; Shropshire, 200; Southdown, 187; Welsh mountain, 199
World's Poultry Congress, 231
World's Poultry Science Association, 231
World War, 42–5; reclamation work dur-ing, 43–4; work during, in Orkneys, 44–5
Worshipful Company of Farriers, 244
Wright, Lewis, 225, 231

INDEX

BATH AND WEST, *names mentioned in connection with:*

HIGHLAND AND AGRICULTURAL SOCIETY, *names mentioned in connection with:*

337

INDEX

ROYAL AGRICULTURAL SOCIETY OF ENGLAND, *names mentioned in connection with:*